To Ellen
with Much Love,
Doug

UNDERSTANDING BASIC MATHEMATICS
FOR ADULTS

A Workbook Containing Objectives and Self Evaluation
by the Reader

By
DOUGLAS POTVIN

ISBN 978-0-9876983-0-8

24-08-11

Cover Illustration by Carl Dettman

Published by Dalpot International Consultants
Printed in Canada

TABLE OF CONTENTS

	Page
Table of Contents	i
Preface	xii
To the Reader – An Overview	xii
Acknowledgements	xvi
Section I – Sets, Numbers, Addition, Subtraction, Multiplication and Division of Whole Numbers	1
Pre–Test I	1
Unit 1 – Addition, Subtraction, Multiplication, Division of Whole Numbers	3
Objectives	3
What is a Set? What is a Number? Order of Numbers	4
Addition	5
Order of Addition..	7
Adding Three Digits...	8
Addition that Results in a Two–Digit Number......................	10
Addition of Two–Digit Numbers.....................................	10
Addition that Results in a Three–Digit Number....................	12
Addition Using Three–and Four–Digit Numbers	14
Subtracting of One–Digit Numbers	15
Subtracting a One–Digit Number from a Two–Digit Number....	16
Subtracting a Two–Digit Number from A Two–Digit Number....	17
Verification of Subtraction	19
Subtraction of Two–Digit Numbers from Three–Digit Numbers	19
Subtraction Using Four–Digit Numbers............................	20
Multiplication of One–Digit Numbers..............................	21
Multiplication of Numbers with Two or More Digits	23
Multiplication of a Three–Digit Number by a One–or Two–Digit Number	25
Division	27
Division by Zero	28
Factors, Prime and Composite Numbers...........................	30

Division of a Three–Digit Number by a One–Digit Number........................... 31

Division of a Three–Digit Number by a Two–Digit Number 33

Division With a Remainder 35

Addition of Numbers that are in a Special Sequence 36

Another Type of Addition and Subtraction – Hours, Minutes, Seconds.................. 36

Multiplication by Decomposition 40

Self-Assessment of the Attainment of the Objectives........................... 41

Post–Test I 42

**Section II – The Use of a Calculator, Patterns, Ordinal Numbers
Roman Numerals, Estimation and Measurement, Graphs** 44

Pre–Test II.. 44

Unit 2 – The Use of a Calculator.................................. 47

Objectives.. 47

Introducing the Calculator.. 47

Observing Patterns... 48

Operating With Small Numbers... 49

Square Roots Using a Calculator... 49

Self-Assessment of the Attainment of the Objectives 51

Unit 3 – Patterns 52

Objectives 52

Self-Assessment of the Attainment of the Objectives........................... 53

Unit 4 – Ordinal Numbers 54

Objectives.. 54

Self-Assessment of the Attainment of the Objectives 55

Unit 5 – Roman Numerals 56

Objectives.. 56

Rules for Writing Roman Numerals 56

Changing from One System to the Other One... **57**

Self-Assessment of the Attainment of the Objectives................................. **58**

Unit 6 — Estimation and Measurement **59**

Objectives.. **59**

English Units of Measurement **59**

The Metric System of Measurement **59**

Conversion Tables **60**

Converting Length, Area, Weight and Volume **60**

Measurement Conversion Chart **61**

Converting Temperatures **63**

Estimating Measures and Performing Measuring Tasks **64**

Measuring Solids **67**

Self-Assessment of the Attainment of the Objectives................................. **68**

Unit 7 — Graphs **69**

Objectives.. **69**

Bar Graphs **69**

Using a Scale for Bar Graphs **71**

Bar Graphs Used for Comparison **72**

Line Graphs **72**

Pie Graphs or Pie Charts **73**

Self-Assessment of the Attainment of the Objectives................................. **76**

Post—Test II... **77**

Section III — Geometrical Facts and Concepts **80**

Pre—Test III... **80**

Unit 8 — Geometrical Facts and Concepts........................... **83**

Objectives **83**

Plane Shapes and Measurements **83**

Point.. **83**

Straight Line 83

Line Segment 84

Angles 84

Triangles 84

Four Types of Triangles 84

The Perimeter of Triangles 85

Squares 86

Perimeter and Area of Enclosed Shapes 86

Area of Squares 86

Area of Rectangles 86

The Area of Triangles 87

The Area of Parallelograms and Rhombuses 87

The Area of a Rhombuses 87

Filling a Square or a Rectangle 90

Pentagons 91

Hexagons 92

Octagons 92

Finding the Sum of the Interior Angles of Polygons 92

Solids 93

Prisms 93

Cubes 94

Spheres 94

Circular Cylinders 94

Cones 94

To Construct a Circle 95

Construct a Triangle Having Been Given the Measure of the Three Sides 97

To Draw a Line Perpendicular to Another Line 97

To Bisect an Angle 99

To Draw an Angle Equal to Another Angle 99

To Draw a Line Perpendicular to Another Line Through a Point Outside of the Line 100

To Bisect a Straight Line Segment 100

To Draw a Line Parallel to Another Line Through a Given Point 100

Lines of Symmetry 102

Congruent Shapes 103

Self-Assessment of the Attainment of the Objectives 105

iv

Post–Test III **106**

Section IV – The Number System from the Natural Numbers to the Real Numbers **109**

Pre –Test IV **109**

Unit 9 – The Number System from the Natural Numbers to the Real Numbers **112**

Objectives **112**

The Natural Numbers (Positive Whole Numbers) **113**

Properties of the Set of Natural Numbers **113**

The Set of Integers **114**

Properties of the Set of Integers **115**

Operations Using Integers **116**

Vectors **116**

Addition by Using Vectors **116**

Patterns for Operations **117**

Addition of Integers **117**

Using the Properties of the Integers to Verify Addition **118**

Subtraction Using Vectors **119**

Definition of Subtraction **120**

Multiplication of Integers **121**

Multiplication by Zero **121**

Multiplication Using Negative Integers **121**

Rules for Multiplication of Integers **122**

The Absolute Value of a Number **122**

Division of Integers **123**

Rules for Division of Integers **123**

The Set of Rational Numbers **124**

Terminating and Recurring Decimal Fractions **125**

The Multiplicative Inverse **125**

Properties of the Set of Rational Numbers **126**

Operations Using Rational Numbers **126**

The Meaning of a Fraction **126**

Equivalent Fractions **127**

Proper and Improper Fractions **128**

Reducing Fractions **129**

Addition of Proper Fractions **131**

Mixed Numbers **133**

Addition of Improper Fractions **135**

Subtraction of Fractions **135**

Addition of Mixed Numbers **136**

Extending Addition and Subtraction to More than Two Terms **136**

The Comparison of Fractions **141**

Multiplication of Fractions **142**

The Use of the word "of" **143**

Division of Fractions **146**

The Set of Real Numbers **149**

Self-Assessment of the Attainment of the Objectives **150**

Post—Test IV **152**

Section V – Decimal Fractions, Percent, The Solution of Equations, Ratios **155**

Pre—Test V **155**

Unit 10 – Decimal Fractions **158**

Objectives **158**

Increasing and Decreasing Amounts Using Decimal Fractions **161**

Decimal Numbers Using Whole Numbers and Fractions **163**

Self-Assessment of the Attainment of the Objectives **166**

Unit 11 – Using Percent **167**

Objectives **167**

Percent **167**

Changing from Percent to Common Fractions and from Common Fractions to Percent **168**

Changing a Percent to a Decimal Fraction and a Decimal Fraction to a Percent **168**

Operations Using Percent as a Fraction **169**

Calculating the Percent of a Number **171**

Determining the Percentage of Increase or Decrease of a Number **173**

Self-Assessment of the Attainment of the Objectives **176**

Unit 12 – The Solution of Equations **177**

Objectives **177**

Solving Equations by Using the Cancellation Properties **177**

Solving Equations in which Both Sides are Fractions **178**

Solving Equations in which Variables are Used in Fractions **179**

Self-Assessment of the Attainment of the Objectives **181**

Unit 13 – Ratios **182**

Objectives **182**

Self-Assessment of the Attainment of the Objectives **185**

Post–Test V **186**

Section VI – Problem Solving Strategies **189**

Pre–Test VI **189**

Unit 14 – Problem Solving Strategies **192**

Objectives **192**

Problem Solving **192**

Strategies for Solving Problems **193**

Dramatize It **193**

Draw a Diagram **193**

Guess and Test **193**

Extend the Thought Beyond the Problem **194**

Look for a Pattern **195**

Do the Problem **195**

More Strategies for Problem Solving... **201**

Create a Simpler Problem **201**

List All of the Possibilities... 201

Try Special Numbers of Cases 201

Work Backwards 202

Solve Part of the Problem and Make a Conjecture 202

Find a Counter-example 203

Use Definitions 203

Use Formulas 203

Read the Problem Aloud 203

Self-Assessment of the Attainment of the Objectives 207

Post–Test VI.. 208

Section VII – Simple Interest and Compound Interest, Break-Even Analysis, Frequency Distributions and Measures of Central Tendencies, Probability, Practical Applications of Mathematics.......... 211

Pre –Test VII... 211

Unit 15 – Simple Interest and Compound Interest 214

Objectives 214

Simple Interest 214

Compound Interest 218

Finding the Amount 219

Self-Assessment of the Attainment of the Objectives.......................... 221

Unit 16 – Break– Even Analysis 222

Objectives 222

Fixed Costs 222

Variable Costs 222

Break–even Point 222

Profit Included in the Break-even Analysis 224

Self-Assessment of the Attainment of the Objectives 226

Unit 17 – Frequency Distributions and Measures of Central Tendencies 227

Objectives 227

viii

Using Percentages or Ratios to Display Information 227

Using Percentages Based on Hundreds or Thousands.. 228

Using Frequency Distributions 230

Charts Used for Displaying Data 231

Measures of Central Tendencies 232

The Mean.. 232

The Median 234

The Mode 235

Self-Assessment of the Attainment of the Objectives 236

Unit 18 – Probability 237

Objectives 237

Probability 237

Self-Assessment of the Attainment of the Objectives 241

Unit 19 – Practical Applications of Mathematics 242

Objectives 242

Perpetuities 242

Self-Assessment of the Attainment of the Objectives 244

Post–Test VII 245

Section VIII – Operations Using Sets 248

Pre–Test VIII.. 248

Unit 20 – Operations Using Sets.. 250

Objectives 250

Operations Using Sets 250

Number Lines and Venn Diagrams 250

Venn Diagrams 250

Complement of a Set... 251

The Intersection of Sets.. 251

Disjoint Sets.. 251

The Operation of Intersection 252

Properties of Sets Using Intersection... 254

The Operation of Union 257

Properties of Sets Using Union.. 258

The Distributive Property Using Union 259

Problems Solved by Venn Diagrams 260

Self-Assessment of the Attainment of the Objectives 263

Post–Test VIII 264

Section IX – Unit 21 – Relations and Graphs........................... 266

Pre–Test IX 266

Objectives 268

A Review of the Number System 268

Plotting Points on a Line 269

Ordered Pairs 271

The Cartesian Plane 272

Plotting Linear Equations and Inequalities 275

The Union or Intersection of Relations 279

The Solution of Simultaneous Equations 279

The Slope of a Line Segment 283

Determining the Length of a Line Segment 286

Separating a Line Segment in a Given Ratio 286

Finding the Conditions of a Linear Relation 288

Self-Assessment of the Attainment of the Objectives 291

Post–Test IX.. 293

Section X – Mathematical Logic 295

Pre–Test X 295

Objectives 296

Mathematical Logic 296

The Nature of Mathematics 296

Inductive and Deductive Reasoning 296

Inductive Reasoning 297

Deductive Reasoning 297

Other Useful Conjectures 298

Negating a Statement 301

Conjunctions 301

Disjunctions 302

Implications 303

Equivalences 303

Contrapositives 304

Tautologies 306

Converse Statements 306

Self-Assessment of the Attainment of the Objectives 308

Post–Test X 309

Answers to Pre–Tests and Post–Tests 310

Answers to the Exercises 315

Symbols Used in this Book 340

Preface

This book is intended for adults who did not understand mathematics when they were younger; have had difficulty remembering their earlier schooling in mathematics; or did not have the opportunity to study mathematics at an earlier age. It also serves as a useful resource book for teachers of mathematics at the Elementary level and the Secondary level up to about the ninth level. This book will help a person who is not prepared for a Pre–Calculus program. There are many Pre–Calculus books on the market that can be used to prepare a person for the study of advanced mathematics.

The widespread use of calculators and computers became a substitute for learning and practicing the basic operations. While the introduction of the calculator has provided a means of performing operations that would require unnecessary time without its use, calculators should not be used as a substitute for determining results that may be made mentally or by using a pencil and a piece of paper.

Although this book was written for formal classroom learning in an Adult Education environment, it may be used for home study on an individual basis. It is also recommended for government training programs because it is written in simple language and explains "why" many of the operations used in mathematics are performed.

Each Section begins with a Pre–Test and ends with a Post–Test. A satisfactory performance on the Pre–Test will determine the amount of study required. A comparison of Pre–and Post–Test results will indicate how much the reader has mastered the concepts in each Section. In general, some Units and some Sections may not require intensive study or may be omitted because you are not interested in the particular topics or you have sufficient experience with the subject matter.

Some topics that are covered in many Elementary School curricula are intentionally omitted because they are not found in real life situations. Some topics that are not included in the Elementary School curriculum, but will be of interest to the adult learner, are included.

Although the metric system is used in most cases, mathematical competencies are not compromised. For example, the mathematical ability to add 120 kilometers to 325 kilometers is the same as adding 120 miles to 325 miles. After completing the exercises in this Workbook, participants will be able to function successfully in adult life-like situations.

To The Reader – An Overview

A Pre–Test will be found at the beginning of each Section. Without looking within the Section, complete the Pre–Test and check the answers that can be found at the back of the book. The number of correct responses and your interest in the topics will determine the amount of time that you wish to spend on the Section.
Read the text and do as many of the exercises as possible.

A list of objectives can be found at the beginning of each Unit. The purpose of this list is to highlight the main concepts of the Unit. There is a self-assessment of the attainment of the objectives at the end of each Unit. The scale is from 5 to 1, 5 being the highest attainment and 1 being the lowest. You can record your score at the end of your assessment.

After doing this, complete the Post–Test. Check your answers and compare your results with those of the Pre–Test to determine the amount of learning that has occurred.

Section I consists of the basic operations of addition, subtraction, multiplication and division of Whole numbers. It is recommended that a calculator not be used until Section II. The main goals of this Section are to provide number sense and to provide accurate computational practice. Properties of the number system are used but not named. For example, when we write $3 + 2 = 2 + 3$, we also state that the order in which numbers are added will not alter the sum. The naming and organization of the number system will be the major topics of Section IV.

Section II consists of: The Use of a Calculator, Patterns, Ordinal Numerals, Roman Numerals, Estimation and Measurement, and Graphs. Calculators that have an eight digit display window should be used for Unit II. (A calculator that contains the power function will be necessary for later Units.) Number sense can be obtained by completing exercises similar to those contained in Section I. Patterns play an important role in mathematics and an introduction to patterns also contributes to a development of number sense. Ordinal Numbers are used by the reader in many ordinary daily situations. Roman Numerals are seen in many daily situations. Much practice and observation is necessary in order to learn the skills of Estimation and Measurement. Graphs have become a part of our daily life. Data have become so readily available that they are sometimes difficult to interpret in their original form. By organizing the data and portraying these data in picture form (graphs), readers are more readily able to interpret the findings. (Some people prefer to use the word, data, in the singular case but in this book it will be used in the plural.)

Section III, Geometrical Facts and Concepts is a general review of plane shapes and solids. In addition, basic constructions are included and these may become useful by applying them to real life situations. Lines of symmetry and congruent shapes are also included.

Section IV, the Number System from the Natural numbers to the Real numbers, deals with the properties of each set of numbers. In the set of Natural numbers (positive whole numbers), only addition and multiplication are always possible. Therefore, more numbers are needed and we add 0 and the negative Whole numbers to the set and we now have the set of Integers (positive whole numbers, negative whole numbers and 0). It is now possible to subtract any numbers within the set of Integers. The rules for the addition, subtraction and multiplication of negative numbers are given special attention. But we can't always divide within the set of

Integers. Therefore, the Rational numbers are required. The set of Rational numbers consists of the Natural numbers, the Integers, and any number that can be written in the form of $\frac{a}{b}$ where a and b are Integers and b ≠ 0. It is shown that all Rational numbers can be written in the form of a terminating decimal fraction or a recurring decimal fraction.

We say that the set of Rational numbers is dense. Between any two Rational numbers, other Rational numbers may be placed on the number line. These are numbers that may be written as non–terminating, non–recurring decimal numbers such as $\sqrt{2}$ and this in its decimal form is 1. 4142 . . . and they are called Irrational numbers. When the Irrational numbers are included on the number line, there is a one–to–one correspondence between all Real numbers and all points on the number line.

The operations of addition, subtraction, multiplication and division are illustrated by using vectors, number patterns, and the application of the properties of the number system. The reason for inverting the divisor and then multiplying when one fraction is divided by another is explained.

Section V illustrates the basic operations using common fractions, decimal fractions, percents, and ratios. A number expressed in any one of these forms can be changed to an equivalent number in the other two forms. For example, $\frac{3}{4}$ (a Rational number or fraction) = 75% (a percent) = 0.75 (a decimal fraction). The solution of linear equations is included because they will be necessary to solve problems in subsequent Units. The number properties are used to explain why certain operations are mathematically logical.

Section VI outlines a number of strategies for approaching the solution of problems. These strategies may give the reader a new understanding for the development of problem–solving skills.

Section VII is aimed at those who are interested in the practical applications of mathematics. Simple and compound interest as well as the nominal and effective rates are included. Break–even Analysis may be helpful to those who are beginning a business or are having difficulty in showing a profit in their current business. Frequency Distributions and measures of central tendency, and probability have useful applications. The Unit on Practical Applications of Mathematics consists of a set of problems and may be considered as an extension of the Unit on Problem–solving Strategies.

Section VIII demonstrates the use of the operations of Intersection and Union of Sets. Since both Union and Intersection are binary operations, some of the properties of the set of Real Numbers are also properties when dealing with operations on sets. Venn Diagrams make the solution of many interesting problems much easier.

Section IX includes plotting points on a line and on a plane and this leads to the graphing of linear equations. The separation of a plane into three regions "equal to", "less than" and "greater than" are illustrated. Union and intersection of linear relations show the graphic solution of simultaneous equations. The slope of a line, the length of a line segment, and the determination of the condition of a linear relation are included.

Section X is a brief introduction to Mathematical Logic. The nature of mathematics, the differences between inductive and deductive reasoning, and the use of syllogisms in mathematics are included. Some geometrical proofs and conjectures provide facts without the rigor of Euclidean geometry. Truth tables are introduced to illustrate the meaning of topics such as: negating a statement, the use of conjunctions and disjunctions, equivalence, implications, converse statements, the use of contrapositives, and tautologies.

This book was written for adults and one of the differences between adult learners and non–adult learners is that adult learners have a much wider range of experiences – both practical and mathematical. In addition, adults are responsible for their own learning and as a consequence their self evaluation of their learning may be more accurate than that of a non–adult learner.

Most books require the reader to begin on page 1 and continue page by page until the end. Although there is something of interest in each Unit, it is recommended that the reader selects and begins at those Sections or Units in which he/she has the greatest interest or need.

If the vocabulary or use of symbols is unfamiliar to you, refer to a previous section of the book that you may have overlooked.

If this book is being used in a classroom setting, the instructor – in consultation with the participants – will administer the Pre–Test for each Section and determine the level of competence in order to ensure that adequate time is allotted for those topics that are of the greatest interest to the participants.

This book contains 22 units (major topics), exercises and problems. The amount of concentrated study in a formal classroom setting should be determined by the instructor who should assess the abilities of the participants before the course begins. The individual reader should examine the contents of the book and make personal decisions regarding the amount of learning she/he requires.

Acknowledgments

The author wishes to thank Steve Potvin for his many hours of patiently clearing viruses from my computer and formatting the text whenever I touched the wrong key or misused the various commands for making changes to the text.

I wish to acknowledge the contributions of problems given to me by Allan Potvin, Carol Potvin, and Angela Potvin.

I wish also to thank Rex Buckland, Roger Carter, Frank Jarka, Paul McGuire, Ellen Potvin and Kenneth Watson for their suggestions after having read parts of the text.

Special thanks are also extended to Bob Shaughnessey for his assiduous reading of the text and his diligent attention to detail in providing the answers to the Exercises.

Section I – Addition, Subtraction, Multiplication, Division of Whole Numbers
Pre–Test I

Complete the following Exercises and then check the answers which can be found at the back of the book.   If your score is 18–20, go on to the next Section. If your score is 15–16, review those sections that contain material relevant to the problems that were not solved correctly. If your score is less than 15, begin at page 1, read the text, and do most exercises. Then complete the Post–Test at the end of the Unit to check your improvement. Do not use a calculator until you have completed Unit 1.

1. What does each of the following symbols mean?

< means   = means   > means

2. If you have 16 tiles and you need 23 tiles, how many more tiles must you buy?

3. Add 9 + 8 + 7 + 6 in two different ways;

4 Add 1 8 8
       3 5 7
       2 3 4

5. Subtract 1 2 3
           2 5

6. Multiply 2 4
          3 6

7. Divide $11\overline{)165}$

8. Add 7 3 8 5
      1 9 2 7

9. Subtract 3 7 5
         7 8

10. Multiply 2 1 8
         2 6

11. Divide $18\overline{)666}$

12. Janet went to the market and bought 20 kg of carrots, 9 kg of green beans, and 16 kg of broccoli. What was the weight of Janet's purchase?

13. Joan bought 112 pills. She used 84 of them. How many pills does Joan have now?

14. Mary made 23 ornaments for the bazaar. Helen made 15 times as many. How many ornaments did Helen make? Calculate by using decomposition.

15. Circle the numbers that are divisible by 3. Explain how you did this.

32 33 34 35 36 37 38 39 40 41 42 43 44 45 46 47 48

16. List all of the factors of 64.

17. Determine the sum of 1 to 26 without using addition. Demonstrate how this was done.

Score _____   Date _____

2

Unit 1 — Sets, Numbers, Addition, Subtraction, Multiplication, Division of Whole Numbers

OBJECTIVES

- identify a set
- demonstrate the difference between a number and a numeral
- determine if one number is greater than or less than or equal to another number
- demonstrate that 0 added to a number does not alter the sum
- add numbers consisting of up to four digits
- add numbers in any order without altering the sum
- solve problems using addition
- subtract numbers of up to four digits
- demonstrate that multiplication is a shortcut for repeated addition
- demonstrate that 0 subtracted from any number leaves that number unchanged
- demonstrate that the order of subtraction cannot be changed
- solve problems using subtraction
- identify the multiplicand, the multiplier and the product
- identify the factors of a given number
- demonstrate that any number multiplied by 0 is equal to 0
- demonstrate that any number multiplied by 1 is equal to that number
- demonstrate that the order of multiplication will not alter the product
- identify the difference between a row and a column in an array of numbers
- multiply numbers in which the multiplicand has three digits and the multiplier has two digits
- solve problems using multiplication
- identify the divisor, dividend and the quotient
- demonstrate that division is the separation of a number into equal parts
- demonstrate why division by 0 is undefined
- demonstrate that the order of division cannot be changed
- demonstrate that division is a shortcut for repeated subtraction
- demonstrate how it can be determined that a number is divisible by 2, 3, 5, 9, 10 or 11
- demonstrate the difference between a prime and a composite number
- divide three digit numbers by two digit numbers
- demonstrate what is done with a remainder
- demonstrate the addition of numbers that are in a special sequence
- demonstrate the ability to add or subtract hours, minutes and seconds
- demonstrate the ability to multiply by decomposition
- solve problems using division of numbers, adding special sequences and multiplying by decomposition

What is a Set? What is a Number? Order of Numbers

A set is a collection of objects.

It should be noted that the only thing common among the sets below is that each contains three objects. The idea of 'threeness' is what we call the number of objects in each collection (set). When we answer the question, "How many objects are there in each set?" we may write 3.

Here, 3 is a symbol (numeral) that stands for the number three. We may use many symbols to denote 3. Some examples are: 2 + 1, 5 − 2, iii, ///, 1 + 1 + 1, 6 ÷ 2, III etc. Numbers that answer the question, "How many?" are called cardinal numbers.

Each set in the diagram below contains three elements even though the elements are not the same.

If we say that "5 is greater than 8", (5 > 8) we mean that the numeral 5 (the symbol for five) is greater in physical size than the numeral 8 (the symbol for eight), but the number 5 is less than the number 8.

For any positive Whole number 1, 2, 3, 4, 5, 6 . . . (the three dots mean "and so on") it can be determined that one number is less than, the symbol is (<), equal to (=), or greater than (>) another number.

Numbers may be represented on a number line as follows:
0 1 2 3 4 5 6 7 8 9 10 11 12 13 14 15 16 17 18 19 20 21 22 23 24 →

The arrow at the end of the line means "and so on".

Any number to the right of another number on the number line is greater than the number to the left on a number line.

1 2 3 4 5 6 7 8 9 10 11 12 13 14 15 16 17 18 19 20 21 22 23 24 25 →

Example 1: 7 > 4 because 7 is to the right of 4.   6 < 12 because 6 is to the left of 12.
9 = 6 + 3 because 6 + 3 is just another way of writing 9. Comparisons may be made easier by knowing that if seven is greater than four (7 > 4), then 4 must be less than seven (4 < 7). Another way of determining if a number is greater than, less than, or equal to another number is by matching.

4

Example 2: Is 6 greater than, equal to, or less than 4?

There are 6 objects in the column on the left and four objects in the column to the right. (Rows are horizontal and go from left to right. Columns are vertical and go up and down.) When we match the objects on the left to those on the right, we notice that there are two objects that cannot be matched. Therefore, we say that 6 is greater than 4 by 2 and we write this as $6 - 4 = 2$.

Exercise 1

1. Insert the correct symbol between each of the following:

a) 5   8   b) 6   4   c) 8   2 + 4   d) 12   9

e) 11   14   f) 7   (5 + 3)   g) (4 + 5)   9   h) 5   6

2. Write each of the following numbers in three different ways:

Example: $8 = 5 + 3, 8 = 4 + 4, 8 = 7 + 1$.

a) 5 =   b) 7 =
c) 9   d) 4 =

3. Insert the symbol <, =, > between each of the following:

a)

b)

c)

d)

Addition

When we write $3 + 4 = 7$, this means that $3 + 4$ is just another way of writing 7. This may be shown by the following illustration.

X X X + X X X X = 7   and X X X X + X X X = 7
   3   +   4   = 7   4   +   3   = 7

This means that a set of three plus a set of four equals a set of seven. It is also true that $0 + 7 = 7$, $1 + 6 = 7$, $2 + 5 = 7$, $4 + 3 = 7$, $5 + 2 = 7$, $6 + 1 = 7$ and $7 + 0 = 7$

5

6 + 4 = 10 may be illustrated as follows:

X X X X X X + X X X X = X X X X X X X X X X
    6   +   4   =   10

Exercise 2

1. How many objects are there in each of the following sets?

a)
b)
c)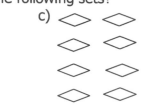
d)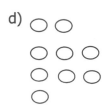

e)
f)
g)

2. Add the following as shown in the Example:

Example: 6 + 4 = 10   X X X X X X + X X X X = X X X X X X X X X X

a)   1 + 4 =

b)   3 + 5 =

c)   4 + 5 =

d)   6 + 5 =

e)   7 + 7 =

3. John has $6 and Paul has $7 more than John. How much money does Paul have?

4. If 8 kilograms of nails are added to 9 kilograms of nails, how many kilograms of nails are there?

5. If you have 6 tiles and you need 13 tiles, how many tiles do you have to buy?

6. A store sold 5 shirts on Friday, 7 on Saturday, and 6 on Sunday. How many shirts were sold during the three days?

7. You have a set of 5 dinner plates. You have invited 8 people for dinner. How many more dinner plates do you need? Draw a diagram to show this as an addition fact and do not forget to include yourself.

8. The following triangle is called a magic triangle because if you place each of the following numbers, 1, 2, 3, 4, 5, 6 in the circles in a certain way, each side of the triangle will have a sum of 9. Some guessing may be required. Complete this in more than 1 way.

$$\begin{array}{cc} \bigcirc & \bigcirc \\ \bigcirc\bigcirc & \bigcirc\bigcirc \\ \bigcirc\bigcirc\bigcirc & \bigcirc\bigcirc\bigcirc \end{array}$$

Order of Addition

X X X + X X X X = X X X X ׀ X X X = X X X X X X X
 3   +   4   =   4 + 3 =   7

Check the Addition Table 0 – 9 and you should notice that the order in which numbers are added does not alter the sum. Choose any two numbers from 0 to 9. Fill in the spaces below by reversing the order of addition.

_____ + _____ = _____   _____ + _____ = _____

Addition Table 0 – 9

+	0	1	2	3	4	5	6	7	8	9
0	0	1	2	3	4	5	6	7	8	9
1	1	2	3	4	5	6	7	8	9	10
2	2	3	4	5	6	7	8	9	10	11
3	3	4	5	6	7	8	9	10	11	12
4	4	5	6	7	8	9	10	11	12	13
5	5	6	7	8	9	10	11	12	13	14
6	6	7	8	9	10	11	12	13	14	15
7	7	8	9	10	11	12	13	14	15	16
8	8	9	10	11	12	13	14	15	16	17
9	9	10	11	12	13	14	15	16	17	18

The following observations should be made: When 0 is used in addition, the sum is equal to the other addend. In other words, the addition of 0 does not alter the sum.

Examples: $0 + 3 = 3, 0 + 7 = 7, 8 + 0 = 8$

Adding Three Digits

Let us now add $3 + 4 + 6$

We will associate the 4 with the 3 and then add 6. Or, we may associate the 4 with the 6 and this sum will be added to 3. Note that the result is the same, 13. Therefore, to add three numbers, we may: associate the middle number with the first number and then add the third number: or we may associate the middle number with the third number and then add the first number: or we may associate the first and the third numbers and then add the middle number. This is another example showing that the order in which numbers are added will not alter the sum.

```
(X X X + X X X X) + X X X X X X          X X X  +  (X X X X + X X X X X X)
   (3    +   4)  +     6                    3 +     (4    +      6)
         7       +     6    = 13            3 +          10         = 13
```

That is, $3 + 4 + 6 = (3 + 4) + 6$ is the same as $3 + (4 + 6)$ and is the same as $(3 + 6) + 4$.

Exercise 3

1. Add each of the following:

a) $6 + 3 =$ b) $7 + 6 =$ c) $5 + 7 =$ d) $8 + 9 =$

e) $6 + 8 =$ f) $7 + 8 =$ g) $6 + 9 =$ h) $7 + 9 =$

2. Add the following and make a statement about the order in which numbers are added:

Example: $1 + 5 + 3 = 9$ and $1 + (5 + 3) = 9$ and $(1 + 5) + 3 = 9$ and $(1 + 3) + 5 = 9$

a) $(2 + 3) + 4 =$ $(4 + 2) + 3 =$ $2 + (4 + 3) =$ $4 + (3 + 2) =$

b) $(1 + 2) + 3 =$ $1 + (3 + 2) =$ $(3 + 1) + 2 =$ $(2 + 3) + 1 =$

c) $(5 + 3) + 7 =$ $3 + (5 + 7) =$ $(7 + 3) + 5 =$ $(5 + 7) + 3 =$

d) $4 + (6 + 0) =$ $(6 + 4) + 0 =$ $6 + (0 + 4) =$ $0 + (4 + 6) =$

Statement

e) Choose b) from above. Are there any other ways of adding these numbers? List them.

3. In how many ways can 5 + 6 + 7 be added?   List these.

The following exercises illustrate the reason why you should form the habit of examining the numbers before you begin the solution of a problem.

4. Add each of the following in the easiest way:

1 + 8 + 9 + 2 = (8 + 2) + (9 + 1) = 10 + 10 = 20

Example: 4 + 7 + 6 + 3 = (4 + 6) + (7 + 3) = 10 + 10 = 20

a) 7 + 2 + 8 + 3 =

b) 4 + 5 + 5 + 6 =

c) 3 + 5 + 7 + 5 =

d) 9 + 4 + 4 + 2 =

5. Since the order of addition will not alter the sum, examine each of the following sets of numbers and add the four numbers in the easiest way. Show how you added these numbers.

a) 9 + 8 + 6 + 7 =

b) 4 + 7 + 3 + 6 =

c) 5 + 9 + 0 + 1 =

d) 4 + 0 + 6 + 1 =

e) 2 + 7 + 8 + 3 =

f) 9 + 5 + 1 + 7 =

g) 7 + 8 + 3 + 2 =

h) 8 + 9 + 2 + 4 =

i) 5 + 7 + 4 + 3 =

Addition that Results in a Two–Digit Number

Consider the following set of objects.

The number of objects may be determined by counting. The number of this set is thirteen and the numeral for this number is 13. Since 13 is greater than ten, we can see by grouping that 13 is equal to 1 set of ten and 3 ones. Notice that the objects may be grouped in any way that results in 1 set of ten and 3 ones, such as:

    X X X XX + X X X X X + X X X 5 + 5 + 3
or, X X X X X X X X X + X X X 10 + 3

or, X X X + X X X X X X + X X X X   3 + 6 + 4

In the same way, 16 is equal to 1 set of ten and 6 ones:

16 = X X X X X X X X X X + X X X X X X

The number 24 is equal to 2 sets of ten and 4 ones:

24 = X X X X X X X X X X + X X X X X X X X X X + X X X X

24 may be considered as 2 tens and 4 ones. Or, it may be considered as 1 set of 10 and 14 ones. The 14 ones can be considered as 1 set of ten and 4 ones. 24 is equal to 2 tens and 4 ones. In the same way, 36 is equal to 3 sets of ten and 6 ones.

Addition of Two–Digit Numbers

Example 1: If we wish to add numbers in which more than one digit results, we proceed as follows: 12 + 15 = 1 ten and 2 ones + 1 ten and 5 ones and this equals 2 tens and 7 ones or 27. Note that we added 2 ones and 5 ones to get 7 ones and we added 1 ten and 1 ten to obtain 2 tens. Therefore, the sum is 27.

Example 2: If we wish to add two–digit numbers, we may proceed in many different ways.

Method 1: Add 12 + 14
12 = 1 ten and 2 ones
14 = 1 ten and 4 ones
12 + 14 = 2 tens and 6 ones or 26 because 10 + 2 + 10 + 4 = 20 + 6 or 26.

Example 3: Now consider the following addition: 24 + 17 =?

Method 2:

24 = 2 tens and 4 ones
17 = 1 ten and 7 ones
Add 2 tens and 1 ten to obtain 3 tens. Then add 4 ones and 7 ones to obtain 11 ones. 11 ones is 1 ten and 1 one. Therefore, we have 3 tens plus 1 ten (that is 4 tens) and 1 one. Therefore, the sum of 24 and 17 is 41.

Method 3:

x x x x x x x x x x   x x x x x x x x x x   x x x x   x x x x x x x x x x   x x x x x x x
     10   +   10   + 4 +   10   +   7

or, 10 + 10 + 10 + 11. But 11 = 10 + 1. This gives us 10 + 10 + 10 + 10 + 1. Therefore, 24 + 17 = 41.

Method 4:

T O   (T is the tens column and 0 is the ones column.)
2 4
1 7
  11   7 ones plus 4 ones = 11 ones or 1 ten and 1 one.
1+ 1   1 ten + 1 ten + 2 tens = 4 tens. Therefore, 24 + 17 = 41.
4 1

Exercise 4

1. Add each of the following (T indicates the Tens column and 0 indicates the Ones column):

a) T O	b) T O	c) T O	d) T O	e) T O	f) T O
4 7	8 5	3 4	4 6	2 8	3 6
5 3	6 6	2 7	4 8	5 2	3 4

2. You have $43 in your pocket. Your friend gives you $21. How much money do you now have?

3. James had 27 liters of gas in his car. He then bought 31 liters of gas. How many liters of gas does James have in his tank now?

4. Peter had 43 nails. He bought 37 more. How many nails does Peter have?

5. Mary made 33 dolls for the bazaar. She then made 24 more. How many dolls did Mary make?

6. A grocery store sold 12 apples on Monday, 8 on Tuesday, and 13 on Wednesday. How many apples were sold during the three days?

7. At a car wash, John washed 14 cars, Bill washed 22 cars, and Henry washed 21 cars. How many cars were washed?

8. Add 18, 14, and 12. Then add 12, 18, and 14. Then add 14, 18, and 12. What do you notice?

18 + 14 + 12 =   12 + 18 + 14 =   14 + 18 + 12 =

9. Mary wrote three numbers on a piece of paper. The sum of the numbers was seventeen. All of the numbers were different and each number was less than 8. What were the numbers?

10. Add the following in the easiest way and show the order of your addition:

a) 23 + 13 + 7 =   b) 7 + 6 + 24 =   c) 6 + 16 + 4 =

d) 22 + 7 + 8 =   e) 32 + 36 + 8 =   f) 44 + 19 + 6 =

Addition that Results in a Three–Digit Number

Consider the following objects. Separate the X's into sets of ten to determine how many there are.

```
X X X X X X X X X X X X X X X X X X X X X X X X X X X X X X X X X X X X X
X X  X X X X X X X X X X X X X X X X X X X X X X X X X X X X X X X  X X X
X X X X X X X X X X X X X X X X X X X X  X X X X X X X X X X
```

It can be determined by counting that there are 104 objects. We may also group the objects in sets of tens and ones.

12

```
X X X X X X X X X X    X X X X X X X X X X    X X X X X X X X X X    X X X X X X X X X X
X X X X X X X X X X    X X X X X X X X X X    X X X X X X X X X X    X X X X X X X X X X
X X X X X X X X X X    X X X X X X X X X X    X X X X
```

We now have ten sets of ten and four ones. The ten sets of ten may be combined into one set of one hundred. If we add the four ones, we will have one hundred and four or 104.

If we wish to add 46 + 24 + 57, we will proceed by adding the ones and then adding the tens.

```
H T O        H will indicate the Hundreds column.
  4 6        Add the ones to get 17.
  2 4        17 ones = 1 ten and 7 ones.  We will add one ten to the tens column.
  5 7        Add the tens column including the 1 ten from the ones column.
1 2 7        12 tens = 1 hundred and 2 tens.  Therefore, the sum is 127.
```

Exercise 5

1. Write the number of hundreds, tens and ones in each of the following:

	Hundreds	Tens	Ones			Hundreds	Tens	Ones
a) 947 =					b) 435 =			
c) 308 =					d) 726 =			
e) 500 =					f) 638 =			

2. Group the following into sets of ten by circling each set of ten and determine the three-digit number that results:

```
X X X X X X X X X X X  X X X X X X X X X X X X X X X X X X X X X X X
X X X X X X X X X X X X X X X X X X X X X X X X X X X X
X X X X X X X X X X X X X X X X X X X X X X X
X X X X X X X X X X X X X X X X X X X X X X X X X X X X X X X
```

3. Add the following numbers:

```
a)  H T O        b)  H T O        c)  H T O        d)  H T O
      6 7              2 8              5 6              9 7
      8 6              3 9              3 8              5 8
      4 7              6 2              4 7              6 6
```

4. You had $74 in your pocket. Your friend gave you $27. How much money do you have now?

5. A merchant sold 26 shirts on Monday, 32 on Tuesday, 29 on Wednesday, and 42 on Thursday. How many shirts did he sell during the four days?

Addition Using Three-Digit and Four-Digit Numbers
100 is equal to 10 tens. To add numbers using 3 digits, we proceed in the same way as we did with adding of two-digit numbers.

Example 1: Add 236 + 144
```
H T O
2 3 6        4 + 6 = 10.
1 4 4        4 + 3 = 7 tens (plus 1 ten from above) gives 8 tens.
3 8 0        1 + 2 hundreds = 3 hundreds.
```

Example 2:   Add 526 and 357
```
H T O
5 2 6
3 5 7        7 + 6 = 13 = 1 ten and 3 ones.
8 8 3        5 + 2 + 1 = 8 tens and 3 + 5 = 8 hundreds.
```

Example 3:   Four-digit numbers are added in the same way that three-digit numbers are added.
```
4 7 1 6        5 + 6  = 11 ones which is 1 ten and 1 one.
3 4 7 5        7 tens + 1 ten + 1 ten = 9 tens.
8 1 9 1        4 hundreds + 7 hundreds = 11 hundreds which is 1 thousand and 1
                                             hundred.
```
1 thousand + 3 thousands + 4 thousands = 8 thousands.

Exercise 6

1. Add each of the following:

a) 5 3 4   b) 2 5 5   c) 5 6 4   d) 6 4 7   e) 3 5 6
   3 2 7   4 3 9   3 8 6   2 9 8   4 5 5

2. Add each of the following:

a) 3 7 4   b) 4 3 7 5   c) 6 4 9 5   d) 3 8 4 7   e) 5 7 0 7
   6 2 4 8   3 7 4 1   2 8 3 5   5 4 6 2   3 4 5 7

3. Paul drove 320 km before he stopped for coffee. He then drove another 268 km. How far did Paul drive?

4. A truck driver picked up 560 kg of scrap metal in one city. He added 493 kg in the next city. He then went to a third city where he loaded another 423 kg. How much weight is the truck now carrying?

5. Shirley was earning $32,524 a year. She received an increase in her pay of $326 a year. What is Shirley's new yearly salary?

6. A truck driver unloaded 320 kg of stones at one house, 450 kg at another house, and 526 kg at a third house. He still had 52 kg of stones in his truck. How many kg of stones did the truck have when it left the quarry?

Subtraction of One–Digit Numbers

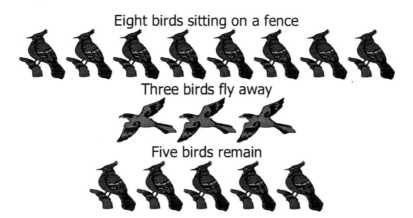

Eight birds sitting on a fence

Three birds fly away

Five birds remain

Subtraction is the operation of taking away. For example, if 8 birds were sitting on a fence and 3 of them flew away, there would be 5 birds still sitting on the fence. This may be written as $8 - 3 = 5$. For example, if Robert had 9 cookies and he ate 4 of them, he would have 5 left.

Notice the relationship between addition and subtraction. When we subtract 3 from 8, the answer is 5 and this is called the difference. The difference plus the number that was subtracted will give a sum that was the original number. That is, if $8 - 3 = 5$, then $5 + 3 = 8$. Unlike addition, the order in which numbers are subtracted cannot be altered. $8 - 5$ is not the same as $5 - 8$.

Observe the following table for subtraction:

It should be noted that: 0 subtracted from any number is that number. Each row consists of the first number and each subsequent entry decreases by 1.

The diagonal consists of 0's only.
This table shows the positive differences only.

-	0	9	8	7	6	5	4	3	2	1
0	0	9	8	7	6	5	4	3	2	1
9	9	0	1	2	3	4	5	6	7	8
8	8	1	0	1	2	3	4	5	6	7
7	7	2	1	0	1	2	3	4	5	6
6	6	3	2	1	0	1	2	3	4	5
5	5	4	3	2	1	0	1	2	3	4
4	4	5	4	3	2	1	0	1	2	3
3	3	6	5	4	3	2	1	0	1	2
2	2	7	6	5	4	3	2	1	0	1
1	1	8	7	6	5	4	3	2	1	0

Exercise 7

1. Find the difference of each of the following by using the Table.

a) $5 - 3 =$ b) $6 - 4 =$ c) $5 - 2 =$ d) $7 - 5 =$

e) $4 - 3 =$ f) $7 - 3 =$ g) $8 - 4 =$ h) $6 - 3 =$

i) $8 - 5 =$ j) $9 - 6 =$ k) $7 - 2 =$ l) $8 - 3 =$

m) $7 - 0 =$ n) $5 - 0 =$ o) $6 - 2 =$ p) $3 - 3 =$

q) $9 - 4 =$ r) $8 - 1 =$ s) $9 - 5 =$ t) $9 - 2 =$

2. Roberta went to the store with $9. She bought some batteries for $6. How much money does Roberta have now?

3. Jim had a piece of string that was 8 meters long. He cut off 3 meters. How much string was there in the larger piece?

Subtracting a One–Digit Number from a Two–Digit Number

Example 1: Note the pattern in the following subtractions. As the number to be subtracted decreases by 1, the difference decreases by 1.

$$
\begin{array}{r} 2\,5 \\ -\,0 \\ \hline 2\,5 \end{array}
\qquad
\begin{array}{r} 2\,5 \\ -\,1 \\ \hline 2\,4 \end{array}
\qquad
\begin{array}{r} 2\,5 \\ -\,2 \\ \hline 2\,3 \end{array}
\qquad
\begin{array}{r} 2\,5 \\ -\,3 \\ \hline 2\,2 \end{array}
\qquad
\begin{array}{r} 2\,5 \\ -\,4 \\ \hline 2\,1 \end{array}
\qquad
\begin{array}{r} 2\,5 \\ -\,5 \\ \hline 2\,0 \end{array}
$$

When we want to subtract 6 from 25, we will observe the following sets:

Example 2: Subtract 25 − 6

```
25 = X X X X X X X X X X + X X X X X X X X X X + X X X X X
 6 =                                                 X X X X X X
25 − 6 = 25 = X X X X X X X X X X + X X X X X X X X X X X X X X X X
    − 6 =                                               X X X X X X
      25 − 6 = X X X X X X X X X X + X X X X X X X X X X
            =           10            +          9              = 19
```

The above subtraction can be accomplished without drawing the above diagram.

2 5   1 set of ten is taken from two sets of ten. We now have 1 ten and 15 ones.
− 6   15 ones − 6 ones is equal to 9 ones. 0 tens from 1 ten = 1 ten.
1 9   Therefore, 25 − 6 = 19.

The process by which we combined the set of 10 with the set of 5 has been incorrectly called "borrowing". What really happens is that one set of ten is combined with the set of ones. For instance, if a grocer has a bag of 10 apples and 3 single apples, he may open the bag of ten apples and add the 3 single apples to have 13 apples when a customer wants to buy 12 apples. The grocer will have 1 apple after the purchase. If we want to perform the following operation: 23 − 7 =? We know that 23 is 2 tens and 3 ones or 1 ten and 13 ones. We will separate the set of 23 into a set of 10 and a set of 13. Notice that we still have two sets of 10 and a set of 3. We can now subtract the set of 7 from the set of 13 to obtain a set of 6 ones. We now have 1 set of ten and 6 ones, or 16.

```
  23 = X X X X X X X X X X  +  X X X X X X X X X X  +  X X X
 − 7 =                                               X X X X X X X
23 − 7 = 23  = X X X X X X X X X X + X X X X X X X X X X X  X X X
   − 7 =                                             X X X  X X X X
23 − 7 =         X X X X X X X X X X + X X X  X X X = 16
                      10            +      6        = 16
```

Diagrams cannot be drawn every time a subtraction is made. The combining of sets is done mentally and becomes easier with practice.

2 5   1 set of ten is taken from 2 sets of ten.
− 7   15 ones minus 7 ones = 8 ones. 1 ten − 0 tens =1 ten. Therefore, 25 − 7 =18.
1 8.

Subtracting a Two–Digit Number from a Two–Digit Number

A shorter method may be used for subtracting 23 − 15.

Example 1: 23 − 15 =? Now the problem looks as follows.

```
23 = 10 + 10 + 3 X X X X X X X X X X + X X X X X X X X X X + X X X
15 = 10 + 5      X X X X X X X X X X + X X X X X
```
Notice that we cannot subtract a set of 5 from a set of 3. We will combine one set of ten to obtain one set of ten and one set of 3 or 13.

```
23 = X X X X X X X X X + X X X X X X X X X X    X X X
15 = X X X X X X X X X X +                      X X    X X X
23 − 15 = X X X X X X X X = 8
```

We can now subtract 5 ones from 13 ones to obtain 8 ones. One ten subtracted from one ten is 0 tens. Therefore, 23 − 15 = 8.

Example 2: Subtract 54 − 36

```
5 4
3 6
1 8
```
1 set of ten is taken from 5 sets of ten and this leaves 4 sets of ten. The set of ten is combined with the set of 4 ones to make a set of 14 ones.
14 ones minus 6 ones = 8 ones and 4 tens − 3 tens = 1 ten.
Therefore, 54 − 36 = 18.

Exercise 8

1. Perform the following subtractions without using diagrams:

a) 3 8
    1 6

b) 3 6
    2 4

c) 4 6
    2 3

d) 8 8
    5 3

e) 9 4
    4 8

f) 8 4
    2 7

g) 5 7
    4 6

h) 6 9
    5 3

i) 6 3
    3 7

j) 5 6
    2 8

k) 6 8
    1 9

l) 7 0
    3 1

2. Pauline went to the store with $90. She spent $37. How much money does Pauline have now?

3. Fred rode his bicycle west for 47 km and then he rode back east on the same route for 29 km. How far is Fred from his starting point?

4. Maria has a rug that is 82 m^2 and she wishes to cut off 14 m^2. What is the size of the larger piece?

5. Joan bought 112 pills. She used 84 of them. How many pills does Joan have now?

6. George received a paycheck for $750. The employer deducted $56 for taxes and $12 for medical insurance. How much was the net amount of pay? Solve this problem using two different methods.

7. Frank filled his gas tank with 53 liters. He drove and used 27 liters. How many liters remain in the gas tank?

Verification of Subtraction

Subtraction may be verified by adding the result of the subtraction (the difference) to the number being subtracted. For example, 36 – 15 = 21. It is also true that 21 + 15 = 36.

$$
\begin{array}{r}
3\ 6 \\
-1\ 5 \\
\hline
=2\ 1 \\
+1\ 5 \\
\hline
=3\ 6
\end{array}
$$

8. Subtract each of the following and then add the difference to the number being subtracted:

a)   9   b)   7   c)   8   d)   12   e)   15

   – 4   – 3   – 3   – 7   – 8

    =   =   =   =   =

  + 4   + 3   + 3   + 7   + 8

    =   =   =   =   =

Subtraction of Two-Digit Numbers from Three-Digit Numbers
Remember that the number 375 tells us that there are 3 hundreds, 7 tens and 5 ones. We also know that 375 = 300 + 70 + 5. If we wish to perform the following subtraction 375 – 78, we will proceed as follows:

$$
\begin{array}{lll}
3\ 7\ 5 & = 3\ 6\ 15 & = 2\ 16\ 15 \\
\quad 7\ 8 & & =\ -7\quad 8 \\
\hline
2\ 9\ 7 & & \ \ 2\quad 9\quad 7
\end{array}
$$

1 set of tens was combined with the ones and 1 set of hundreds was combined with the tens.

Exercise 9

1. Perform the following subtractions:

a) H T O   b) H T O   c) H T O   d) H T O

       5 1   8 5   6 3 8   5 5 6

       3 7   3 4   4 6 7   2 0 8

2. Use subtraction to find the difference. Check the answers by adding the difference to the number that was subtracted.

a) 1 4 5   b) 2 1 6   c) 4 5 9   d) 1 3 2   e) 2 9 0   f) 1 1 6
   −   5 4   − 1 7   − 6 3   − 3 5   − 8 1   − 9 3
   =   =   =   =   =   =
   +   5 4   + 1 7   + 6 3   + 3 5   + 8 1   + 9 3
   =   =   =   =   =   =

Subtraction Using Four-Digit Numbers

Subtract the following: 3, 4 5 7 − 1, 5 4 2

```
T H T O
3 4 5 7
1 5 4 2
    1 5                7 − 2 = 5 ones and 5 − 4 = 1 ten
3 4 5 7  =  2 14 5 7   We cannot subtract 5 hundreds from 4 hundreds.  We will
                       take 1 thousand which is 10 hundreds.  Now there are 14
1 5 4 2  =  1   5 4 2  hundreds  and 2 thousands.
         =  1   9 1 5
```

Exercise 10

1. Perform the following subtractions and check by addition:

a) H T 0   b) H T 0   c) H T 0   d) H T 0
    3 5 7   5 8 3   7 2 1   5 9 7
    1 6 4   4 7 4   4 3 2   3 2 8
   =   =   =   =
   +1 6 4   4 7 4   +4 3 2   +3 2 8
   =   =   =   =

2. Use subtraction to find the difference and check by addition.

a) 1 5 2 7   b) 4 0 3 6   c) 5 1 7 9   d) 3 6 0 2
      6 3 1   2 1 5 0   2 0 8 4   3 0 4 6
    =   =   =   =
    + 6 3 1   +2 1 5 0   +2 0 8 4   +3 0 4 6
    =   =   =   =

3. John drove 1,280 meters on his motorcycle. Joyce drove 435 meters less. How far did Joyce drive?

4. Paul earned $3,136 every two weeks. Income tax of $940 was deducted from each payment. How much money did he receive every two weeks?

5. 5,375 kilograms of sand were used to fill Cheryl's sandbox. Sylvia's sandbox required 425 kg less. How many kilograms were used to fill Sylvia's sandbox?

Multiplication of One-Digit Numbers

Consider the following sets. X X X X X X   X X X   X X X and X X X X   X X X X   X X X
There are four sets of three and there are three sets of four.

In 3 sets of 4, it can be determined that there are 12 objects in the sets by counting. We would be thinking that $4 + 4 + 4 = 12$. Or, we could say that $3 \times 4 = 12$. Notice that multiplication is a shortcut for repeated addition.

It is also true that 4 sets of 3 is also 12. XXX XXX XXX XXX. 4 sets of 3 is equal to 3 sets of 4.

Multiplication Table 0 – 9

x	0	1	2	3	4	5	6	7	8	9
0	0	0	0	0	0	0	0	0	0	0
1	0	1	2	3	4	5	6	7	8	9
2	0	2	4	6	8	10	12	14	16	16
3	0	3	6	9	12	15	18	21	24	27
4	0	4	8	12	16	20	24	28	32	36
5	0	5	10	15	20	25	30	35	40	45
6	0	6	12	18	24	30	36	42	48	54
7	0	7	14	21	28	35	42	49	56	63
8	0	8	16	24	32	40	48	56	64	72
9	0	9	18	27	36	45	54	63	72	81

The numbers that are multiplied are called factors (the multiplicand and the multiplier), and the result of the multiplication is called the product.

The following observations should be made:

In $4 \times 5 = 20$, 4 is called the multiplicand, 5 is called the multiplier, and 20 is called the product.

4 and 5 are also said to be factors of 20. A factor of a number divides into that number so that the remainder is equal to 0. The factors of 20 are: 1, 2, 4, 5 10, and 20.

Any number multiplied by 0 is equal to 0. For example, if you have 0 sets of 3, you have 0. Or, $3 \times 0 = 0 + 0 + 0 = 0$

Any number multiplied by 1 leaves the product equal to the multiplicand. For example: $4 \times 1 = 4$, $8 \times 1 = 8$, $0 \times 1 = 0$, etc.

In the multiplication table, if we examine any row, it will be noted that each product going from left to right is increased by a constant. In the fourth row, the constant is 3. Since the multiplicand (at the top of the chart) is increasing by 1, there is one more factor of 3 in each subsequent product.

| 0 | 3 | 6 | 9 | 12 | 15 | 18 | 21 | 24 | 27 |

Select any number, say 7, in the column on the left and 5 in the row at the top. Move your finger along the row until you reach the number for which 5 is at the top. You will notice that the product is 35. Now go to the column on the left and choose 5. Move your finger along that row until you reach the number 7 at the top of the chart. You will note that the product is also 35. Follow the same procedures to check other numbers. It will be noted that the order in which two numbers are multiplied will not change the product.

Note the diagonal from upper left to lower right on the multiplication chart. These are the squares of the numbers. For example, $4 = 2 \times 2$, $25 = 5 \times 5$, $49 = 7 \times 7$, etc. These numbers may be written as $2^2 = 4$, $5^2 = 25$, $7^2 = 49$, etc. 2^2 is read "two squared".

Notice the diagonal beginning at 0 and ending at 81. List the difference between each number.   Do you see a pattern?   What is it?
            Check to see if this difference exists between 9^2 and 10^2.

The number facts found in the multiplication table can be easier to remember if, for example, you know that $7 \times 9 = 63$, you also know that $9 \times 7 = 63$.

Let us now examine the following multiplication: $5 \times 4 \times 3$.

```
0 0 0 0   0 0 0 0   0 0 0 0        0 0 0   0 0 0   0 0 0   0 0 0   0 0 0
0 0 0 0   0 0 0 0   0 0 0 0        0 0 0   0 0 0   0 0 0   0 0 0   0 0 0
0 0 0 0   0 0 0 0   0 0 0 0        0 0 0   0 0 0   0 0 0   0 0 0   0 0 0
0 0 0 0   0 0 0 0   0 0 0 0        0 0 0   0 0 0   0 0 0   0 0 0   0 0 0
0 0 0 0   0 0 0 0   0 0 0 0           4 rows x 3 columns x 5 sets= 60
5 rows x 4 columns x 3 sets = 60
```

Notice that the product in each case is the same. The order in which three (or more) numbers are multiplied will not alter the product.

Exercise 11

1. Write the product of each of the following:

a) 5 x 6 = _____   b) 8 x 7 = _____   c) 6 x 8 = _____   d) 7 x 4 = _____
e) 5 x 7 = _____   f) 3 x 8 = _____   g) 9 x 4 = _____   h) 4 x 9 = _____
i) 6 x 7 = _____   j) 5 x 1 = _____   k) 9 x 1 = _____   l) 1 x 0 = _____
m) 7 x 0 = _____   n) 0 x 8 = _____   o) 0 x 5 = _____   p) 9 x 7 = _____
q) 7 x 6 = _____   r) 7 x 9 = _____   s) 8 x 9 = _____   t) 1 x 11 = _____

2. Write the product of each of the following:

a) 5 x 7 x 3 = _____   b) 7 x 5 x 3 = _____   c) 3 x 7 x 5 = _____

d) 4 x 6 x 3 = _____   e) 6 x 3 x 4 = _____   f) 6 x 3 x 4 = _____

g) 5 x 1 x 4 = _____   h) 6 x 0 x 1 = _____   i) 1 x 1 x 5 = _____

j) 3 x 8 x 2 = _____   k) 9 x 2 x 4 = _____   l) 0 x 0 x 0 = _____

3. Agnes had 8 photographs and Sandra had 6 times as many. How many photographs did Sandra have?

4. A football team was winning 9 – 0. The other team then scored 6 times as many points as the other team had. How many points did the winning team score?

5. Andrew had four books. Matthew had 7 times as many. Anthony had 3 times as many books as Matthew had. How many books did Anthony have?

6. Why is 6 X 8 x 7 = 7 x 6 x 8?

7. What is the product of 10 x 10 x 10?

8. Write a problem in words such that a multiplication is necessary to find the solution. Solve the problem and indicate the product.

Multiplication of Numbers With Two or More Digits

If we wish to multiply 15 x 26, the ones are multiplied by the ones and the tens are multiplied by the ones. Then the ones are multiplied by the tens and the tens are multiplied by the tens.

```
H T O
  1 5        6 ones x 5 = 30 ones or 3 tens
  2 6        6 ones x 1 ten − 6 tens
2 16 30      2 tens x 5 ones = 10 tens and 2 tens x 1 ten = 2 hundred
2 19  0      19 tens = 9 tens and 1 hundred
3  9  0
```

Exercise 12

1. Write each of the following as a three-digit number:

a) 4 hundreds, 13 tens, 12 ones =

b) 6 hundreds, 16 tens, 19 ones =

c) 5 hundreds, 21 tens, 21 ones =

d) 8 hundreds, 15 tens, 32 ones =

e) 4 hundreds, 42 tens, 48 ones =

f) 7 hundreds, 21 tens, 18 ones =

2. Multiply each of the following:

a) H T O	b) H T 0	c) H T O	d) H T O	e) H T O	f) H T O
1 3	8 3	9 5	1 9	8 6	4 8
5 6	2 7	4 8	5 9	2 5	1 3

3. Perform the following multiplications:

a) 2 6	b) 6 4	c) 5 6	d) 1 6	e) 2 2	f) 4 7	g) 5 1
1 8	1 5	1 3	1 9	2 2	1 9	1 7

4) John laid 14 bricks today. Henry laid 11 times the number of bricks that John laid. How many bricks did Henry lay?

5. Mary made 23 ornaments for the bazaar. Helen made 15 times as many. How many ornaments did Helen make?

6. 33 waiters each served 20 people at a banquet. How many people attended the banquet?

7. Paul's house is 11 meters high. His office building is 17 times as high. How high is his office building?

8. Alone Dairy produced 76 cans of milk each day. Barlow Dairy produced 12 times as many cans as Alone Dairy. How many cans did Barlow Dairy produce each day?

9. A basketball team averaged 78 points a game. How many points were scored in 12 games?

10. Newton Furniture Company has 68 employees. The closest competitor has 8 times as many employees. How many employees does the competitor have?

Multiplication of a Three-Digit Number by a One-Digit or Two-Digit Number

Set up a place value chart that includes thousands, hundreds, tens, and ones in order to multiply a three-digit number by a one-digit number or a two-digit number. There are 10 groups of 100 in 1,000. There are ten thousands in 10,000. Ten 10,000 equals one hundred thousand 100,000 and ten one hundred thousands are equal to one million 1,000,000.

```
T   H   T   O
    3   7   5
_____    4      4 ones x 5 ones = 20 ones = 2 tens.
    12  28  20      4 ones x 7 tens = 28 tens = 2 hundreds and 8 tens.
    12  30   0      4 ones x 3 hundreds = 12 hundreds =1 thousand and 2 hundreds.
1   5   0   0      That is, 1,200 + 280 + 20 = 1,500.
```

Or, without using the place value chart,
```
    3 7 5
        4
    ─────
  1 5 0 0
```

Another way of multiplying 375 x 4 is as follows:
4 ones x 5 ones = 20 ones which is equal to 2 tens and 0 ones.
4 ones x 7 tens plus 2 tens is equal to 30 tens. 30 tens equal 300 or 3 hundreds.
4 x 3 hundreds = 12 hundreds plus 3 hundreds = 15 hundreds or 1,500.

Observe the following multiplications and notice what is done mentally:

Multiply 13 4 x 32

```
      1 3 4
        3 2
      ─────
      2 6 8
    4 0 2
    ───────
    4 2 8 8
```

Multiply 256 x 47

```
        2 5 6
          4 7
        ─────
      1 7 9 2
    1 0 2 4
    ─────────
    1 2 0 3 2
```

Exercise 13

1. Find the product of each of the following:

a) 6 3 2
     7

b) 3 8 6
     5

c) 5 7 3
     6

d) 8 3 9
     8

e) 4 2 4
   3 4

f) 3 8 6
   2 7

g) 6 4 2
   5 1

h) 5 0 0
   2 6

2. Sheila's salary was $623 every two weeks. Taxes of $126 were deducted from each paycheck. She received 26 payments each year.

What was Sheila's gross annual salary?

How much did Sheila pay in taxes each year?

What was Sheila's net salary each year?

3. A machine was used for 17 hours each day for 326 days. How many hours was the machine used?

4. A company distributed 1,234 bottles to each of 146 outlets in one day. How many bottles were distributed each day?

The reason for moving the product to the left is that in the first instance we are multiplying ones by ones and so the product will be ones. In the next instance, we are multiplying by tens and therefore the product will be in tens. A similar thing happens when we are multiplying by hundreds or thousands. To see a picture of this, observe the following multiplication.

```
    1 3 5 6
      4 1 2
    2 7 1 2
  1 3 5 6 0      Note that 6 ones multiplied by 1 ten = 60 ones or 6 tens.
5 4 2 4 0 0      6 ones multiplied by 4 hundreds is 24 hundreds or 2,000 + 400
5 5 8 6 7 2
```

It is conventional to omit all of the zeros that are not followed by a non zero number.

Division

Division is an operation in which a number is separated into equal parts. For example, the following set contains 15 elements, and we wish to separate it into three equal parts.

```
    0 0 0 0 0        0 0 0 0 0        0 0 0 0 0
```

If the above markers were objects, we could separate them into 3 sets of five. That is, $5 \div 3 = 5$.

Notice that 3 sets of 5 equal 15. We have separated, that is, divided 15 into 3 sets of 5. Therefore, 15 divided by 3 equals 5. This is written $15 \div 3 = 5$.
The following observations should be noted: if $15 \div 3 = 5$, then $5 \times 3 = 15$:
if $15 \div 5 = 3$, then $3 \times 5 = 15$.

Or, the set of 15 could have been separated (divided) into 5 sets of 3. Therefore, we see that a set of 15 may be divided into 3 sets of 5 (observe the rows below) or 5 sets of 3 (observe the columns below).

```
0 0 0 0 0  or   0 0 0    0 0 0
0 0 0 0 0       0 0 0    0 0 0
0 0 0 0 0       0 0 0
3 sets of 5     5 sets of 3
```

In $15 \div 3 = 5$, 15 is called the dividend, 3 is called the divisor, and 5 is called the quotient.

Multiplying the quotient by the divisor can provide a check for division. If the division is correct, the product will be the dividend.

Another example: $32 \div 4 = 8$. Note that $8 \times 4 = 32$.

Division by Zero

Division by 0 is undefined. $14 \div 0 =$? What number multiplied by 0 equals 14? We have seen that 0 multiplied by any number is 0 (see Multiplication Table.) Therefore, there is no number that will satisfy the operation $14 \div 0$.

Division by 1 leaves the dividend unchanged.

For example, $7 \div 1 = 7$, $9 \div 1 = 9$, $263 \div 1 = 263$, etc.

Multiplication Table Used for Division Facts 0 – 9

X	0	1	2	3	4	5	6	7	8	9
0	0	0	0	0	0	0	0	0	0	0
1	0	1	2	3	4	5	6	7	8	9
2	0	2	4	6	8	10	12	14	16	18
3	0	3	6	9	12	15	18	21	24	27
4	0	4	8	12	16	20	24	28	32	36
5	0	5	10	15	20	25	30	35	40	45
6	0	6	12	18	24	30	36	42	48	54
7	0	7	14	21	28	35	42	49	56	63
8	0	8	16	24	32	40	48	56	64	72
9	0	9	18	27	36	45	54	63	72	81

A multiplication table used in a different manner will provide a means of knowing the basic facts of division.

Choose any number, say 28. If we move our finger on the row and to the left, we will find 4 or 7. If we move the finger upwards in the column, we will find 7 or 4. This means that $28 \div 4 = 7$ and $28 \div 7 = 4$. Note that we are using a multiplication chart that also tells us that $4 \times 7 = 28$ and $7 \times 4 = 28$. If we wish to divide 45 by 3 we would ask the question, "What number, when multiplied by 3, is equal to 45?" The answer is 15. That is, $15 \times 3 = 45$.

The following number facts will assist in performing the operation of division:

If a number is even, it is divisible by 2. Another way of saying this is: if a number is divided by 2, and there is no remainder (other than 0), the number is even. All other whole numbers are odd and are not divisible by 2. An even number may be written as $2n$ (where n is any whole number), and an odd number may be written as $2n + 1$ or $2n - 1$. If we take any even number and add (or subtract) 1, the number will be odd.

If the last digit of a number (the Ones digit) is an even number, the number can be divided by 2. Note that 0 can be divided by 2 and the quotient is 0 because 2 x 0 = 0.

Example: 16 is divisible by 2, i.e. 16 ÷ 2 = 8 which is a Whole number and 8 x 2 = 16. However, when 17 is divided by 2, the result is not a Whole number. Therefore, 17 is an odd number.

If a number ends in 5 it is divisible by 5. Example: 5, 15, 25, 35, 45, 55, 65, 75, 85, 95, 105, 225, etc. are all divisible by 5.

If the ones digit of a two (or more) digit number is 0, the number is divisible by 10. 10, 20, 30, 40, 50, 60, 70, 80, 90, 100, etc. are divisible by 10. It should also be noted that each of these numbers may be divided by 5 and by 2 since 10 is divisible by both 5 and 2. If a number is divisible by another number, then it is also divisible by all of the other factors of the other number.

If the sum of the digits of a number is divisible by 3, the number is divisible by 3. The sum of the digits of 27 is 2 + 7 = 9. 9 is divisible by 3. Therefore, the number 27 is divisible by 3.

If the sum of the digits is divisible by 9, the number is divisible by 9. The sum of the digits of 36, (3 + 6) = 9. 9 is divisible by 9. Therefore, 36 is divisible by 9. It should be noted that the number is also divisible by 3 since 3 x 3 = 9.

If the last two digits of a two-digit number are the same, the number is divisible by 11. For example, 55 ÷ 11 = 5 and 77 ÷ 11 = 7.

If we wish to divide a three-digit number by a one-digit number, we would check to see if 100 is divisible by the one-digit number. If it is, then 200, 300 . . . are divisible by the divisor. Therefore, we just have to look at the last two digits of the hree-digit number. For example, 4 divides into 324 because 4 divides into 100 and therefore, divides into 300 and 4 divides into 24. However, 5 does not divide into 324. 5 divides into 300, but it does not divide into 24.

Exercise 14

1. Perform the following divisions:

a) 18 ÷ 6 = _____   b) 20 ÷ 4 = _____   c) 35 ÷ 7 = _____   d) 48 ÷ 6 = _____

e) 36 ÷ 6 = _____   f) 63 ÷ 7 = _____   g) 48 ÷ 8 = _____   h) 72 ÷ 9 = _____

i) 48 ÷ 4 = _____   j) 28 ÷ 7 = _____   k) 28 ÷ 4 = _____   l) 45 ÷ 5 = _____

2. Betty served 32 pieces of pizza. She had cut each pizza into 8 pieces. How many pizzas were cut?

3. Paula has 5 pies. She wants to serve 39 people. Into how many equal pieces must she cut each pie?

4. Without dividing, circle the numbers that are divisible by 2.

5 8 9 4 10 35 29 44 56 37 17 33 36 48 55

72 81 98 16 75 21 43 66 18 27 39 40 50 51 87

92 99 47 32 64

5. Without dividing, circle the numbers that are divisible by 5.

4 15 17 27 45 80 23 55 33 29 35 65 70 75 95 100

6. Without dividing, circle the numbers that are divisible by 10.

26 40 44 55 60 90 10 15 30 80 36 49 70

Are any of the circled numbers in number 6 also divisible by 5?

Explain

7. Without dividing, circle the numbers that are divisible by 3.

45 33 22 21 35 60 18 48 51 55 68 69 72 81 87 91 96

8. Without dividing, circle the numbers that are divisible by 9.

6 25 27 35 45 51 54 57 62 63 69 72 79 81 85 90 95

9. Are any of the circled numbers in number 8 also divisible by 3?

Explain

10. Without dividing, circle the numbers that are divisible by 11.

1 13 15 22 25 32 33 38 42 44 55 59 65 66 77 82 88 98 99

Factors, Prime and Composite Numbers

A factor of a number divides into that number without having a remainder (other than 0).

Example: 2 is a factor of 6 because 6 ÷ 2 = 3. 3 is a factor of 6 because 6 ÷ 3 = 2.

We say that 2 and 3 are factors of 6. 1 and 6 are also factors of 6.
The factors of 12 are 1, 2, 3, 4, 6, and 12 because each of these numbers divides into 12 with a remainder of 0.

A number that has factors other than one and itself is called a composite number. For example, 4, 6, 8, 9, 10, 12, 14, 15 . . . are examples of composite numbers. A number is called a prime number if it is greater than one and has no factors other than 1 and itself.   For example, 2, 3, 5, 7, 11, 13, 17 are some examples of prime numbers. All whole numbers are either prime or composite numbers.

Exercise 15

1. Write the factors of each of the following numbers:

a)   15   b) 14

c)   12   d) 17

e)   16   f) 31

g)   51   h) 55

i)   27   j) 72

k)   36   l) 22

m)   32   n) 24

o)   64

2. Circle the prime numbers.

  1   2   3   4   5   6   7   8   9   10   11   12   13   14   15   16   17   18   19   20   21

22   23   24   25   26   27   28   29   30   31   32   33   34   35   36   37   38   39   40

3. Circle the composite numbers.

   36 37 38 39 40 41 42 43 44 45 46 47 48 49 50 51 52 53 54 55

      56 57 58 59 60 61 62 63 64 65 66 67 72 87 75 81 83 90

4. If n is a prime number, can n + 1 be a prime number?   Give an example.

Division of a Three–Digit Number by a One–Digit Number

We will use an algorithm (a systematic procedure for performing a task) to divide a three-digit number by a one-digit number.

Example 1: 125 ÷ 5. We check to see if 5 divides into 125. Because the ones digit of 125 is 5, we know that 5 will divide into 125. We will use the following symbol for division: ⟍ We now have 5⟌125 . 5 is called the divisor: 125 is called the dividend: the answer, 25, is called the quotient. We look to see if 5 divides into the first digit 1. It does not. Then we look to see if 5 divides into the first 2 digits 12. It does. Therefore, we will divide.

125 ÷ 5 = ?

```
      2 5      We divide 5 into 12.
  5)125        The quotient is 2.

      10       Now we multiply 2 x 5 to get 10.
      2 5      Subtract 12 – 10 = 2. "Bring down" the 5.
      2 5      5 divides into 25.  5 x 5 = 25.
        0      Subtract to obtain 0.  Therefore, 125 ÷ 5 = 25.
```

Example 2: 342 ÷ 9 = ?

```
      3 8
  9)3 4 2      34 ÷ 9 = 3.

    2 7        3 x 9 = 27.   34 – 27 = 7.
      7 2      "bring down" 2   72 ÷ 9 = 8.
      7 2      9 x 8 = 72.     Subtract to obtain 0.
        0      Therefore, 342 ÷ 9 = 38.
```

Exercise 16

1. Complete the following divisions. Check by multiplying the quotient by the divisor.

a)   8)128   b)   6)792   c) 5)760   d) 7)364

<u>8</u> x ___ = ___   <u>6</u> x ___ = ___   <u>5</u> x <u>5</u> = ___   <u>7</u> x ___ = ___

e) 8)1712   f) 4)1460   g) 3)1962   h) 7)1477

<u>8</u> x ___ = ___   <u>4</u> x ___ = ___   <u>3</u> x ___ = ___   <u>7</u> x ___ = ___

2. Peter filled his gas tank 7 times and traveled 8,554 kilometers and had very little gas left in the tank. How many kilometers did he travel on average for each tank of gas?

3. Joan sold 1,224 raffle tickets at a three-day long bazaar. How many sales did she average each day?

4. A mother had 756 pictures of her 6 daughters. She wanted to divide these pictures equally among her daughters. How many pictures did each daughter receive?

5. Workers at an auto repair shop repaired 180 cars during a 5-day work-week. On average, how many cars were repaired each day?

6. 1,200 paperclips were equally divided among 8 people. How many paperclips did each person receive?

Division of a Three–Digit Number by a Two–Digit Number

Example: $322 \div 14 =?$

$$\begin{array}{r} 23 \\ 14\overline{)322} \end{array}$$

28	$32 \div 14 = 2$ and $2 \times 14 = 28$.
42	$32 - 28 = 4$. Bring down 2.
42	$42 \div 4 = 3$ and $3 \times 14 = 42$.
0	$42 - 42 = 0$. Therefore, $322 \div 14 = 23$ and $23 \times 14 = 322$.

Exercise 17

1. Complete the following divisions and verify the answer by multiplying the quotient by the divisor:

a) $36\overline{)864}$ b) $33\overline{)693}$ c) $19\overline{)798}$ d) $23\overline{)598}$

36 x   =   33 x   =   19 X   =   23 x   =

e) $36\overline{)900}$ f) $19\overline{)513}$ g) $47\overline{)846}$ h) $27\overline{)810}$

36 x   =   19 x   =   47 x   =   27 x   =

2. John shuffled 3 decks of playing cards. Each deck contained 52 cards. He then dealt them in turn to 4 players. How many cards did each player receive?

3. Betty baked 255 chocolate squares. She divided them equally among her 17 office staff. How many squares did each person receive?

4. Tom bought 576 candies for Halloween. He decided to give 12 candies to each child. How many children did he give candies to if he gave away all of his candies?

5. 728 bricks were to be laid in 1 day. There were 14 bricklayers working and each was to lay the same number of bricks. How many bricks did each worker lay?

6. A train traveled 1,230 miles in 15 hours. What was the average speed of the train?

Division With a Remainder

There will be many times in which one number does not divide exactly into another number. The remainder is not trivial. For example, Peter's mother baked 40 small cakes. She wanted to divide them equally among 13 of Peter's friends. How much cake did each person receive? The answer is: each friend received 3 cakes and $\frac{1}{13}$ of a cake. In order to check that the division is correct, multiply the quotient by the divisor and add the remainder. The result should be the dividend.

Example: (3 x 13) = 39 and 39 + 1 = 40.

$$
\begin{array}{r}
3 \\
13\overline{)40} \\
39 \\
\hline
1
\end{array}
$$

We call 1 the remainder and we write 40 ÷ 13 = 3 and R = 1.

(R being the remainder) or 40 ÷ 13 = $3\frac{1}{13}$

Note that 13 x 3 = 39 and 39 + 1 = 40.

Exercise 18

1. Maria has $11,000 to invest and she wants to place the money equally in 3 financial institutions. How much change will Maria have after she has made these investments?

2. George is dealing 3 decks of cards (52 cards per deck) to 7 people. All players are to receive the same number of cards. How many cards will George have left when he cannot deal a card to every person? Solve this in two different ways.

3. Bertha is knitting scarves. She has 19 balls of wool. Each scarf requires 5 balls of wool.
How many scarves can Bertha knit?

How much wool will she have when she is finished?

4. Steve had 927 liters of water that he wanted to share equally among 4 of his friends. How much water was left over?

Addition of Numbers that are in a Special Sequence

Observing certain patterns of numbers might save some time and effort. For example, if we wish to add $1 + 2 + 3 + 4 + 5 + 6 + 7 + 8 + 9 + 10$, we could group the numbers in twos by adding the first number and the last number. $1 + 10$ equals 11. Now look at the second number and the second to last number: $2 + 9 = 11$. Similarly, $3 + 8 = 11$. There are 5 such groups because we have 10 numbers. Therefore, $5 \times 11 = 55$. Check by ordinary addition.

We would proceed as follows to add 1 to 100. $1 + 2 + 3 + 4 \ldots + 97 + 98 + 99 + 100$.

$1 + 100 = 101$, $2 + 99 = 101$, $3 + 98 = 101$. We see that each pair is equal to 101. There are 50 such pairs. Therefore, the sum is $50(101)$, which is equal to $50(100 + 1)$ which equals $5,000 + 50$ or $5,050$.

It should be noted that the above method can be used only when there is a constant difference between any number and its succeeding number.

For example, add $3 + 7 + 11 + 15 + 19 + 23 + 27 + 31$. Note that each number after the first is the preceding number plus 4. Therefore, we have 4 groups of 34. That is, 4×34 or 136 and this is the sum of the numbers above.

What happens if there is an odd number of numbers to be added? For example, add $6 + 9 + 12 + 15 + 18 + 21 + 24$. We would add the first 6 numbers by the method above and then add 24. We have 3 groups of 27 or 3×27 or 81. Then we must add 24. $81 + 24 = 105$. Or, we could add the last 6 numbers and have 3 groups of 33 or $3 \times 33 = 99$. Then we must add 6. $99 + 6 = 105$.
The point to be made is that you should examine the numbers before you begin solving the problem.

Another Type of Addition and Subtraction-Hours, Minutes, Seconds
Not all additions are made using ones, tens, hundreds, and thousands. For example, if we wish to add time on a clock, we consider 60 seconds equal 1 minute, 60 minutes

equal 1 hour, 12 hours equal 1 revolution of the hour arm, and 2 revolutions equal 1 day. Some clocks have the 24 hours included in 1 revolution of the hour hand. Many societies use the 12 hour clock by distinguishing between a.m. and p.m. However, there is a growing tendency towards the use of the 24-hour clock.

Example 1: It is now 8:20. What time will it be in a) 30 minutes, b) 45 minutes, c) 2 hours and 55 minutes?

a) 8:20   b) 8:20   8:20   c) 8:20   8:20
   + :30   +:45   +:45   + 2:55   + 2:55
    8:50   8:65   9:05   10:75   11:15

(65 minutes = 1 hour and 5 minutes)   (75 minutes = 1 hour and 15 minutes)

Example 2: The time is now 10:22:35. What time will it be in 1 hour and 20 minutes and 30 seconds? What time will it be in 2 hours 40 minutes and 25 seconds?

10:22:35   10:22:35
 1:20:30   2:40:25
11:42:65 = 11:43:05   12:62:60 = 13:03 hrs.

(65 seconds = 1 minute and 5 seconds.)   (60 seconds = 1 minute and 63 minutes
                                            =1 hour and 3 minutes.)

Example 3: The time is now 8:15. What time was it 50 minutes ago? 8:15 − 50. We cannot subtract 50 minutes from 15 minutes. Therefore, we combine 1 hour which is 60 minutes. We now have 7:75. The problem becomes 7:75 − :50 or 7:25.

Example 4:   The time is now 7:30:25. What time was it 3:30:30 ago?
7: 30:25
3: 30:30   We cannot subtract 30 seconds from 25 seconds. Therefore, we
                combine 1 minute which is 60 seconds. We now have:
7:29:85
3:30:30
      55   We cannot subtract 30 minutes from 29 minutes. Therefore, we
                change 1 hour to 60 minutes. We now have:
6:89:85
3:30:30
3:59:55

Example 5: If we use the 24 hour clock and it is now 18:00 hours, what time will it be in 7 hours? In 10 hours?

18 + 7 = 25 hours. 25 − 24 = 1 hour.
18 + 10 = 28 hours. 28 − 24 = 4 hours.

Exercise 19

1. Add the first three rows of the Addition Chart by the method of adding numbers in a sequence. Write the sum of the remaining rows without adding. Put the sums in the blank spaces.

+	1	2	3	4	5	6	7	8	9	
1	2	3	4	5	6	7	8	9	10	
2	3	4	5	6	7	8	9	10	11	
3	4	5	6	7	8	9	10	11	12	
4	5	6	7	8	9	10	11	12	13	
5	6	7	8	9	10	11	12	13	14	
6	7	8	9	10	11	12	13	14	15	
7	8	9	10	11	12	13	14	15	16	
8	9	10	11	12	13	14	15	16	17	
9	10	11	12	13	14	15	16	17	18	

2. Use the addition chart to add the first three columns. Write the sums of the remaining columns without adding the numbers? Use the blank spaces in the diagram.

3. Use the 24 hour clock. The time is now 5:45. What time will it be in:

a) 2 hours and 20 minutes?   b) 3 hours and 10 minutes?

c) 5 hours and 45 minutes?   d) 3 hours and 25 minutes

4. The time is now 17:40. What time was it?

a) 2 hours and 25 minutes ago?   b) 3 hours and 45 minutes ago?

c) 4 hours and 50 minutes ago?   d) 6 hours and 55 minutes ago?

5. The time is now 9:30:45. What time will it be in:

a) 2 hours, 40 minutes and 20 seconds?   b) 2 hours 30 minutes and 30 seconds?

c) 5 hours 25 minutes and 25 seconds?

6. The time is now 6:50:50. What time was it?

a) 3 hours, 20 minutes and 20 seconds ago? b) 1 hour, 55 minutes and 45 seconds ago?

c) 2 hours, 50 minutes and 55 seconds ago?

7. It is now 9:15 hrs. What time will it be in:

a) 4 hours and 20 minutes?   b) 7 hours and 50 minutes?

c) 6 hours and 30 minutes?

8. List four instances where the 24 hour clock is useful.

9. A clock that looses 2 minutes a day shows the correct time at 10:00 a.m. What will it show at 10:00 p.m.?

10. It was 3:45 by Bill's watch when he left to go to the store. While at the store, he corrected his watch by setting it forward from 4:09 to 4:15. He arrived home at 4:45. How many minutes was he away?

Multiplication by Decomposition

There is another way to multiply a 2-digit number by a 1 or 2-digit number. This method is called decomposition.

Example: Multiply 23 x 32.
Write 23 in the form (20 + 3) and multiply by 32.
32(20 + 3) = 640 + 96 or 736. (Note that each term within the parentheses was multiplied by 32.)

Or, write 32 in the form of (30 + 2) and multiply by 23.
23(30 + 2) = 690 + 46 or 736.

Exercise 20

1. Multiply each of the following by decomposition.

a) 13 x 21 =   b) 23 x 45 =
          =   =
          =   =

c) 38 x 41 =   d) 55 x 18 =
          =   =

          =   =

e) 28 x 30 =   f) 47 x 12 =
          =   =

          =   =

Self-Assessment of the Attainment of the Objectives

	5	4	3	2	1
- identify a set					
- demonstrate the difference between a number and a numeral					
- determine if one number is greater than, less than, or equal to another number					
- demonstrate that 0 added to a number does not alter the sum					
- add numbers consisting of up to four digits					
- add numbers in any order without altering the sum					
- solve problems using addition					
- subtract numbers consisting of up to four digits					
- demonstrate that multiplication is a shortcut for repeated addition					
- demonstrate that 0 subtracted from any number leaves that number unchanged					
- demonstrate that the order of subtraction cannot be changed					
- solve problems using subtraction					
- identify the multiplicand, the multiplier and the product					
- identify the factors of a given number					
- demonstrate that any number multiplied by 0 is equal to 0					
- demonstrate that any number multiplied by 1 is equal to that number					
- demonstrate that the order of multiplication will not alter the product					
- identify the difference between a row and a column in any array of numbers					
- multiply numbers in which the multiplicand has three digits and the multiplier has two digits					
- solve problems using multiplication					
- identify the divisor, dividend and quotient					
- demonstrate that division is the separation of a number into equal parts					
- demonstrate that division by 0 is undefined					
- demonstrate that the order of division cannot be changed					
- demonstrate that division is a shortcut for repeated subtraction					
- demonstrate how it can be determined that a number is divisible by 2, 3, 5, 9 10 or 11 (if it is less than 100)					
- demonstrate the difference between a prime and a composite number					
- divide three–digit numbers by two–digit numbers					
- demonstrate what is done with a remainder					
- demonstrate the addition of numbers that are in a special sequence					
- demonstrate the ability to add and subtract hours, minutes and seconds					
- demonstrate the ability to multiply by decomposition					
- solve problems using division of numbers, adding special sequences and multiplying by decomposition					

Score /165 Date _____

Section I – Addition, Subtraction, Multiplication, Division of Whole Numbers
Post–Test I

Do not use a calculator until you have completed Unit 1. Answers may be found at the back of the book.

1. What does each of the following symbols mean?

< means   = means   > means

2. If you have 16 tiles and you need 23 tiles, how many more tiles must you buy?

3. Add 9 + 8 + 7 + 6 in two different ways;

_____ = _____   _____ = _____

4 Add 1 8 8   5. Subtract 1 2 3   6. Multiply 2 4   7. Divide 11)165
       3 5 7   2 5   3 6
       2 3 4

8. Add 7 3 8 5   9. Subtract 3 7 5   10. Multiply 2 1 8   11. Divide 18√666
      1 9 2 7   7 8   2 6

12. Janet went to the market and bought 20 kg of carrots, 9 kg of green beans, and 16 kg of broccoli. What was the weight of Janet's purchase?

13. Joan bought 112 pills. She used 84 of them. How many pills does Joan have now?

14. Mary made 23 ornaments for the bazaar. Helen made 15 times as many. How many ornaments did Helen make? Calculate by using decomposition.

15. Circle the numbers that are divisible by 3. Explain how you did this.

   32 33 34 35 36 37 38 39 40 41 42 43 44 45 46 47 48

16. List all of the factors of 64.

17. Determine the sum of 1 to 26 without using addition. Demonstrate how this was done.

Score _____   Date _____

Section II – The Use of a Calculator, Patterns, Ordinal Numbers, Roman Numerals, Estimation and Measurement, Graphs
Pre–Test II

The answers to these problems can be found at the back of the book.

Numbers 1 – 6 are from Unit 2, the Use of a Calculator; numbers 7 – 8 are from Unit 3, Patterns; number 9 is from Unit 4, Ordinal Numbers; numbers 10 – 11 are from Unit 5, Roman Numerals; numbers 12 – 15 are from Unit 6, Estimation and Measurement; numbers 16 – 20 are from Unit 7, Graphs.

After completing the Pre-Test, the reader should spend the amount of time necessary on each Unit. When sufficient understanding has been achieved, complete the Post-Test at the end of the Section and compare your results.

1. Perform the following multiplications using a calculator. List the next product in the sequence.

11 x 11 =   12 x 11   13 x 11 =   14 x 11 =

The next product in the sequence is

2. The positive square root of 169 is

3. Perform the following operation: 6 ÷ 0 =

Explain

4. A car uses 9.8 liters of gas to travel 200 km. How much gas is required to travel 380 km?

5. I wish to multiply 102 by 99 using a calculator. However, the 9 key does not work on my calculator. How can I determine the product using my calculator?

What is the product?

6. Use the Memory key of a calculator to find (23 x 4) + (37 x 26). List the steps in the process that you used.

7. Write the next two numbers in the following sequence:

2, 3, 5, 8, 12, _____   _____

8. Write the pattern in Number 7 in words.

9. In the following grid, list the entry in a) the third row and fourth column and b) in the fourth row and third column:

2	7	11	14	27
13	9	4	22	8
16	5	3	12	15
20	31	44	6	1
10	33	27	29	30

a)   b)

10. Change 257 into Roman Numerals. 257 =

11. Change C X I I into the Hindu–Arabic system. C X I I =

12. Paul has a truck with a capacity of 432 cubic meters. What is the capacity in cubic feet? $(1\ m^3 = 35.315\ f^3)$. List the answer with 3 decimal places.
$432\ m^3 = \ ft^3$

13. Square tiles were required to cover Sarah's floor that measured 13 m by 12 m. The only tiles available measured $\frac{1}{2}\ m^2$. How many square tiles did Sarah have to buy?

14. Change 25º Celsius to Fahrenheit   25º Celsius =   Fahrenheit

15. Change 95º Fahrenheit to Celsius   95º Fahrenheit =   Celsius

16. Construct a tally sheet having a sample of 18 people who have a preference for walking or swimming or cycling (see next page).

			%
walking	swimming	cycling	

17. Construct a bar graph using the data from number 16.

18. Construct a pie chart using the same data.

19. Construct a line graph to display the sales of cars at an auto sales dealer who sells cars on Monday to Friday.

20. Construct a graph to display the following data. A municipality employs 12 secretaries, 20 maintenance workers, 25 policemen, 10 fire fighters and 5 administrators.

Score _____ Date _____

Unit 2–The Use of a Calculator

OBJECTIVES

- demonstrate the use a calculator to add, subtract, multiply and divide numbers
- demonstrate the use a calculator to show the properties of numbers as outlined in Unit 1
- demonstrate multiplication by 0
- demonstrate multiplication and division by 1
- show that multiplication is a shortcut for repeated additions
- show that division is a shortcut for repeated subtractions
- demonstrate the ability to recognize and continue patterns
- demonstrate the use a calculator to solve problems using very small numbers
- demonstrate the use a calculator to square a number
- demonstrate the use a calculator to find the positive square root of a number
- solve problems using a calculator

Introducing the Calculator

The following exercise will assist those who have not experienced activities using a simple calculator. Read the instructions carefully after purchasing a calculator.

Exercise 21

1. Press as many keys with numerals as are necessary to fill the display box. How many digits are accommodated on the display box?   If your answer is 8, then you have a basic calculator. (If the answer is greater than 8, make sure that you read the instruction booklet that comes with the calculator.)

2. Press 4. Press +. Press 3. Press =. The answer is

3. Press 3. Press +. Press 4. Press =. The answer is

4. What general statement can be made about the addition of numbers?

5. Press 35. Press ÷. Press 5. Press =. The answer is

6. Press 35. Press −. Press 5. Press =. Press −, Press 5. Press =. Press −. Press 5. Press =. Press −. Press 5. Press =. Press −. Press 5. Press =. Press −. Press 5. Press =. Press −. Press 5. Press =. The answer is

7. Press 35. Press. Press 5. Press =. Press =. Press =. Press =. Press =. Press =. Press =. What does this tell us about 35 ÷ 5?

8. Use the calculator to multiply 5 x 4. The answer is
Use the calculator to add 4 + 4 + 4 + 4 + 4. The answer is
You can see that multiplication is a shortcut for repeated additions.

9. Press 0. Press ÷. Press 6. The answer is

10. Press 6. Press ÷. Press 0. The answer is

Explain

11. Perform the following operations and explain the mathematical concept involved.
37 + 41– 41 =   45 x 51 ÷ 51 =

Explain

12. Enter any two–digit number. Multiply this number by 10 five times. Note the movement of the decimal point. Clear the calculator. Now enter the same two digit number and divide by 10 five times. Note the movement of the decimal point. Multiplication moves the decimal point to the ___ . Division moves the decimal point to the ___ .

Observing Patterns

A calculator may be used for observing patterns.

Example 1: Insert 3. Multiply this number by 2. Then multiply this number by 2. Multiply this number by 2. Multiply this number by 2. The products that resulted are 6, 12, 24, 48.

Observe the difference between these.

12 – 6 = 6, 24 – 12 = 12, 48 – 24 = 24. Do you see a pattern? What is the next number in the sequence 6, 12, 24, 48, _____. Explain two ways that may be used to reach this result.

List the next 6 numbers of the sequence.

Example 1: Add 40 +   41 + 42   =
                      42 +   43 + 44   =
                      44 +   45 + 46   =

Now write the sum of 46 + 47 + 48 without using addition.

Example 2: Perform the following operations with your calculator: What pattern is developing?

If you do not see the pattern, continue the sequence.

11 x 11 = _____ ,   12 x 11 = _____ ,   13 x 11 = _____ , 14 x 11 = _____ ,

15 x 11 = _____ .

48

The next set of products is 176 because adding one factor of 11 to the preceding term forms the sequence. Therefore, the product will increase by 11.

Operating With Small Numbers

Sometimes, problems are too tedious to calculate with a pen or pencil. In such cases, it is better to use a calculator.

Example: If a telephone book has 1,856 pages and is 5.2 cm thick, what is the thickness of each page? 0.0028 cm. That is, $5.2 \div 1856 = 0.0028017$ or 0.0028 cm or 0.003 cm.

Square Roots Using a Calculator

We have seen that numbers can be squared. For example, $2^2 = 4$, $3^2 = 9$, $4^2 = 16$, and so on.

It is useful to know the squares of numbers to 12 and then to know some numbers that are often used in squaring. Therefore, to continue from above, the following squares should be committed to memory.

$5^2 = 25$, $6^2 = 36$, $7^2 = 49$, $8^2 = 64$, $9^2 = 81$, $10^2 = 100$, $11^2 = 121$, $12^2 = 144$, $15^2 = 225$, $20^2 = 400$, $25^2 = 625$, $30^2 = 900$, $40^2 = 1,600$, $50^2 = 2,500$, $60^2 = 3,600$, $70^2 = 4,900$, $80^2 = 6,400$, $90^2 = 8,100$, $100^2 = 10,000$.

Observe the differences of the results from 30^2 to 100^2. Why is this so?

The square root of a number is that number which when multiplied by itself will equal the number. For example, the positive square root of 9 is 3: the positive square root of 100 is 10. However, there are some numbers whose square root is not committed to memory such as 169. Although there exists an algorithm to find the square root of any number, it is much more efficient to use the calculator.

To find the square root of 169, insert 169 and then press the square root key. The symbol $\sqrt{}$ means "the square root of". The number 13 should be displayed on the screen.

There are some numbers that do not have a square root that is a whole number. For example, $\sqrt{2} = 1.4142135 \ldots$ by using a calculator. (The square root of 2 is a non-terminating, non–recurring decimal number. That is, it will never come to an end and the numbers will not repeat.) This number, 1.4142135, multiplied by itself will equal 1.9999998 and this is close to, but not exactly 2. Insert any number in the calculator and press the $\sqrt{}$ key. You will notice that there are more numbers that do not have a perfect square root than there are numbers that do have a perfect square root. (A perfect square root is a whole number.)

It should be noted that only the positive square root of a number is being considered at this time. All numbers have two square roots. For example $\sqrt{9}$ = 3 and –3. After a study of the Integers in Unit 9, we will see that – 3 x – 3 = + 9.

Exercise 22

1. Perform the following operations with your calculator and fill in the fourth term.

a) $\frac{1}{3} =$ $\frac{1}{33} =$ $\frac{1}{333} =$ =

b) $\frac{1}{9} =$ $\frac{1}{99} =$ $\frac{1}{999} =$ =

2. A car uses 9.8 liters of gas to travel 200 km. How much gas would be required for the car to travel 380 km?

3. A dictionary has 2,177 pages and is 7.2 cm thick. What is the thickness of each page?

4. Multiply 124,565 x 358,752 using a calculator that displays exactly 8 digits?

5. I wish to multiply 102 by 99. However, the 9 key of my calculator does not work. How can I determine the product?

What is the product?

6. Make up a problem of multiplication using a calculator that has a 7 key that does not work.
The problem is:

The solution can be found by:

The answer is

7. Find the positive square root of each of the following by using a calculator:

a) $\sqrt{196} =$ b) $\sqrt{289} =$ c) $\sqrt{8,100} =$ d) $\sqrt{8,100} =$

50

e) $\sqrt{576} =$ f) $\sqrt{961} =$ g) $\sqrt{495} =$ h) $\sqrt{217} =$

i) $\sqrt{5} =$ j) $\sqrt{7} =$ k) $\sqrt{11} =$ l) $\sqrt{28} =$

Exercise 23

1. Use a calculator to compute each of the following. When parentheses are used, complete the computation of those numbers within the parentheses first.

a) 6 + 7 + 9 =   b) 14 x 11 x 6 =   c) 36 x 0 x 51 =

d) 19 x 1 x 24 =   e) (24 x 12) + (10 x 6) =

f) (43 x 26) + (24 x 13) =

2. John bought 8 shirts at $23.00 each and 9 pairs of pants at $40.00 each. How much did John spend for his clothes?

3.   Mary bought 11 cans of soup for $1.23 a can and 15 kilograms of carrots for $1.93 a kilogram. How much money did Mary spend? (Use a calculator.)

SELF-ASSESSMENT of the ATTAINMENT of the OBJECTIVES

	5	4	3	2	1
- demonstrate the use a calculator to add, subtract, multiply and divide numbers					
- demonstrate the use a calculator to show the properties of numbers as outlined in Unit 1					
- demonstrate multiplication by 0					
- demonstrate multiplication and division by 1					
- show that multiplication is a shortcut for repeated additions					
- show that division is a shortcut for repeated subtractions					
- demonstrate the ability to recognize and continue patterns					
- demonstrate the use a calculator to solve problems using very small numbers					
- demonstrate the use a calculator to square a number					
- demonstrate the use a calculator to find the positive square root of a number					
- solve problems using a calculator					

Score   /55 Date _____

Unit 3 – Patterns

OBJECTIVES

- demonstrate the ability to recognize patterns
- continue patterns
- solve problems involving patterns

The recognition of patterns is an important component in the study of mathematics. Normally, patterns should be recognized after the presentation of three items of data. Patterns may appear in the form of numbers or in the form of objects and mostly in the form of shapes.

Example 1: continue the following pattern: 1, 4, 7. . .   Answer: 1, 4, 7, 10. . .
In words: add 3 to the preceding number.

Example 2: Continue the following pattern 4, 8, 12. . .   Answer: 4, 8, 12, 16. . .
In words: add 4 to the preceding number.

Exercise 24

1. Complete each of the following patterns and describe the pattern in words.

a) 5, 10, 15,

In words

b) 2, 4, 6,

In words

c) 1, 4, 9,

In words

d) 11, 22, 33,

In words

e) 1, 8, 27,

In words

f) 37, 49, 60,

In words

g) 87, 78, 71,

In words

h) 1, 3, 7, 15, 31,

In words

i) 96, 48, 24,

In words

j) 6, 10, 8, 13, 10, 16, 12,

In words

k) 8, 3, 8, 9, 8, 27,

In words

l) 2, 3, 5, 8, 12,

In words

m) 75, 74, 72, 68, 60, 44,

In words

2. John's dog weighed 2 kg when she was born. After a month, she weighed 7 kg and after two months 11 kg. After three months she weighed 14 kg. How much did the dog weigh after five months if the same pattern of weight increases continued?

3. Write the next three rows of each of the following:

a) $1 \times 8 + 1 = 9$
$12 \times 8 + 2 = 98$
$123 \times 8 + 3 = 987$

b) $1 \times 9 + 2 = 11$
$12 \times 9 + 3 = 111$
$123 \times 9 + 4 = 1111$

c) $9 \times 9 + 7 = 88$
$98 \times 9 + 6 = 888$
$987 \times 9 + 5 = 8888$

SELF-ASSESSMENT of the ATTAINMENT of the OBJECTIVES

- demonstrate the use of a calculator to add, subtract, multiply and divide numbers
- demonstrate the use of a calculator to show the properties of

5	4	3	2	1

Score   /10   Date _____

Unit 4 – Ordinal Numbers

OBJECTIVES

- demonstrate the meaning of a cardinal number

- demonstrate the meaning of an ordinal number

- identify cells in any row and any column

There are two types of numbers in the Hindu-Arabic system. A cardinal number answers the question, "How many?" It is this number that determines how many elements are in a set. Ordinal numbers answer the question, Which one? The ordinal numbers are written 1st, 2nd, 3rd, 4th, 5th, and so on. Ordinal numbers are identified by position.

We have seen many number fact charts. It should be noted that the rows are on a horizontal line (across) and the columns are vertical (up and down). The top row is the first row and the rows are numbered from top to bottom. The first column is at the left side as a person looks at the grid.

	1	2	3	4	5	6	7	8	9	10
1	1	2	3	4	5	6	7	8	9	10
2	11	12	13	14	15	16	17	18	19	20
3	21	22	23	24	25	26	27	28	29	30
4	31	32	33	34	35	36	37	38	39	40
5	41	42	43	44	45	46	47	48	49	50
6	51	52	53	54	55	56	57	58	59	60
7	61	62	63	64	65	66	67	68	69	70
8	71	72	73	74	75	76	77	78	79	80
9	81	82	83	84	85	86	87	88	89	90
10	91	92	93	94	95	96	97	98	99	100

Now let us look at the 3rd row and the 5th column in the above grid. The entry is 25: the entry in the 5th row and 3rd column is 43. The identification of positions of rows and columns is an important skill for later studies in mathematics.

Exercise 25

1. Identify the contents of the cells using the grid on the following page.

a) 4th row, 5th column

b) 6th row, 3rd column

c) 7th row, 1st column

d) 6th row, 2nd column

e) 1st row, 2nd column

f) 8th row, 3rd column

g) 8th row, 5th column

h) 2nd row, 8th column

2. Identify the contents of the cells using the grid below.

a) 4th column, 5th row   b) 6th column, 3rd row

c) 7th column, 1st row   d) 8th column, second row

e) 1st column, 2nd row   f) 8th column, 3rd row

g) 8th column, 5th row   h) 2nd column, 8th row

Notice the difference in the answers for numbers 1 and 2.

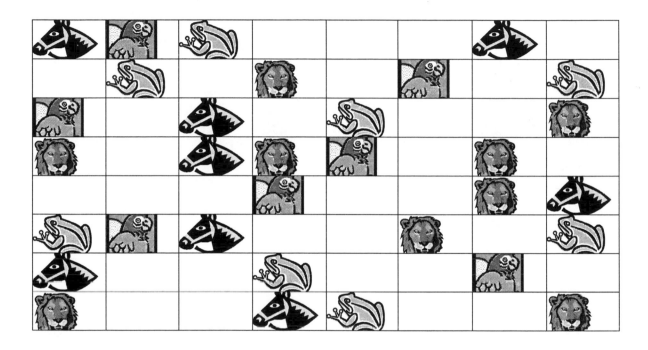

SELF-ASSESSMENT of the ATTAINMENT of the OBJECTIVES

- demonstrate the meaning of a cardinal number
- demonstrate the meaning of an ordinal number
- identify cells in any row and any column

5	4	3	2	1

Score /15   Date _____

Unit 5 — Roman Numerals

OBJECTIVES

- identify the seven basic numbers in the Roman system of notation
- demonstrate when a special numeral is used to increase or decrease a number
- change numbers from the Hindu-Arabic system to the Roman Numeral system of notation
- change numbers from the Roman Numeral system to the Hindu-Arabic system of notation
- solve problems involving Roman Numerals

Although Roman Numerals are not in common use, there is some benefit in knowing these and observing and comparing the Roman system of numeration to the Hindu-Arabic system of numeration.

The Hindu-Arabic system uses only the ten digits 0, 1, 2, 3, 4, 5, 6, 7, 8, 9 and this is why it is called the decimal system of notation. Note that after all ten digits have been used, the next numbers become 10, 11, 12, and 13, and so on.

Rules for Writing Roman Numerals

The Roman system of notation uses italicized letters. Lower case letters such as iv are used sometimes. Capital letters, such as IV are used at other times.

The basic rule is that only three of the same symbols may be contained in any number. Note that the symbols I, II, III are the numerals 1, 2, 3. We have now used I three times for the number 3. The numeral for 5 is V and to obtain the number 4, we subtract I from V to get IV. The lesser (smaller valued) symbols preceding a special symbol imply subtraction i.e., 4 = 5 − 1. Similarly, symbols following a special symbol imply addition. For example, VI = 5 + 1 or 6. The special numbers are I for 1, V for 5, X for 10, L for 50, C for 100, D = 500 and M = 1,000. These are the only letters commonly used.

There are three rules regarding numerals that are placed to the left of a bigger one and subtracted:

1) Only I, X, and C can be used in this way.

2) Only one smaller number can be placed to the left of a bigger one. For example, 29 may be written as XXIX. But 28 cannot be written as XXIIX. 28 must be written as XXVIII.

3) The subtracted number must be a tenth or more of the number from which it is subtracted. An X can be placed to the left of an L or a C, but not to the left of a D or an M.

Convert each digit separately when converting to a Roman numeral. For example,

953 = 900 + 50 + 3 or CM (1,000 − 100), L which is 50, and III which is 3. Therefore, the Roman numeral for 953 is CMLIII.

An examination of the Roman Numeral Chart 1–100 will provide a greater understanding of the Roman system of notation.

I	II	III	IV	V	VI	VII	VIII	IX	X
XI	XII	XIII	XIV	XV	XVI	XVII	XVIII	XIX	XX
XXI	XXII	XXIII	XXIV	XXV	XXVI	XXVII	XXVIII	XXIX	XXX
XXXI	XXXII	XXXIII	XXXIV	XXXV	XXXVI	XXXVII	XXXVIII	XXXIX	XL
XLI	XLII	XLIII	XLIV	XLV	XLVI	XLVII	XLVIII	XLIX	L
LI	LII	LIII	LIV	LV	LVI	LVII	LVIII	LIX	LX
LXI	LXII	LXIII	LXIV	LXV	LXVI	LXVII	LXVIII	LXIX	LXX
LXXI	LXXII	LXXIII	LXXIV	LXXV	LXXVI	LXXVII	LXXVIII	LXXIX	LXXX
LXXXI	LXXXII	LXXXIII	LXXXIV	LXXXV	LXXXVI	LXXXVII	LXXXVIII	LXXXIX	XC
XCI	XCII	XCIII	XCIV	XCV	XCVI	XCVII	XCVIII	XCIX	C

Changing From One System to the Other One

Example 1: Change CLXXI to the decimal system of notation.

CLXXI = C   L   X   X   I

           100 + 50 + 20 + 1 = 171

Example 2: Change DCLXVII to the decimal system of notation.

DCLXVII = D   C   L   X   VII

           500 + 100 + 50 + 10 + 7 = 667

Example 3: Change 1,666 to Roman numerals.

1,666 = 1,000   +   600   +   60   +   6
          M   +   DC   +   LX   +   VI = MDCLXVI

Exercise 26

1. Change the following to the Roman numeral system:

a) 257 =   b) 429 =   c) 837 =   d) 902 =

e) 235 =   f) 3,299 =   g) 1,002 =   h) 989 =

i) 1,510=   j) 364 =   k) 2,138 =   l) 1,001 =

2. List three places where you may see Roman numerals.

3. Change the following Roman numerals to the Hindu-Arabic system:

a) CXI =

b) MCDXCI =

c) CXII =

d) MCDLIII =

e) MCMIII =

f) MDC =

g) C C X XIV =

h) MD C C C XLII =

i) MDX =

j) M D C C L XXI =

k) C C C X LV =

l) MDLVII =

SELF-ASSESSMENT of the ATTAINMENT of the OBJECTIVES

	5	4	3	2	1
- identify the seven basic numbers in the Roman system of notation					
- demonstrate when a special numeral is used to increase or decrease a number					
- change numbers from the Hindu-Arabic system to the Roman Numeral system					
- change numbers from the Roman Numeral system to the Hindu-Arabic system					
- solve problems involving Roman Numerals					

Score   /25 Date _____

Unit 6 – Estimation and Measurement

OBJECTIVES

- convert lengths among the metric, Imperial and U.S. systems
- convert areas among the metric, Imperial and U.S. systems
- convert weights among the metric, Imperial and U.S. systems
- convert a Celsius temperature to a Fahrenheit temperature
- convert a Fahrenheit temperature to a Celsius temperature
- estimate measures
- perform measuring tasks accurately
- determine the volume of shapes
- solve problems involving estimation and measurement

The following information should be used for reference only.

English Units of Measure

Length	Volume	Weight
1 foot (ft) = 12 inches (in)	pint (pt) = 16 Fluid ounces	6 ounces (oz) = 1 pound
1 yard = 3 feet (ft)	quart (qt) = 2 pints (pt)	1 ton = 2,000 lb
1 mile (mi) = 5,280 ft	4 qt = 1 gallon (gal)	

The Metric System of Measurement

Length	Weight
1 centimeter (cm) = 10 millimeters (mm)	1 centigram (cg) = 10 milligrams (mg)
1 meter (m) = 100 cm	1 gram (g) = 100 cg
1 kilometer (km) = 1,000 m	1 kilogram (kg) = 1,000 mg

Liquid

1 centiliter(cl) = 10 milliliters (ml)

1 liter (ℓ) = 100 (cl)

1 kiloliter (kl) = 1,000 ℓ

Cooking

1 cup = 8 oz = 16 tbsp = 48 tsp = 237 ml

$\frac{3}{4}$ cup = 6 fl.oz = 12 tbsp = 36 tsp = 177ml

$5\frac{1}{3}$ fl.oz = $10\frac{2}{3}$ tbsp = 32 tsp = 158 ml = 0.24 ℓ

$\frac{1}{2}$ cup = 4 fl.oz = 8 tbsp = 24 tsp = 118 ml

$\frac{1}{3}$ cup = $2\frac{2}{3}$ fl.oz = $2\frac{2}{3}$ tbsp = 16tsp = 79 ml

$\frac{1}{4}$ cup = 2 fl. oz = 4 tbsp = 12 tsp = 59ml

Conversion Tables

Lengths: Imperial and U.S. to Metric

1 inch = 2.54 cm or 0.054 m
1 foot = 0,3048 meters
1 yard = 0.9144 meters
1 statute mile = 1609.344 meters
1 nautical mile = 1853.18 meters
(international nautical mile is 1,852 meters)

U.S. Liquid Measure to Metric

1 fluid dram = 3.6967 cc
1 fluid ounce = 29.5735 cc
1 pint = 473.176 cc
1 quart = 946.353 cc
1 gallon = 3785.41 cc

Areas: Imperial and U.S. to Metric

1 square inch = $6.4516 \times 10^{-4} \, m^2$
1 square foot = $0.0929 \, m^2$
1 square yard = $0.8361 \, m^2$
1 acre = 0.4047 hectares
1 square mile = 258.9990 hectares

Volume and Capacity; Imperial to Metric

1 cubic inch = 16.3871 cc
1 fluid ounce = 28.4131 cc
1 pint = 568.261 cc
1 quart = 1136.52 cc
1 gallon = 4546.09 or 4.546091879 cc

Weight and Mass: Imperial to Metric

1 ounce = 28.35 grams
1 troy ounce = 31.1035 grams
1 pound = 0.4536 kg (by definition)
1 ton = 1.01605 tonnes

Weight and Mass: U.S. to Metric

1 ounce = 28.35 grams
1 troy ounce = 31.1035 grams
1 pound = 0.4536 kg (by definition)
1 ton = 0.907185 tonnes

Converting Length, Area, Weight and Volume

The unit to be used in making the estimate and in measuring for accuracy of the estimate must be determined. There are three systems of measurement: the metric system and the English system (sometimes called the Imperial system). In addition, the Customary United States measures are used. Equivalence charts are available for the above types of measurements on the internet.

The following is a Measurement Conversion Chart in which each measurement is expressed in 1 unit. If we wish to convert 5 inches to centimeters, we see from the chart that 1 in = 2.54 cm. Therefore, 5 inches will be 5 x 2.54 or 12.7 cm.

Measurement Conversion Chart

LENGTH						
1inch (in)	=	2.54 centimeters (cm)	and	1 cm	=	0.3937 in
1 foot (ft)	=	30.48 centimeters		1 cm	=	0.0328 ft
1 yard (yd)	=	0.9144 meters (m)		1 m	=	1.0936 yd
1 mile (mi)	=	1.60934 kilometers		1 km	=	0.62137 mi
AREA						
1 in^2	=	6.45 cm^2		1 cm^2	=	0.1550 in^2
1 ft^2	=	929.03 m^2		1 m^2	=	0.09 ft^2
1 yd^2	=	0.84 m^2		1 m^2	=	1.2 yd^2
1 mi^2	=	2.59 km^2		1 km^2	=	0.39 mi^2
WEIGHT						
1 ounce (oz)	=	28 grams		1 g	=	0.04 ounces
1 pound (lb)	=	0.45 kilograms (kg)		1 kg	=	2.2 pounds
1 short ton	=	0.91 metric tons		1metric ton	=	1.1 short tons
				1metric ton	=	2,204.62 (lbs)
IMPERIAL		**METRIC**		**U.S.A.**		**METRIC**
1 oz		28.413 ml		1 oz		29.574 ml
1 pint (pt)		0.5683 ℓ		1 pt		0.4731 ℓ
1 gallon		4.5461 ℓ		1 gallon		3.7854 ℓ

Rather than try to memorize these equivalencies, it is better to use the chart as a reference.

Example 1: Judith required 5 gallons of paint. The store sold paint in cans using the metric system only. How many liters of paint did Judith have to buy? 4.5 liters is equal to 1 gallon (from the conversion table). Judith required 5 gallons. Therefore, 5 times 4.5 = 22.5 liters. If the paint was available in both one-liter and half-liter cans, then Judith would buy 22 one-liter cans and 1 half-liter can. If the paint was not available in half-liter cans, Judith would have to buy 23 one-liter cans. If the paint was available in half-liter cans only, Judith would have to buy 45 cans.

If for some reason we wanted to convert the number of liters back to gallons, we would divide 5 by 22.5 and obtain 0.222222 . . . But the conversion chart lists the factor as 0.2. If we multiply 22.5 x 0.2 we would get 4.5 gallons. If we multiplied 22.5 x 0.22 the product would be 4.95 gallons. If we multiplied 22.5 x 0.222 the product would be 4.995. If we multiplied 22.5 x 0.2222 the product would be 4.9995. If we multiplied by 0.22222 the product would be 4.99995. Notice the increase in the number of nines. The number is approaching 5 and for all practical purposes, we can regard the product as 5.

Unless we are searching for an exact conversion as is necessary in science and research, we can do the following:

1. Use the conversion chart going one way only. In the above Example, we do not know if the conversion factor that 1 gallon equals 4.5 liters requires more digits.

2. If we are talking about gallons of paint, it does not require much thought to round off 4.99995 to 5 gallons.

Example 2: Paul weighed 186 pounds. How many kilograms did he weigh? 1 pound = 0.45 kg. Therefore, 186 pounds equals 186 x 0.45 = 83.7 kilograms. If we wanted to convert 83.7 kg to pounds, we would multiply by 2.2. 2.2 x 83.7 equals 184.14 pounds. The discrepancy can be attributed to the fact that the decimal fractions have been rounded off or truncated.

Exercise 27

1. Maria required 8 tablespoons of raisins for her cake. The packaging was done in milliliters only. How many milliliters did Maria have to buy?

2. John measured the runner on his stairwell and it was 9 yards. How many meters of runner did John have to buy?

3. Paul has a truck whose capacity is 432 cubic meters. What is the capacity in cubic feet? ($1 \text{ m}^3 = 35.315 \text{ ft}^3$.) Round off answer to three decimal places.

4. A linoleum covering was required to cover Sarah's kitchen floor that measured 13 ft by 12 ft. How many square meters of linoleum did Sarah have to buy?

5. The distance between two cities is 495 miles. If Tom is driving at the average rate of 110 km per hour, how much driving time will it take him to complete the journey?

Converting Temperatures

Although there are other types of temperatures, we will limit ourselves to the Celsius (or Centigrade) system and the Fahrenheit system.

To convert a Celsius temperature to a Fahrenheit temperature, multiply the Celsius temperature by 9, divide by 5 and add 32. (Some people will multiply by 2 and add 30 to obtain an approximate conversion.)

Or, to convert from Celsius to Fahrenheit, subtract 32 and then multiply by $\frac{5}{9}$.

$F = \frac{9}{5} C + 32^{\circ}$.

Example 1: Change 25° C to Fahrenheit.
$\frac{9}{5}$ x 25 = 45 and 45 + 32 = 77° Fahrenheit.

To convert a Fahrenheit temperature to a Celsius temperature, subtract 32 from the Fahrenheit temperature, multiply by 5 and divide by 9. $C = \frac{5}{9} (F - 32)$

Example 2: Change 77° F to C°
$77 - 32 = 45$ and $45 \times \frac{5}{9} = 25°C$

Exercise 28

1. Pat was in Florida where the temperature was 92° F. What was the temperature in Celsius?

2. Sophie was in Toronto where the weather was reported to be 17° C. What was the temperature in Fahrenheit?

3. If water boils at 212° F, what is the boiling point of water in Celsius measure?

4. If water freezes at 32° F, at what Celsius degree level will water freeze?

5. When is the number of degrees in Celsius equal to the number of degrees in Fahrenheit?

Estimating Measures and Performing Measuring Tasks

The ability to make estimates of lengths, weights, capacities, etc. must be practiced. The development of this ability is a major goal of mathematics learning. Although accuracy is the ultimate achievement, there are some instances in which close estimates are the best that can be achieved. For instance, if you walk into a sports arena and look at the crowd, you may estimate that there are 15,000 people in attendance. You did not count the number of people. What you are estimating is that there are approximately 15,000. Since the unit being used is thousands, an actual attendance of from 14,500 to 15,500 would be sufficiently accurate. Notice that the range is one-half of the unit used on both sides of the estimate. However, the accountant in charge of maintaining financial records for the owners or the government will not have a range of 1,000 people. If taxes are to be paid for each ticket sold, the government will want to know and be able to verify the exact number.

The above distinction is an illustration of the fact that you must know what you are estimating and why you are making the estimate.

In addition, the unit to be used for measuring must be determined. For instance, a football field would not be measured in inches or centimeters. The measurement to be used is either yards or meters.

It is instructive to measure objects in the metric and then in the English system. Pour fluid into a graduated cylinder to show what 8 oz is and to show that twice this amount is 1 cup. It is also useful to use a one-liter milk container to get an idea of what a liter is.

When estimating and then measuring, it is useful to make a chart as follows:
Make your estimate and record your estimate.

Item	Estimate	Measurement	Difference
Perimeter of a book	72 cm		

Measure and record the measurement and then calculate the difference between your estimate and the measurement.

Item	Estimate	Measurement	Difference
Perimeter of a book	72 cm	76 cm	4 cm

Exercise 29

1. Tell what unit of metric measurement would be used to measure the size of each of the following:

a) a table top   b) a bucket of water   c) a person's weight

d) five cement bricks   e) two inches of water in a bathtub   f) a football field

g) the length of your middle finger   h) your height   i) a car

2. Choose 5 items to measure. Using meters and centimeters, complete the chart below.

Item	Estimate	Measurement	Difference

3. Estimate the measure of each of the following in centimeters. Then measure each length and compare with your estimate. Record your measurement to the nearest half centimeter.

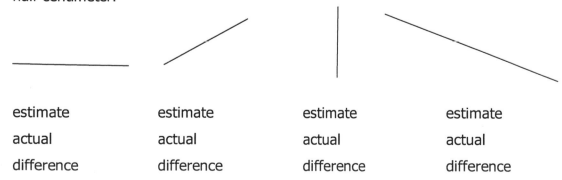

estimate   estimate   estimate   estimate

actual   actual   actual   actual

difference   difference   difference   difference

4. Use a piece of string to measure another person's height. Measure that person's arm span (i.e. the arms are extended outwards and parallel to the floor.) Compare the results and give a general statement.

5. What are the dimensions of a tank that will hold 50 liters of water if 1 liter fills an area of 10 cm^3?

6. If a dripping tap loses 31.7 metric gallons a day, estimate the number of U.S. gallons that are lost in one week? Then calculate the amount. (1 metric gallon = 266.5 U.S. gallons.)

Estimate   Calculation   Difference

7. If a dishwasher uses 75 liters each time it is used and washing the dishes by hand uses 35 liters, estimate the difference in water consumption after 5 times of washing dishes by each method.

Estimate

After you have recorded your estimate, do the calculation and record it.

What is the difference between your estimate and the amount calculated?

8. What measurements may be used in baking a cake?

9. List three instances in which measurements must be accurate:

10. List three instances in which measurements may be approximate:

11. Use an empty large cola bottle and a plastic measuring cup. Estimate how much of the bottle will be filled with 400 ml of water by placing an elastic around the bottle at the level that you think the water will reach. Measure 400 ml in a graduated cup. Then pour the water into the cola bottle and compare the estimated and the actual results. Then place the elastic around the bottle at the level you think the water will be after 500 ml has been added. Repeat the previous procedure. Compare your estimates with the actual levels of the water.
Difference between estimate and actual level of the water is:

12. Estimate the perimeter of a rectangle in inches and then estimate it in centimeters. Compare the results.

Item	Estimate	Measurement	Difference
Perimeter	in	in	in
	cm	cm	cm

13. Measure one square foot in a corner of the room. Then estimate the length, width, and height of the room. Then measure each dimension and compare the results with your estimates.

estimate of length   measure of length

estimate of width   measure of width

estimate of height   measure of height

14. The seating of a theater was designed to accommodate 1 person in 1.5 m^2. The theater accommodated 650 people. What were some of the possible dimensions of the seating area?

What was the best choice of dimensions of the seating area?

15. If 25 paper clips are interlocked lengthwise, how would you calculate the total length of the paper clips?

Record your estimate   Then measure the string of paper clips   What is the difference?

16. Without measuring, list an object whose measurement is equal to or close to the measurement given.

a) 1 inch	b) 3 inches	c) 6 inches
d) 1 foot	e) 6 feet	f) 10 feet
g) 1 yard	h) 3 yards	i) 10 yards
j) 1 mile	k) 5 miles	l) 200 miles
m) 3 cm	n) 0 cm	o) 100 cm
p) 1 m	q) 5 m	r) 100 cm
s) 1 km	t) 5 km	u) 100km

Measuring Solids

Linear measure, for example 2 cm, is a one dimensional measure. Square measures such as 2 cm^2 are two dimensional measures, and cubic measures such as 2 cm^3 are three dimensional measures. These measures are used to give the measurement of solids and volumes that have three dimensions.

The volume of some shapes such as prisms, spheres, cones, cylinders, etc. can be determined by inserting the given measurements into a general formula. However, there are a number of solids with an irregular shape and which have no formula to use to find the volume. The volume of such objects may be determined by submerging them in a graduated container of water. The volume of the displaced water is equal to the volume of the object submerged. For example, if an object is submerged in a graduated cylinder containing 10.0 cm^3 of water before and 14 cm^3 of water after an object has been submerged, then we know 4 cm^3 (14 − 10) has been displaced and the volume of the object is 4 cm^3.

SELF-ASSESSMENT of the ATTAINMENT of the OBJECTIVES

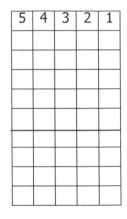

5	4	3	2	1

- convert lengths among the metric, Imperial and U.S. systems
- convert areas among the metric, Imperial and U.S. systems
- convert weights among the metric, Imperial and U.S. systems
- convert a Celsius temperature to a Fahrenheit temperature
- convert a Fahrenheit temperature to a Celsius temperature
- estimate measures
- perform measuring tasks accurately
- determine the volume of shapes
- solve word problems involving estimation and measurement

Score   /45   Date _____

Unit 7 – Graphs

OBJECTIVES

- gather and organize data by using a tally sheet
- construct a bar graph after having gathered the data
- use a scale when constructing a bar graph
- read the data contained on a bar graph
- construct a line graph
- read the data contained on a line graph
- construct a pie chart
- read the information contained on a pie chart
- solve problems containing graphs

A graph is a picture or an illustration of data. As a consequence of the widespread use of computers and calculators, an increasing amount of data is now being made available to the general public. These data are very difficult to read in their original form. Therefore, graphs are used to enable people to look at the picture and interpret the data quickly.

Although there are many types of graphs, we will consider bar graphs, line graphs, and pie charts because these are the three types of graphs that are most often encountered in everyday life. Although it is important to construct a graph, it is more important to be able to interpret the data, and list as much as possible of the data contained in the graph.

We construct a graph taking a horizontal line and a vertical line (although we will see other types of graphs later) and draw them as follows:

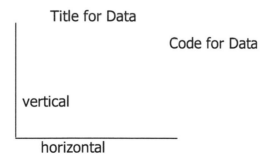

Note that the title for the data should be included at the top and the code that distinguishes the data is indicated at the right side of the graph. The first thing that a person must do when reading or constructing a graph is to determine what is being displayed on the horizontal line and what is being displayed on the vertical line.

Bar Graphs

Let us assume that we wish to determine the favorite sport of individuals in a group. We will restrict the choices to hockey, cricket, baseball, football, and tennis. A bar graph will be used because bar graphs show the relationships among groups. The data must be gathered. These data may be gathered by asking many people to list his/her favorite sport on a piece of paper. The papers are collected and the data may be organized by using a tally sheet. The tally sheet for the data collected will look like the following:

Tally Sheet			
hockey	~~////~~	/	6
cricket	~~////~~		5
baseball	//		2
football	~~////~~	///	8
tennis	////		4
		Total	25

Now that we have the data, we will construct the following diagram that shows the sports listed on the horizontal line and the number of choices listed on the vertical line. (We could have chosen the horizontal line for the number of choices and the vertical line for the listing of the sports.)

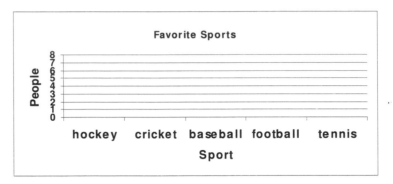

We are now able to complete the graph by inserting bars on each sport and making them equal to the distance that represents the number of choices. The graph will look like the following:

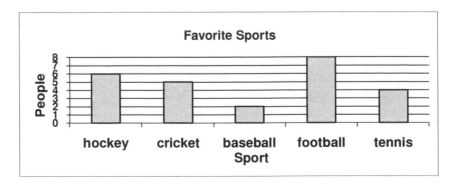

The above bar graph indicates that 25 people selected their favorite sport. Six chose hockey, 5 chose cricket, 2 chose baseball, 8 chose football, and 4 chose tennis.

70

Using a Scale for Bar Graphs

Sometimes when the data becomes larger, it is not possible to use each number on the vertical line. In these cases, 1 space may represent 2 or more units. The numbers are indicated and this makes the reading of the graph easier.

Example: Draw a bar graph indicating the age of each person in a group. We proceed by gathering the data and recording it on a tally sheet.

> 50	/ /	2
41-50	TTHL /	6
31-40	TTHL TTHL	10
20-30	TTHL / / /	8
< 20	/ / / /	4
		30

The drawing of the graph will differ in that the age range may be fairly large. Therefore, we will start at less than 20, and then 20 and increase each by 10 until 50 and then add greater than 50. This information will go on the horizontal line. In this case, it is expected that most people will be aged between 20 and 40. Therefore, we will use the following age categories: < 20, 20 – 30, 31 – 40, 41 – 50, and > 50.

This graph tells us that there are 30 persons in the group, 4 of whom are aged less than 20, 8 are between 20 and 30 years old, 10 are between 31 and 40 years old, 6 are between 41 and 50 years old, and 2 are older than 50.

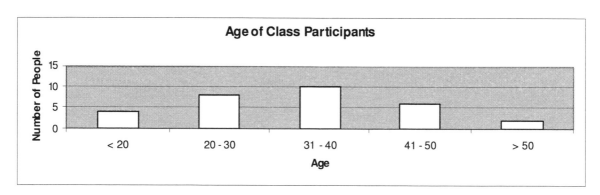

There is no hard and fast rule that says that specific data must be on the horizontal line and the other data on the vertical line. The above graph could have been constructed as follows:

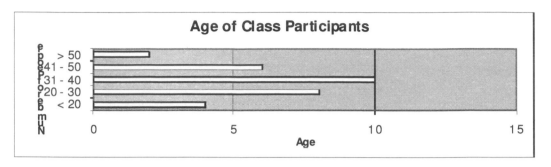

Bar Graphs Used for Comparison

Bar graphs may also be used for comparison of data during two or more different time periods. For example, the following graph compares the number of admissions to the Emergency Department of a hospital during a period of four months over a two year period. The darker bars indicate last year's admissions and the lighter bars will indicate this year's admissions.

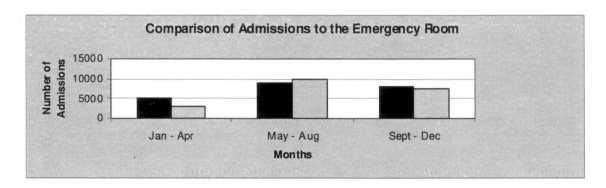

It can be seen from the above graph that compared to four months ago, admissions were down by approximately 2,000 during the periods of January to April; up by about 1,000 during the period May to August; and down by about 500 during the period September to December.

Line Graphs

Line graphs are used to show the variance of a single event over a period of time. They may be used to show continuing data, that is, how one thing affects another; and may be used to compare two or more sets of data.

Example 1: If we wish to find a special trend in the purchase of a particular model of car over any given period of time, we may make a tally sheet of purchases for each day of the week to see if there is a trend.

72

Tally Sheet		
Sunday	ⅢⅠ ///	8
Monday	ⅢⅠ ⅢⅠ ⅢⅠ /	16
Tuesday	ⅢⅠ ⅢⅠ ////	14
Wednesday	ⅢⅠ ⅢⅠ //	12
Thursday	ⅢⅠ ⅢⅠ ⅢⅠ ⅢⅠ	20
Friday	ⅢⅠ ⅢⅠ ⅢⅠ ⅢⅠ ////	24
Saturday	ⅢⅠ ⅢⅠ ⅢⅠ ⅢⅠ //	22
	Total	116

If the data are gathered and organized by putting it on a tally sheet, the following numbers may result: Sunday 8, Monday 16, Tuesday 14, Wednesday, 12, Thursday 20, Friday 24, and Saturday 22. We may use these data to construct a line graph. The graph will look like the following:

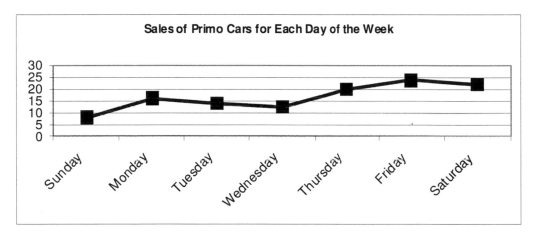

Example 2: If we wanted to show a continuous change in the pulse rate of two individuals who are exercising, we may measure and record their pulse at 1- minute intervals.

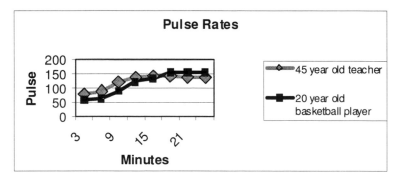

Pie Graphs or Pie Charts

A pie chart displays parts of the data as they relate to the whole. In order to ensure that the data are read properly, it is useful to indicate either the numbers or the percentage of each sector of the circle.

73

The circle that is used for a Pie Chart is a whole circle and is equal to 100%. In order to construct parts of the circle (sectors), draw a horizontal diameter and use a protractor. For instance, in the diagram of Example 1, one quarter of the circle is 25%. 25% of 360º = $\frac{1}{4}$ x 360° = 90° : 20% of 360º = $\frac{1}{5}$ x 360° =72 º: and 10% of 360º = 36º. This would be done only if you are not familiar with the Excel program.

Example: A food company produces 5 kinds of cereals. The sales indicated that 25% resulted from the sale of corn flakes, 20% from shredded wheat, 30% from raisin bran, 15% from oatmeal, and 10% from wheat bran. Construct a pie chart to display these data.

Cereal Sales

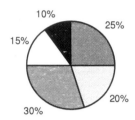

Exercise 30

1. Look at a number of people and record the color of the sweater, shirt, blouse, etc. of each person. Organize the data and construct a bar graph and a pie chart to display this information.

2. Ask 31 people to write his/her favorite fruit from among the following: apples, bananas, oranges, and mangoes. Organize the data and construct a bar graph and a pie chart to display this information.

3. Draw a bar graph in which 5 types of fertilizer are applied to 5 plants of the same type and show how each type of fertilizer affected the growth of the plants.

4. Draw a bar graph and a line graph to show a comparison of dollar sales of a furniture store for each quarter during the past year and the previous year.

5. Construct a line graph of the temperature for each day of one week. (Be sure to observe the temperature at approximately the same time each day.)

6. List all of the data that each of the following graphs display:

a)

b)

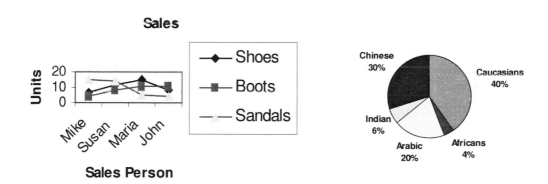

7. Construct a line graph that displays the gross sales (in dollars) and the net profit of a small company during the past five years.

8. A municipality employed the following number of people: 15 secretaries, 25 blue collar workers, 20 policemen, 10 firemen, and 5 administrators. Construct a pie chart to display these data.

9. A survey was taken to determine the favorite flavor of ice cream. The following data resulted: 25% chose vanilla, 20% chose pecan, 5% chose chocolate, 10% chose strawberry, 15% chose banana, 20% chose peach, and 5% chose raspberry. Construct a pie graph to display these data. Then explain why it is necessary to indicate the numbers on the chart.

10. Give a title to the following and write all of the information that you can read from the following pie chart:

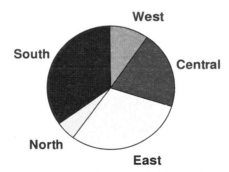

It should be noted that the above data could have been displayed as a bar graph.

SELF-ASSESSMENT of the ATTAINMENT of the OBJECTIVES

	5	4	3	2	1
- gather and organize data by using a tally sheet					
- construct a bar graph after having gathered the data					
- use a scale when constructing a bar graph					
- read the data contained on a bar graph					
- construct a line graph					
- read the data contained on a line graph					
- construct a pie chart					
- read the information contained on a pie chart					
- solve problems containing graphs					

Score ___ / 45   Date _____

Section II – The Use of a Calculator, Patterns, Ordinal Numbers, Roman Numerals, Estimation and Measurement, Graphs

Post–Test II

The answers to these problems can be found at the back of the book.

1. Perform the following multiplications using a calculator. List the next product in the sequence.

11 x 11 =   12 x 11 =   13 x 11 =   14 x 11 =

The next product in the sequence is

2. The positive square root of 169 is

3. Perform the following operation: 6 ÷ 0 =

Explain

4. A car uses 9.8 liters of gas to travel 200 km. How much gas is required to travel 380 km?

5. I wish to multiply 102 by 99 using a calculator. However, the 9 key does not work on my calculator. How can I determine the product using my calculator?

What is the product?

6. Use the Memory key of a calculator to find (23 x 4) + (37 x 26). List the steps in the process that you used.

7. Write the next two numbers in the following sequence:

2, 3, 5, 8, 12, _____   _____

8. Write the pattern in Number 7 in words.

9. In the following grid, list the entry in a) the third row and fourth column and b) in the fourth row and third column:

2	7	11	14	27
13	9	4	22	8
16	5	3	12	15
20	31	44	6	1
10	33	27	29	30

a)   b)

10. Change 257 into Roman Numerals. 257 =

11. Change C X I I into the Hindu–Arabic system. C X I I =

12. Paul has a truck with a capacity of 432 cubic meters. What is the capacity in cubic feet? ($1 m^3 = 35.315 f^3$). List the answer with 3 decimal places.
$432 m^3 = ft^3$

13. Square tiles were required to cover Sarah's floor that measured 13 m by 12 m. The only tiles available measured $\frac{1}{2} m^2$. How many square tiles did Sarah have to buy?

14. Change 25º Celsius to Fahrenheit   25º Celsius =   Fahrenheit

15. Change 95º Fahrenheit to Celsius   95º Fahrenheit =   Celsius

16. Construct a tally sheet having a sample of 18 people who have a preference for walking or swimming or cycling (see next page).

			%
walking	swimming	cycling	

17. Construct a bar graph using the data from number 16.

18. Construct a pie chart using the same data.

19. Construct a line graph to display the sales of cars at an auto sales dealer who sells cars on Monday to Friday.

20. Construct a graph to display the following data. A municipality employs 12 secretaries, 20 maintenance workers, 25 policemen, 10 fire fighters and 5 administrators.

Score _____ Date _____

Section III – Geometrical Facts and Concepts

Pre–Test III

After completing this test, check your answers at the end of the book. If you have ten or more correct answers, review those sections that contain the problems that were not answered correctly. If you have less than 10 correct answers, study the entire Section.

Each person should have a compass, a protractor, a set square, and a ruler to complete this Unit.

1. Name each of the following angles:

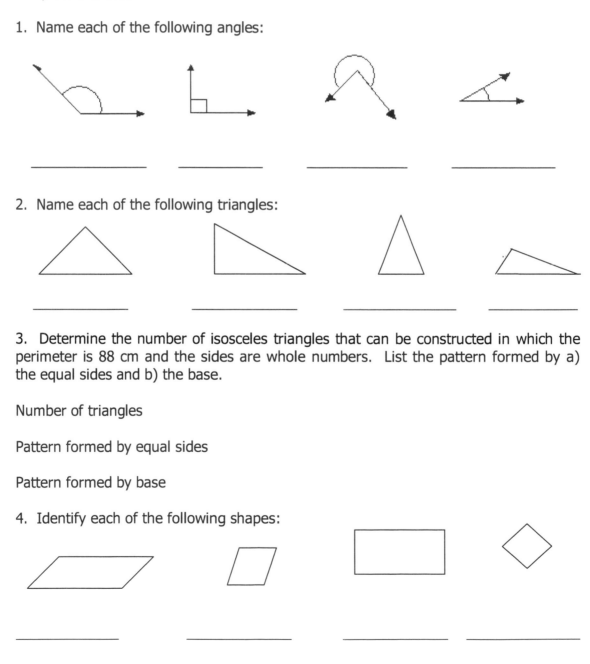

_____   _____   _____   _____

2. Name each of the following triangles:

_____   _____   _____   _____

3. Determine the number of isosceles triangles that can be constructed in which the perimeter is 88 cm and the sides are whole numbers. List the pattern formed by a) the equal sides and b) the base.

Number of triangles

Pattern formed by equal sides

Pattern formed by base

4. Identify each of the following shapes:

_____   _____   _____   _____

80

5. If you have a number of tiles having a measurement of 1 cm² to cover an area of 24 m², how many rectangular shapes may be covered? List these.

6. Construct a triangle so that its area is 12 cm². Indicate the dimensions.

7. What is the sum of the interior angles of a regular pentagon?

8. What is the area of a circle whose radius is 2.8 cm?

9. Using the circle below,

a) name the circle

b) draw and name a radius

c) draw and name the diameter

d) draw and name a chord

e) name an arc

f)   shade a sector

10. What is the circumference of a circle whose diameter is 14 cm?

11. Construct an angle of $22\frac{1}{2}$° without using a protractor and explain how you did this.

12. How many lines of symmetry are there in:

a) a scalene triangle

b) an equilateral triangle

c) an isosceles triangle

d) a right triangle

e) a square

f) a rectangle

g) a parallelogram

h) a rhombus

i) a regular pentagon

j) a regular hexagon

Score _____   Date _____

Unit 8 – Geometrical Facts and Concepts

OBJECTIVES

- identify the three types of lines
- draw a line segment
- identify the four types of angles
- identify the four types of triangles
- determine the perimeter of plane shapes
- determine the area of plane shapes (square, rectangle parallelogram, rhombus, triangle)
- identify pentagons, hexagons, octagons
- determine the sum of the interior angles of polygons
- identify a prism, a triangular prism, a cube, a sphere, a circular cylinder, a cone
- determine the volume of each of the above
- identify the parts of a circle
- construct a triangle having been given the measure of the three sides
- draw a line perpendicular to another line
- bisect an angle
- draw an angle equal to a given angle
- bisect a line segment
- draw a line parallel to another line through a point outside of the line
- use a set square correctly
- identify lines of symmetry
- identify congruent shapes
- solve problems using the facts and methods in this Unit

Plane Shapes and Measurement

Each participant should have in his/her possession a compass, a ruler graded in centimeters, a protractor and a set square.

Plane shapes have position and size (perimeter and area) but no thickness. They can be placed on a plane surface such that all parts of the shape are touching a plane surface. The following are some plane shapes that are most often used:

Point

A point does not have measurable qualities. It has position. If we wish to refer to a point, we name it by a letter. For example .A is read "point A".

Straight Line

The word line when used alone refers to a straight line. A line passes through two points on a plane without changing direction.

There are three types of lines:

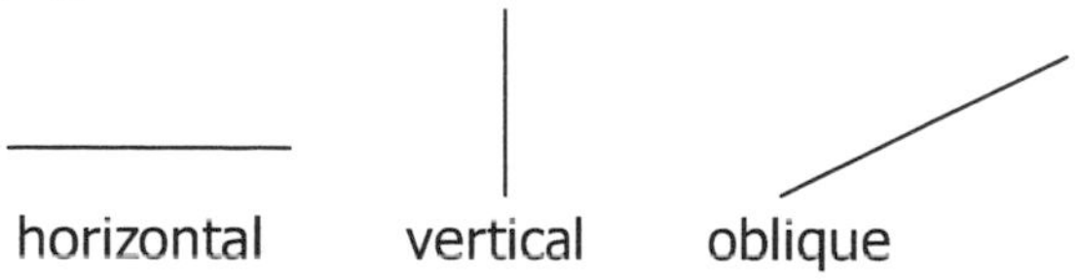

horizontal   vertical   oblique

Line Segment

A line segment is named by its endpoints. For example, A_____B is named the line segment AB. A line segment has length.

Angles

An angle is formed when two lines meet at a point.

 An angle is named by three letters. The angle is written ∠ABC or ∠CBA or ∠B.

If the measure of the angle is less that 90º, the angle is called an acute angle.

A complete revolution – think of the hands of a clock moving in 12 hours – is equal to 360º.

 One half of a complete revolution is 180º and is called a straight angle.

 One quarter of a revolution (or $\frac{1}{2}$ of a straight angle) is called a right angle.

 An angle greater than 90º and less than 180º is called an obtuse angle.

An angle greater than 180º and less than 360° is called a reflex angle.

Triangles

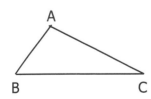 A triangle is an enclosed shape that has three sides and three angles.
The triangle at the left has three sides AB, BC, and CA and three angles ABC, BCA, and CAB. Three letters name the triangle. The triangle is named ABC.

Four Types of Triangles

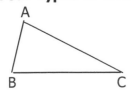 A scalene triangle has three sides each having a different measurement.

An isosceles triangle has two sides that are equal in measurement.
The angles opposite the equal sides are also equal.

 An equilateral triangle has three equal sides and three equal angles.

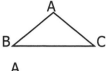 A right angled triangle contains an angle of 90º.

It should be noted that all of the triangles were named by A, B, and C. These can be named as DEF, EFG, MNO, PQR or any other three letters.

Perimeter of Triangles

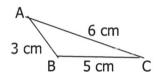 The perimeter of a triangle is the sum of the measurements of the three sides.
For example, in the triangle ABC, AB = 3 cm, BC = 5 cm, and AC = 6 cm   Therefore, the perimeter is 14 cm.

Exercise 31

1. Identify each of the following triangles as scalene, isosceles, equilateral, or right angled:

a) 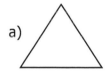   b)   c) 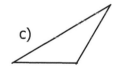   d)

_____   _____   _____   _____

2. Measure (to the nearest half centimeter) each side of the following shapes and determine the perimeter of each:

a) 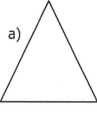   b)   c)   d)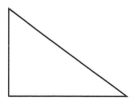

_____   _____   _____   _____

_____   _____   _____   _____

_____   _____   _____   _____

Perimeter_____   _____   _____   _____

3. Use a protractor to measure the angles of each triangle (to the nearest degree).
Then list the measures of the angles and add these measures for each triangle.

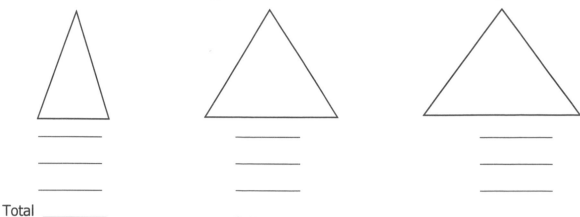

Total _____   _____   _____

Squares, Perimeter and Area of Enclosed Shapes

A square is an enclosed shape that has four equal sides. In addition, each angle within
the square is equal to 90°.

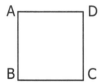

The perimeter of this square is the sum of the measure of the sides
AB + BC + CD + DA, or 4 x the measure of one side.

Area of Squares

Find the area of the square ABCD, if the length is 4 cm.
Draw horizontal and vertical lines 1 cm apart within the
square. We see that there are 16 small squares. Each of the
small squares is 1 cm^2 and the area of the large square is 16
cm^2. The area of a square is the length of one side squared.
It should be noted that if a square is one half the size of another square, then it will
require 4 of the smaller squares to fill the larger square.

Rectangles

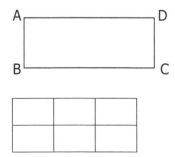

A rectangle is an enclosed shape that has four sides and
each angle within a rectangle measures 90°.
Note that AD = BC and AB = DC. Also note that each of
the angles within the rectangle are equal to 90°.
If a unit is 1 cm^2, then the area is 3 x 2 or 6 cm^2.
Count the number of squares in the diagram or multiply
the number of units in each row (squares in a horizontal
line) by the number of squares in a column (squares in a
vertical line).

Since there are 2 rows and 3 columns, the number of squares is 2 x 3 or 6.   That is, the area of a rectangle is the length multiplied by the width or A = ℓ x w. That is, the area is 6 cm^2.

The Area of a Triangle

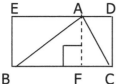

Let ABC be a given triangle. We want to find the area of ABC.

Draw a rectangle on the triangle ABC.   Draw a line from A perpendicular to BC. Use a protractor or a set square.

AF is called the height of the triangle. BC is called the base. The triangle ABE is equal to the triangle ABF, and the triangle AFC is equal to the triangle ACD. Therefore, the triangle ABC is $\frac{1}{2}$ of the area of the rectangle EBCD and is equal to $\frac{1}{2}$ base x height.

The area of the rectangle EBCD is equal to EB x BC.
Since EB is equal to AF, the area of the rectangle is AF x BC.

Therefore, the area of the triangle ABC is equal to $\frac{1}{2}$ (BC x AF) or the area of the triangle is $\frac{1}{2}$ (b x h) where b is the base and h is the altitude (height) of the triangle.

Parallelograms

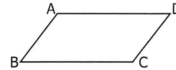

A parallelogram is an enclosed shape that has four sides and the opposite sides are equal and parallel (that is, they will never meet when extended in either direction).

However, no angle within the parallelogram is equal to 90º.

Rhombus

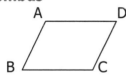

A rhombus is a parallelogram that has four equal sides.

The Area of Parallelograms and Rhombuses

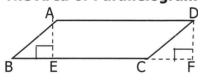

ABCD is a parallelogram. Extend BC to F. Construct or use a protractor to draw AE and DF perpendicular to BF.
Since BE is equal to CF, the area of the rectangle AEFD is AE x EF.
Since the area of the triangle ABE is equal to the area of triangle DCF, the area of the parallelogram ABCD is equal to the area of the rectangle AEFD.
The area of the rectangle AEFD is AE x EF or base x height. Therefore, the area of the parallelogram is base x height or BC x AE.

Exercise 32

Use Whole numbers in each of the following.

1. Name each of the following shapes:

a)   b)    c) 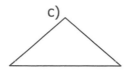   d)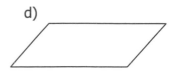

_____   _____   _____   _____

2. List three places where you may find a:
square

rectangle

Measure each side of each shape in number 1 to the closest half centimeter and then write the perimeter of each shape.

a) square   sides   perimeter

b) recta   sides   perimeter

c) triangle   sides   perimeter

d) parallelogram   sides   perimeter

4. Find the area of each of the following rectangles and write the area inside of each rectangle. (Remember that 2 cm x 5 cm = 10 cm^2.):

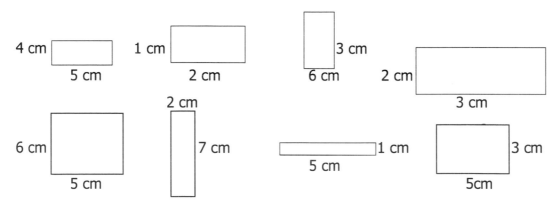

5. Write a general rule for finding the area of a square.

6. If you have a number of tiles to cover an area of 24 m^2, how many different rectangular shapes may be covered?   List the dimensions of each.

88

7. How many squares can you make so that the area is 36 cm^2?

8. How many squares can you make so that the perimeter is 36 cm?

List the dimensions of each.

9. How many squares can you make so that the perimeter is 24 cm?   List them.

10. How many squares can you make so that the area is 13 cm^2?

11. How many rectangles can you make so that the perimeter is 36 cm?
List the dimensions of each.

12. How many rectangles can you make so that the perimeter is 17 cm?

13. If the area of a rectangle is 72 m^2 and one side is 8 m, what is the length of the other side?

14. Name each of the following angles.

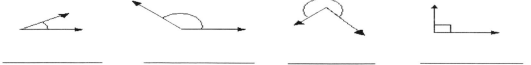

_____   _____   _____   _____

15. Insert the symbol >, <, = to make the following a correct statement.

16. Draw a parallelogram and determine its area.

17. Draw a rhombus and determine its area.

18. Determine the area of each of the following triangles:

a)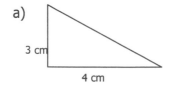

3 cm

4 cm

b)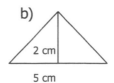

2 cm

5 cm

c)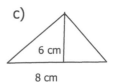

6 cm

8 cm

_____   _____   _____

19. Determine the number of isosceles triangles that can be constructed in which the perimeter is 88 cm and the sides are whole numbers. List the pattern formed by a) the equal sides and b) the base.

Number of triangles

Pattern formed by equal sides

Pattern formed by base

20. Are all squares rectangles?   Explain

21. Are all squares rhombuses?   Explain

22. Are all rhombuses squares?   Explain

23. Are all parallelograms rectangles?   Explain

24. Are all rectangles parallelograms?   Explain

25. Can a right triangle also be an isosceles triangle?   Explain

Filling a Square or a Rectangle

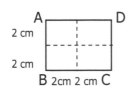

If the sides of a square are doubled, then the area is quadrupled (multiplied by 4). The measurement of each side of ABCD is 4 cm. Therefore, the area of ABCD is 16 cm^2.

The measurement of each side of EFGH is 2 cm. Therefore, the area of EFGH is 4 cm^2. Therefore, the area of ABCD is four times the area of EFGH.

Exercise 33

1. You wish to tile a floor of 24 m². When you go to the store to buy tiles, you find that they are sold only in $\frac{1}{2}$ m x $\frac{1}{2}$ m size. How many tiles will you have to buy to cover the floor?

2. A wall 10 meters long and 5 meters high is to be covered with tiles measuring 10 cm by 5 cm. How many tiles must be used? (1 meter = 100 centimeters)

3. An afghan that measures 105 cm by 60 cm is to be made from squares whose sides measure 15 cm. How many squares must be used? Explain.

4. Determine the different sizes of squares that can be used to make a table ornament that measures 90 cm by 60 cm. List these.

Pentagons

A pentagon is an enclosed shape that has five sides.

There are two types of pentagons

A regular pentagon has 5 equal sides.

An irregular pentagon has 5 sides and the measures of the sides are not all equal.

Hexagons

A hexagon is a closed shape on a plane that has 6 sides.

A regular hexagon has six equal sides.   An irregular hexagon has six sides
                                          and the measures are not the same.

Octagons

An octagon is a closed shape that has 8 sides.

A regular octagon has 8 sides and the   An irregular octagon has 8 sides and
measures of the sides are the same.   the measures of the sides are not the
                                          same.

In all regular pentagons, hexagons and octagons, the interior angles are equal.

Finding the Sum of the Interior Angles of Polygons

We will accept as a fact that the sum of the interior angles of a triangle is 180°. This will be proven in Unit X. If there is any difficulty in accepting this fact, draw a triangle and measure its angles to try to find a triangle in which the sum of the interior angles is not 180°.

Let us now examine the following shapes: a square, a rhombus, a rectangle, and a parallelogram. Note that each shape has 4 sides.

A diagonal (a line drawn from any angle to the opposite angle) will be drawn in each shape and this will separate each shape into 2 triangles.

           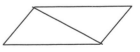

Each shape contains 2 triangles. Therefore, the sum of the interior angles is 2 x 180° or 360°.

Let us now use a regular polygon (5 sides), a hexagon (6 sides), and an octagon (8 sides).

92

We will choose one angle of each shape and draw lines to other angles so that these will not be a part of the perimeter of the shape.

Number of sides	5	6	8
Number of triangles	3	4	6
Sum of interior angles	3 x 180º = 540°	4 x 180º = 720°	6 x 180º = 1080º

Do you see a pattern? Explain

The general formula for finding the sum of the interior angles of a polygon is 180° multiplied by (the number of sides minus 2) or 180º(n − 2), where n is the number of sides.

Exercise 34

1. What is the sum of the interior angles of:

a) a twelve sided polygon   b) a ten sided polygon

2.   What is the measure of each of the angles of a regular pentagon?

 (A regular pentagon has five equal sides and five equal angles.)

Solids

Plane shapes are those that have the whole face completely touching a plane.
Solids are enclosed shapes in which one of many faces is touching a plane.

Prisms

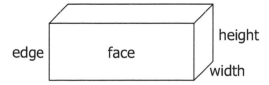

A rectangular prism has 2 ends often called faces and 4 other faces.
The opposite sides (faces) have the same area.

The surface area is the sum of the areas of the 6 faces.
The volume of a rectangular prism is width x the height x the length.

A rectangular right prism is a solid that has 6 faces and in which all of the faces are rectangles and all of the angles are 90º. The volume of a rectangular prism is ℓ X w x h.

A triangular prism has a base that is a triangle. The volume of a triangular prism is equal to the area of the triangle multiplied by the length.

V = area of the triangle x ℓ.

Cube

 A cube is a prism in which all of the faces and all of the edges are equal. The volume of a cube is V = s^3 (where s is the measure of any side) because the sides are equal.

Sphere A sphere is an enclosed shape in which all of the points on the surface are of equal distance from the center.

 The volume of a sphere of radius r is $\frac{4}{3}$ π r^3 where π = 3.14.

Circular Cylinder

 A circular cylinder is an enclosed solid that has a circular base and a height. The volume of a cylinder is the area of one base multiplied by the height. Area = π r^2 h. (Note area of circle is π r^2.)

Cone A cone is a solid that has a circular base and the sides terminate at a given point.

 Since a cone is equal to $\frac{1}{3}$ of a cylinder, the volume of a cone is

equal to $\frac{1}{3}$ of the volume of a cylinder or V = $\frac{1}{3}$ (π r^2 h).

It should be noted that since the volume of solids are three dimensional, the volume is stated in cubic measurement. For example, the volume of a prism is ℓ x w x h. If the length is 2 cm, the width is 8 cm, and the height is 10 cm, the volume will be 160 cm^3. A similar answer would result if inches were used. 6 in x 4 in x 3 in = 72 in^2.

Exercise 35

1. List three examples of each of the following shapes:

a) prism

b) cube

c) sphere

d) cylinder

2. Find the volume of a prism whose length is 5 cm, width is 4 cm, and height is 6 cm.

3. Find the volume of a sphere whose radius is 5 cm.

4. Find the volume of a cube whose edge measures 4 cm.

5. If the edge of the cube in number 4 is doubled, what is the volume of the new cube?

6. Find the volume of a triangular prism in which the base of the triangle is 3 cm, the height is 5 cm and the length of the prism is 8 cm.

7. Find the volume of a cone in which the radius is 3 cm and the height is 8 cm.

8. Find the volume of a cylinder in which the radius is 7 cm and the height is 12 cm.

9. If one edge of a square is doubled, is the area doubled?

What is the area?   Explain

10. If the side of a cube is tripled, is the volume tripled?

Explain

To Construct a Circle

Use a compass and take any measurement. Place the point of the compass on the paper and turn the compass completely (one revolution).

P ← interior or area   A circle is named by three points. In this case, the circle
   R   is called PQR or PRQ.
Q ← circumference

Note the names given to various parts of the circle.

0 is the center of the circle.

PQ is the diameter. It is a straight line that joins two points on the circumference and passes through the center of the circle.

OR is called the radius (plural radii). It is a line drawn from the center to any point on the circumference. Note that OP = OQ = OR.

An arc of a circle is a part of the circumference. In the above diagram, PR, PS, RQ, RS, QS and QP are some of the arcs of the circle.

MS is a chord. It is a line that joins two points on the circumference and does not pass through the center.

A sector is part of the interior that is enclosed by an arc and a chord.

The area of BAC and BEC are sectors.

Exercise 36

1. Draw a circle whose radius is 2.8 cm. What is the measure of the length of the diameter of this circle?

2. Using the same center, draw three circles whose radii (plural of radius) are 1 cm, 1.5 cm and 2 cm. Circles with the same center are said to be concentric.

3. Draw two circles with radii 1 cm and 2 cm so that the circumferences will touch one another at one point only.

4. How many diameters can you draw in a circle?

5. How many radii can you draw in a circle?

6. A field measures 160 m by 120 m. A cow is tethered to a stake at the center of the field and the rope is 60 m long. Draw to scale the area of the field in which the cow may walk. (Use a scale of 1 cm = 40 m.)

7. Draw a circle:

a) name the circumference

b) draw and name a radius

c) draw and name a diameter

d) draw and name a chord

e) name an arc

f) shade a sector

Radius, Diameter, and Circumference

We know that a radius is a line segment from the center of a circle to the circumference. A diameter is a line segment from one point on the circumference to another point on the circumference and which passes through the center of the circle. Therefore, a diameter of a circle is twice as long as a radius. That is d = 2r.

Now imagine cutting a piece of string equal in length to the diameter. Wrap this piece of string around the circumference. You will notice that the string will have to be used three times and there is still a small distance left over. Therefore, the circumference is d x some number that is 3 + a decimal fraction. This number is equal to π (spelled pi and pronounced pie) which is a non–terminating, non–recurring decimal fraction equal to 3.14159... This fraction will never terminate (have a remainder of 0), and the decimal number sequence will never recur. In general, we use 3.14 for calculations using pi. Therefore, the circumference of a circle is π d where π is equal to 3.14 and d is the diameter. It follows that the circumference of a circle is $2\pi r$ because 2 r = d. The area of a circle is πr^2 where π = 3.14. For example, if the diameter of a circle is 6 cm, the radius is 3 cm and the area is πr^2 or 3.14 x 9 which equals 28.26 cm^2.

Construct a Triangle Having Been Given the Measure of the Three Sides

Example 1: Construct a triangle whose sides are 2 cm, 3 cm, and 4 cm.

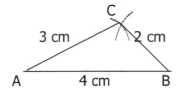

97

Let the base AB be 4 cm.
With a compass point placed at A draw an arc of 3 cm.
With the compass point at B draw an arc of 2 cm intersecting the first arc at C.
Join the point at which the arcs intersect (C) to A and B.
The triangle CAB has sides 2 cm, 3 cm and 4 cm.

Example 2: Construct a triangle ABC with the following measures: the base BC = 3 cm, the side AB = 4 cm, and the side AC = 5 cm.

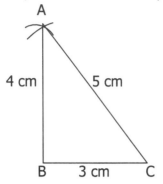

With the compass point placed at B draw an arc of 4 cm.
With the compass point placed at C draw an arc of 5 cm.
Let the intersection of the arcs be A.
Join A to B and A to C. ABC is the required triangle.
Measure the angle ABC. What kind of a triangle is ABC?

Exercise 37

1. Construct triangles in which the measures of the sides are:

a) 4 cm, 6 cm, 5 cm.   b) 6 cm, 8 cm, 10 cm.

What kind of a triangle is this?   What kind of a triangle is this?

c) each side is 4 cm.   d) 6 cm, 6 cm, 10 cm.

What kind of a triangle is this?   What kind of a triangle is this?

2. Draw a triangle whose sides measure 7 cm, 2 cm, 3 cm.

Make a general statement.

98

3 a) What is the circumference of a circle whose diameter is 14 cm?

b) What is the circumference of a circle whose radius is 7 cm?

To Draw a Line Perpendicular to Another Line

Let AB be a line

Let us choose a point C on AB where we want to draw the perpendicular line.

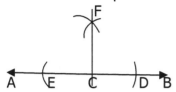

Place the compass at the point C and use any radius to draw arcs cutting AB at E and D.
Place the compass at the point E and use a radius greater than EC and draw an arc.
Place the compass at D and using the same radius, draw a second arc to intersect the previous arc at F. Join FC.
Now FC is perpendicular to AB.
Check that $\angle$FCA = 90° = the angle FCB by using a protractor or a set square.

To Bisect an Angle

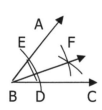

Let ABC be a given angle. With center B and any radius.
Draw an arc ED cutting AB at E and AC at D. Join ED.
With center E and radius ED draw an arc.
With center D and radius ED draw another arc cutting the first arc at F. Join BF.
Use a protractor to show that $\angle$ABF = $\angle$FBC.

To Draw an Angle Equal to a Given Angle

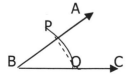 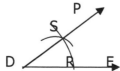

Let ABC be a given angle. With B as center, draw an arc cutting AB and BC at P and Q.
Draw a line DE. With D as center, and using the radius PQ, draw an arc to cut DE at R.

Using the length QP and R as the center, draw an arc cutting the first arc at S. Join DS and extend the line to P.
Using a protractor show that ∠ABC = ∠ PDE.

To Draw a Line Perpendicular to Another Line Through a Point Outside of the Line

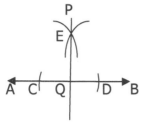

Let AB be a given line and P be a point outside of the line. With center P, draw an arc cutting AB at C and D. With centers C and D and using the same radius, draw arcs intersecting at E.
Join PE intersecting AB at Q.
Use a protractor to show that the angle PQA and PQB are each 90⁰.

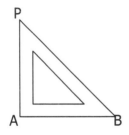

A line may be drawn through a point P perpendicular to a line by using a set square as shown in the diagram.

To Bisect a Straight Line Segment

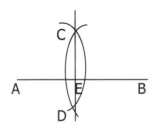

Let AB be a given line segment.
With centers A and B and equal radii, greater than half of AB, draw arcs intersecting each other at C and D. Join CD intersecting AB at E.   AE = EB. Check by measuring with a ruler.

To Draw a Line Parallel to Another Line Through a Given Point

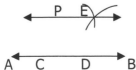

Let AB be a given line and P a point outside of the line. Choose any two points C and D on AB.

With center P and radius CD draw an arc. With center D and radius PC draw another arc cutting the first arc at E. Join PE. PE is parallel to AB.

A set square and a ruler may be used to draw a line parallel to a given line through a point outside of the line.

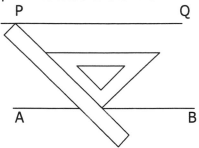 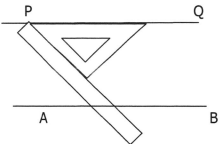

A set square is placed with one corner along AB. The ruler is then placed in contact with the set square. The ruler is held firmly and the set square is moved along the ruler until the edge that was on AB meets the point P. While holding the set square in position, a line is drawn through P along the edge of the set square. This is the line PQ that is parallel to AB.

Exercise 38

1. Draw a line segment AB 6 cm long and draw a line perpendicular to AB from a point C not on AB. Do this by using a ruler and compass only and then do this by using a ruler and a set square only.

2. Draw a line segment PQ 5 cm long. At each endpoint, draw a line perpendicular to PQ.

3. Using a ruler and compass only, draw an angle of 45° and an angle of $22\frac{1}{2}$°.

4. Draw any triangle PQR and extend QR to S. Bisect ∠PQR and ∠PRS and extend the bisectors to meet at T. Measure ∠QPR and ∠QTR. What do you notice?

5. Draw a line AB and mark points C on one side of the line and D on the other side of the line. Draw perpendicular lines from C to AB and from D to AB. Check by using a protractor.

6. Draw a triangle ABC with a base BC 8 cm and the sides 7.5 cm and 5.3 cm. Draw a perpendicular line from A to BC to obtain the altitude of the triangle. Measure the length of the perpendicular with a ruler. Then find the area of the triangle ABC.

7. Draw a line segment AB whose length is 7 cm. At each end of AB draw perpendicular lines of 3 cm length on opposite sides of AB. Join these two endpoints. By measuring, show that this line bisects AB.

8. Draw three parallel lines using a) a ruler and compass only, b) using a ruler and set square only.

9. In the diagram below, mark the points such that AP = PQ = QB. C is any point on AD. Join PC. Draw lines QD and BE parallel to PC. Measure AC, CD, DE. What do you notice?

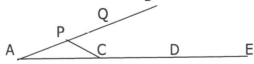

Lines of Symmetry

A line of symmetry divides an enclosed shape into two parts. When one part is folded over the line, it will fit exactly on the other. That is, the two parts are exactly alike in size and shape.

Example: If ABCD is a given square and BD is drawn as a diagonal, we note that the triangle, ABD, when folded on BD will fit exactly on the triangle CBD. Therefore, BD is a line of symmetry.

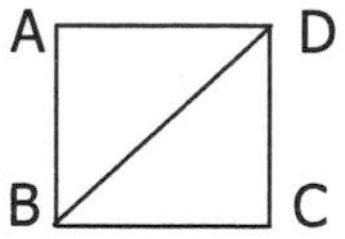

The next question to be asked is, "How many lines of symmetry does the shape have?" We may try to find other lines of symmetry within a square. Observe the following:

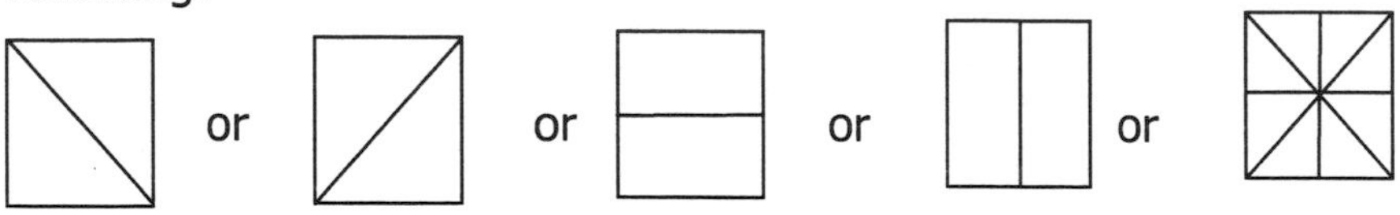

We note that there are 4 lines of symmetry within a square. When we draw the 4 lines of symmetry on the same shape, the resulting shape will appear as the square above to the right. Many enclosed shapes have one or more lines of symmetry. However, there are some shapes that have no line of symmetry.

For example,

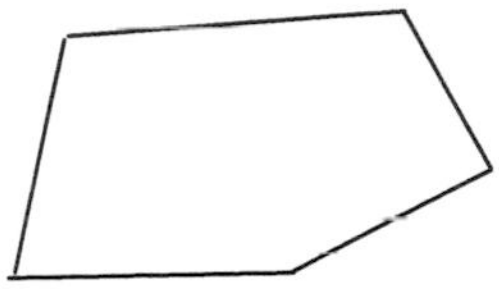

irregular pentagon
An irregular pentagon has no line symmetry.

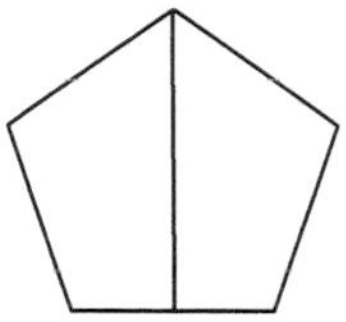

regular pentagon
A regular pentagon has 1 line of symmetry.

Congruent Shapes

Lines or shapes are said to be congruent if they have the same shape and the same size.

Example1:   The line segment A_____B is congruent to the line segment C_____D because if either line segment is moved onto the other line segment, the two line segments will match exactly. That is, the two line segments have the same measurement and the same shape.

Example 2:

The triangle ABC is congruent to the triangle DEF because the two triangles will fit one on top of the other. That is, the triangles have the same shape and the same size.

Example 3:

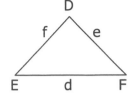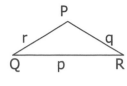

These two triangles are not congruent because, although they have the same shape, they do not have the same size. Neither one will fit exactly if placed one on top of the other. In this case, we say that the triangles are similar. That is, they have the same shape but are not the same size. If two triangles are similar, their corresponding sides are proportional. That is, $\frac{f}{r} = \frac{d}{p} = \frac{e}{q}$.

Exercise 39

1. Can a four leaf clover have lines of symmetry?

Explain

2. List four objects that have a line (or lines) of symmetry.

3. How many lines of symmetry are there in each of the following shapes? Draw a diagram to illustrate your answer.

a) a scalene triangle   b) an equilateral triangle

c) an isosceles triangle   d) a right triangle

e) a rectangle   f) a parallelogram

g) a square   h   a rhombus

i) a regular hexagon   j) a regular pentagon

4. Can 2 irregular polygons be congruent?

Explain

5. List 6 congruent shapes that you may see in everyday life.

6. Construct 2 isosceles triangles that are congruent.

7. Construct 2 isosceles triangles that are not congruent.

8. Draw 2 line segments such that one line segment is twice the measure of the other. Are these line segments congruent? .

Explain

SELF-ASSESSMENT of the ATTAINMENT of the OBJECTIVES

	5	4	3	2	1
- identify the three types of lines					
- draw a line segment					
- identify the four types of angles					
- identify the four types of triangles					
- determine the perimeter of plane shapes					
- determine the area of plane shapes (square, rectangle parallelogram,					
- identify pentagons, hexagons, octagons					
- determine the sum of the interior angles of polygons					
- identify a prism, a triangular prism, a cube, a sphere, a circular cylinder, a cone					
- determine the volume of each of the above					
- identify the parts of a circle					
- construct a triangle having been given the measure of the three sides					
- draw a line perpendicular to another line					
- bisect an angle					
- draw an angle equal to a given angle					
- bisect a line segment					
- draw a line parallel to another line through a point outside of the line					
- correctly use a set square					
- identify lines of symmetry					
- identify congruent shapes					
- solve problems using the facts and methods in this Unit					

Score _____ /105   Date _____

Section III – Geometrical Facts and Concepts
Post–Test III

After completing this test, check your answers at the end of the book and compare your results with your score on the Pre–Test.

1. Name each of the following angles:

_____   _____   _____   _____

2. Name each of the following triangles:

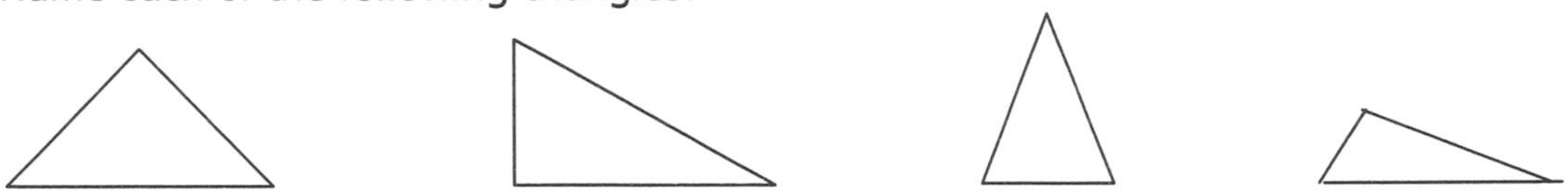

_____   _____   _____   _____

3. Determine the number of isosceles triangles that can be constructed in which the perimeter is 88 cm and the sides are whole numbers. List the pattern formed by a) the equal sides and b) the base.

Number of triangles

Pattern formed by equal sides

Pattern formed by base

4. Identify each of the following shapes:

_____   _____   _____   _____

5. If you have a number of tiles having a measurement of 1 cm² to cover an area of 24 m², how many rectangular shapes may be covered? List these.

6. Construct a triangle so that its area is 12 cm². Indicate the dimensions.

7. What is the sum of the interior angles of a regular pentagon?

8. What is the area of a circle whose radius is 2.8 cm?

9. Using the circle below,

a) name the circle

b) draw and name a radius

c) draw and name the diameter

d) draw and name a chord

e) name an arc

f) shade a sector

10. What is the circumference of a circle whose diameter is 14 cm?

11. Construct an angle of $22\frac{1}{2}$° without using a protractor and explain how you did this.

12. How many lines of symmetry are there in:

a) a scalene triangle

b) an equilateral triangle

c) an isosceles triangle

d) a right triangle

e) a square

f) a rectangle

g) a parallelogram

h) a rhombus

i) a regular pentagon

j) a regular hexagon

Score _____   Date _____

Section IV – The Number System from the Natural Numbers to the Real Numbers
Pre–Test IV

Answers can be found at the end of the book.

1. Write an example of the commutative property of addition.

2. What number is the multiplicative identity?

3. Give an example of the associative property of multiplication.

4. Give an example of the distributive property of multiplication with respect to addition.

5. Give an example of the cancellation property of multiplication.

6. What new operation always becomes possible when we add the negative whole numbers and zero to the positive whole numbers?

7. What is the additive identity in this new set of numbers?

8. Add each row and place the result in each box in column (a). Then add each column and place the result in each box in row (b). Then add column (a) and row (b).

					(a)	
4	− 5	6	− 2	− 3		
− 3	2	− 1	4	6		
− 7	0	− 2	− 3	− 2		
− 4	3	3	6	3		
3	5	− 4	2	− 1		
(b)						

9. Add each of the following:

a) − 7
   − 5

b) 7
   − 5

c) − 7
   − 5

d) 7
   − 5

10. Multiply each of the following:

a) − 7
   − 8

b) 7
    8

c) 7
   − 8

d) − 7
    8

109

11. What is the additive inverse of -5?

12. Subtract each of the following:

a) $-5 - 4 =$ b) $4 - (-5) =$ c) $-7 + 7 =$ d) $7 - (-3) =$

13. Divide each of the following:

a) $16 \div -4 =$ b) $-16 \div 4 =$ c) $-16 \div -4 =$ d) $3 \div -3 =$

14. Determine whether each of the following is a terminating or a recurring decimal fraction

a) $\frac{2}{3}$ is   b) $\frac{3}{5}$ is

15. Perform the following division: $6 \div 0 =$

Explain

16. Calculate each of the following:

a) $\frac{3}{5} + \frac{3}{5} =$ b) $\frac{1}{4} - \frac{1}{6} =$ c) $\frac{3}{7} + \frac{1}{21} =$

d) $\frac{3}{8} - \frac{1}{4} =$ e) $3\frac{1}{4} + 2\frac{5}{6} =$ f) $4\frac{4}{5} - 3\frac{1}{10} =$

g) $5\frac{3}{8} - 4\frac{3}{4} =$ h) $\frac{5}{3} \times \frac{4}{7} =$ i) $2\frac{3}{5} \times 4\frac{3}{4} =$

j) $3\frac{2}{5} \times 3\frac{2}{5} =$ k) $\frac{5}{6} \div \frac{2}{3} =$ l) $\frac{3}{7} \div \frac{4}{5} =$

m) $2\frac{2}{5} \div 4\frac{1}{3} =$

17. Calculate each of the following.

a) increase 60 by $\frac{1}{4}$

b) decrease 45 by $\frac{2}{9}$

c) increase 27 by $\frac{1}{3}$

d) decrease 36 by $\frac{2}{3}$

18. What new operation is possible when we increase the set of Integers to include the set of rational numbers?

Score _____   Date _____

Unit 9 – The Number System from the Natural Numbers to the Real Numbers

OBJECTIVES
- define a Natural number
- define what is meant by a set being closed
- tell what is meant by the commutative property
- give an example of the associative property
- give an example of the distributive property
- give an example using the identity element for multiplication
- tell what is meant by a set being ordered
- list an example using the cancellation property
- name the operations that can be performed using the Natural numbers only
- define the set of Integers
- what new operation is possible using the set of Integers
- demonstrate that the set of Natural numbers is a subset of the set of Integers
- demonstrate the use of the additive identity in the set of Integers
- demonstrate that each Integer has an additive inverse
- define a vector
- demonstrate the ability to use vector addition
- add Integers
- subtract Integers
- multiply Integers
- divide Integers
- demonstrate the ability to subtract Integers using vectors
- define subtraction
- demonstrate that any number multiplied by 0 is 0
- define the absolute value of a number
- define the set of Rational numbers
- give an example of a terminating decimal fraction
- give an example of a non–terminating decimal fraction
- give an example of a recurring decimal fraction
- give an example using the multiplicative inverse of a Rational number
- explain what is meant by saying that the set of Rational numbers is dense
- indicate what new operation is possible when the set of Rational numbers is added to the Integers
- list four fractions that are equivalent to a given fraction
- define a proper fraction
- demonstrate the ability to add, subtract, multiply, and divide proper fractions
- define an improper fraction
- demonstrate the ability to add, subtract, multiply, and divide improper fractions
- demonstrate the ability to add, subtract, multiply, and divide mixed numbers
- demonstrate the ability to reduce fractions to their lowest terms
- demonstrate the ability to find the Lowest Common Denominator
- define a Rational number
- define the set of Real numbers
- give an example of an Irrational number
- solve problems using the various sets of numbers

112

The Natural Numbers (Positive Whole Numbers)

It is instructive to know the number system ranges from the Natural numbers (positive whole numbers) to the Integers (positive whole numbers, negative Whole numbers and zero), to the Rational numbers (fractions that can be written in the form of $\frac{a}{b}$ where a and b are Integers and b $\neq$ 0 (such as $\frac{1}{2}, \frac{3}{4}$, etc.), to the Real numbers that include all Rational and all Irrational numbers.

The following pages will outline the set of Natural numbers and the other sets of numbers.

The set of Natural numbers is the set of all positive Whole numbers.

The number line for the set of Natural numbers is as follows:

N = 1 2 3 4 5 6 . . .   In set notation, N = {1, 2, 3, 4, 5 . . .}.

Properties of the Set of Natural Numbers

The Natural numbers (or the positive whole numbers), {1, 2, 3, 4, 5 . . .}, are governed by certain properties with respect to addition and multiplication.

1. The set of Natural numbers is closed with respect to addition and multiplication. This means that when we add or multiply Natural numbers, the result will be a Natural number.

Example 1: 3 + 5 = 8 (which is a Natural Number) and 5 x 6 = 30 (which is a Natural Number).

2. The Natural numbers are commutative with respect to addition and multiplication. This means that the order in which Natural numbers are added or multiplied will not alter the result.

Example 2: 3 + 5 = 8 and 5 + 3 = 8. Also, 3 x 5 = 15 and 5 x 3 = 15.

3. The Natural numbers possess the associative property with respect to addition and multiplication. This means that we can associate the middle number with the first or the third number.

Example 3: 2 + 3 + 5 = 2 + (3 + 5) = 2 + 8 = 10 and 2 + 3 + 5 = (2 + 3) + 5 = 5 + 5 = 10.

It is also true that 2 + 3 + 5 = 3 + (2 + 5) = 3 + 7 = 10   and 2 + 3 + 5 = (2 + 5) + 3 = 7 + 3 = 10

For multiplication: 2 x 3 x 5 = 2(3 x 5) = 2 x 15 = 30 and (2 x 3) x 5 = (2 x 3)5 = 6 x 5 = 30. (It should be noted that the multiplication sign is omitted when we multiply using parentheses.)   Note also that each term within the parentheses must be multiplied by the multiplier.

4. The Natural numbers have a distributive property of multiplication with respect to addition. This means that when the sum of two Natural numbers is multiplied by another Natural number, that number must multiply each term in the sum.

Example 4: 3(4 + 6) = 3(4) + 3(6) = 12 + 18 = 30.

5. The Natural numbers have a multiplicative identity 1. This means that any positive whole number remains unchanged when it is multiplied by 1. The other factor and the product remain identical.

Example 5: 4 x 1 = 4.

6. The Natural numbers are ordered. That is, given any two Natural numbers, say a and b, then a > b, or a < b, or a = b.

7. The Natural numbers have the property of transitivity.   The property of transitivity states that if a > b and b > c, then a > c: if a = b and if b = c, than a = c; if a < b and b < c, then a < c.

Example 6: If 5 > 4 and 4 > 2, then, 5 > 2.   If 3 = 2 + 1 and 2 + 1 = 1 + 1 + 1 then, 3 = 1 + 1 + 1.   If 4 < 6 and 6 < 7, then 4 < 7.

8. The Natural numbers have a cancellation property.

Example 7. If a + b = c + b then a = c. If ab = cb, then a = c. If a + b > c + b, then a > c, and if a + b < a + c, then b < c. Also, if ab = cb, then a = c. If ab > ac, then b > c. If ab < cb, then a < c.

The Set of Integers

Since the Natural numbers are not closed with respect to subtraction, i.e. $4 - 5 = -1$ which is not a Natural Number, and $4 \div 5$ or $\frac{4}{5}$ which is not a Natural number. We will extend the number line to the left and the number line will include the positive Whole numbers, the negative whole numbers, and zero.

$$\longleftarrow \quad \dots \text{-5 -4 -3 -2 -1} \quad 0 \quad 1 \quad 2 \quad 3 \quad 4 \quad 5 \dots \longrightarrow$$

Zero is neither positive nor negative.

Note that the set of Natural numbers is a proper subset of the set of Integers. That is, the set of Integers contains all of the Natural numbers.

114

In set notation, the Integers are:

I = {. . . −3, −2, −1, 0, 1, 2, 3 . . .}

The set of Natural numbers being a proper subset of the set of the Integers will lead to the following diagram:

Note that $1 > -2$ because 1 is to the right of -2, $-3 < -1$ because -3 is to the left of -1, $4 > 0$ because 4 is to the right of 0, and $0 > -5$ because 0 is to the right of -5.

The operation of subtraction can now be performed within the set of Integers.
$10 - 7 = 3$, $7 - 10 = -3$, $4 - 5 = 4 + (-5) = -1$, $-8 = -5 + (-8) = -13$.

Properties of the Set of Integers

As a consequence of adding the negative numbers and 0 to the set of Natural numbers, the operation of subtraction is now possible. As a result, we can now say that there is also a distributive property of multiplication with respect to subtraction. In general, $x(a - b) = xa - xb$. For example, $3(7 - 4) = (3 \times 7) - (3 \times 4) = 21 - 12$ or 9.

Two new properties can be added. $5 + 0 = 5$ and $5 - 0 = 5$. Any number plus or minus 0 remains unchanged. Therefore, 0 is called the additive identity.

Zero is not nothing — zero is something. 0 has a position on the number line. It is neither positive nor negative. It is undefined as a divisor.

For every Integer there exists a number that when added to the number will produce the additive identity, 0. For example, $5 + (-5) = 0$. In general, $a + (-a) = 0$ where a is any Integer. $-a$ is called the additive inverse of a, just as -5 is the additive inverse of 5.

We can now state that the set of Integers:
− is ordered;
− is closed with respect to addition, multiplication and subtraction;
− has a commutative property of addition and multiplication;
− has an associative property of addition, multiplication, and subtraction;
− has a distributive property of multiplication with respect to addition, multiplication, and subtraction;
− has a multiplicative identity 1;
− for each number there is another number called the additive inverse such that the sum of the two numbers is equal to 0;
− has the property of transitivity;
− has a cancellation property of addition, multiplication and subtraction. For subtraction, if $a - b = c - b$, then $a = c$;

– has an additive identity 0. Any number plus or minus 0 equals that number; 4 + 0 = 4 and, in general, n + 0 = n and n − 0 = n;

Operations Using Integers

Vectors

A vector describes length and direction. If we wish to apply vectors for operations with Integers, we should distinguish between the graph of the number and the graph of the number line vector.

The graph of the number 3 is a point. The graph of 3 is shown below.

-4 -3 -2 -1 0 1 2 3 4

The graph of the vector 3 is the line with the arrow that starts at 0 and goes to the right (because 3 is positive).

The graph of the vector − 4 is the line with the arrow that starts at 0 and goes to the left because − 4 is negative. Vectors can be used to illustrate the addition and subtraction of Integers.

Addition by Using Vectors

Vectors have length and direction. Vectors directed to the right are associated with positive numbers and vectors directed to the left are associated with negative numbers. The sum of two vectors is the length of the vector whose initial point is at the initial point of the first vector and whose terminal point is at the terminal point of the second vector.

Example 1: Show 4 + 3 by number line vectors.

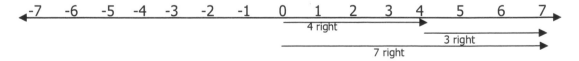

Notice that the vectors are directed to the right because they are associated with positive numbers. It can be seen that 4 + 3 = 7 by using vectors.

Example 2: − 5 + 6 = 1

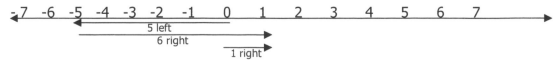

116

Notice that 5 is directed to the left because it is associated with a negative number. By observing the vectors, we see that $-5 + 6 = 1$

Example 3: Show $4 - 7$ by number line vectors. $4 - 7 = 4 + (-7) = -3$

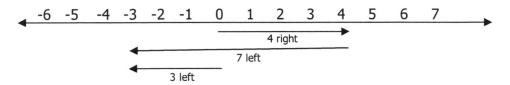

Example 4: Show $6 - 4$ by number line vectors. $6 - 4 = 6 + (-4) = 2$

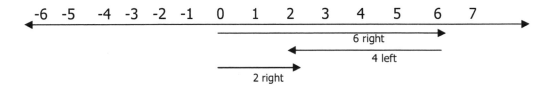

Example 5: Show $6 - 10$ by number line vectors. $6 - 10 = 6 + (-10) = -4$

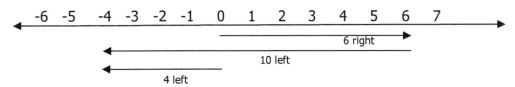

Example 6: Show $(-5) + (-2)$ by number line vectors. $(-5) + (-2) = (-7)$

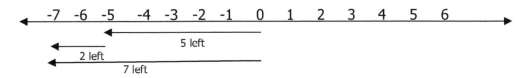

Patterns for Operations - Addition of Integers

6	6	6	6	6	6	6	6	6	6
0	−1	−2	−3	−4	−5	−6	−7	−8	−9
6	5	4	3	2	1	0	−1	−2	−3

Note that as one addend decreases, the sum decreases. Checks may be made at the point in which the additive inverse of a number is added. The sum of $6 + (-6) = 0$. Also, a check may be made when adding the additive identity, 0. $6 + 0 = 6$. Observe the following additions:

−6	−6	−6	−6	−6	−6	−6	−6	−6
6	5	4	3	2	1	0	−1	−2
0	−1	−2	−3	−4	−5	−6	−7	−8

It should be noted that $-6 + (-1) = -7$; $-6 + (-2) = -8$ and $(-6) + (-3) = -9$.

117

Using the Properties of the Set of Integers to Verify Addition

The number facts shown above can be further demonstrated by using the properties of the Integers. The following are examples:

Example 1: Show that $6 + (-5) = 1$

$6 + (-5) = (1 + 5) + (-5)$	We choose the addends 1 and 5 because we want to associate 5 with (-5).
$1 + [5 + (-5)] =$	associative property
$= 1 + 0$	5 and (-5) are additive inverses
$= 1$	0 is the additive identity

Example 2: Show that $(-5) + (-2) = -7$

$7 + [(-5) + (-2)] = (5 + 2) + [(-5) + (-2)$	cancellation property
$= [5 + (-5)] + [2 + (-2)]$	commutative and associative properties
$= 0 + 0 = 0$	additive inverses
Therefore, $7 + [(-5) + (-2)] = 0$	additive inverse
But $7 + (-7) = 0$	additive identity
Hence $7 + [(-5) + (-2)] = 7 + (-7)$	transitive property
$[(-5) + (-2)] + 7 = (-7) + 7$	commutative property
$[(-5) + (-2)] = -7$	cancellation property
Therefore, $(-5) + (-2) = -7$	

Exercise 40

1. Write the additive inverse of each of the following:

a) -7 b) -6 c) $4 + 8$ d) $a - b$

2. Illustrate each of the following by vector addition:

a) $4 + (-6)$ $-10 \ -9 \ -8 \ -7 \ -6 \ -5 \ -4 \ -3 \ -2 \ -1 \quad 0 \quad 1 \quad 2 \quad 3$

b) $4 - 6$ $-10 \ -9 \ -8 \ -7 \ -6 \ -5 \ -4 \ -3 \ -2 \ -1 \quad 0 \quad 1 \quad 2 \quad 3$

c) $(-5) + 2$ $-10 \ -9 \ -8 \ -7 \ -6 \ -5 \ -4 \ -3 \ -2 \ -1 \quad 0 \quad 1 \quad 2 \quad 3$

d) $(-5) + (-3)$ $-10 \ -9 \ -8 \ -7 \ -6 \ -5 \ -4 \ -3 \ -2 \ -1 \quad 0 \quad 1 \quad 2 \quad 3$

118

3. Show that − 5 + (− 3) = − 8 by using properties of the Integers.

4. Write the sum of each of the following:

a) − 7 + 8 =   b) 4 + (− 7) =   c) − 8 + 8 =

d) 22 + (− 7) + 3 + (− 12) =   e) − 18 + (− 5) + (− 2) =

5. Fill in the blanks so that the sums in column a and row b will be correct. Then fill in the remaining spaces.

						a
	2		7	− 3	− 5	5
		− 4	3	− 1	0	− 4
	3	− 6		2	4	3
	− 1	4	− 3		7	1
	− 4	3	− 2	− 1		− 9
b	− 2	1	5	− 9	1	

Subtraction Using Vectors

Subtraction using vectors is done in the same way as addition. For example, 10 − 7 is the same as 10 + (− 7).

Example 1: In vector representation on the number line, it can be shown that 10 − 7 = 3 or 10 + (− 7) = 3.

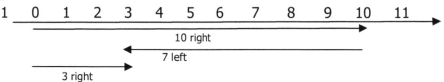

Example 2: Show 9 − 13 = − 4 by vectors. This equals 9 + (− 13).

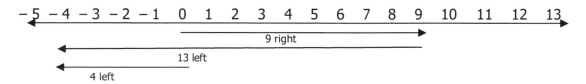

Example 3: Use number vectors to show $10 - (-7) = 17$ or $10 + 7 = 17$

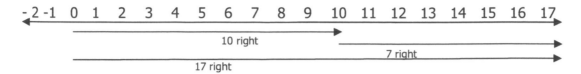

Example 4: Use number line vectors to show : $(-3) - (-7)$ is $(-3) + 7 = 4$

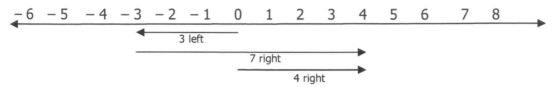

Notice that if you apply vector addition, the following will result.

$10 - 17 = 10 + (-17) = -7$ $10 - (-7) = 10 + 7 = 17$

$(-3) - (-7) = (-3) + 7 = 4$ $(-8) - (-5) = (8) + 5 = -3$

From the above illustrations, the subtraction of an Integer has the same effect as adding the additive inverse of that Integer. An additive inverse is a number that when added to another number gives 0. For example, 3 is the additive inverse of -3 and -5 is the additive inverse of 5, etc.

Definition of Subtraction

Subtraction is the addition of the additive inverse of a number.

Exercise 41

1. Illustrate each of the following by number line vectors:

a) $(-2) - (-4)$

```
 − 4  − 3  − 2  − 1   0   1   2   3   4   5   6   7   8   9   10   11   12
←───────────────────────────────────────────────────────────────────→
```

b) $(-5) - 8$

```
 − 13  − 12  − 11  − 10  − 9  − 8  − 7  − 6  − 5  − 4  − 2  − 1   0   1
←───────────────────────────────────────────────────────────────────→
```

c) $(-5) + 8$

```
 − 8  − 7  − 6  − 5  − 4  − 3  − 2  − 1   0   1   2   3   4   5   6   7
←───────────────────────────────────────────────────────────────────→
```

d) $(-7) - (-3)$

$$\xleftarrow{\qquad} \begin{array}{ccccccccccccccccc} -8 & -7 & -6 & -5 & -4 & -3 & -2 & -1 & 0 & 1 & 2 & 3 & 4 & 5 & 6 & 7 & 8 \end{array} \xrightarrow{\qquad}$$

2. Find the value of each of the following:

a) $20 - (-11) =$ b) $-9 - 0 =$ c) $-8 - (-8) =$ d) $-17 - (-13) =$

3. Perform the following subtractions:

a) $6 - 4 =$ b) $4 - 6 =$ c) $6 - 0 =$ d) $0 - 6 =$

e) $8 - 13 =$ f) $-9 - 0 =$ g) $12 - (-16) =$ h) $1 - (-7) =$

4) Determine the result of each of the following by using subtractions:

a) $-4 + 7 =$ b) $-6 - 4 =$ c) $-7 + 0 =$
d) $-3 - (-4) =$ e) $-7 + 7 =$ f) $7 - (-3) =$
g) $(-4) - 5 =$ h) $4 + (-6) =$ i) $10 - 3 =$
j) $-3 + 4 =$ k) $-5 - 6 =$ l) $0 - (-5) =$

Multiplication of Integers

Multiplication is a shortcut for repeated additions. Compare the following:
$4 \times 3 = 12$ or $4 \times 3 = 3 + 3 + 3 + 3 = 12$

Multiplication by 0

If we were to multiply any number by 0, for instance, 4 multiplied by 0, what would be the product? First, commute the factors and then proceed by repeated addition. $4 \times 0 = 0 \times 4$.

0 multiplied by $4 = 0 + 0 + 0 + 0$. But $0 + 0 + 0 + 0 = 0$. Therefore, any number multiplied by 0 is 0.

Multiplication Using Negative Integers

In the following multiplication chart, note that as the multiplier decreases by 1, the product decreases by 2, the amount equal to the multiplicand.

| $\begin{array}{r}2\\ \underline{\times 3}\\ 6\end{array}$ | $\begin{array}{r}2\\ \underline{\times 2}\\ 4\end{array}$ | $\begin{array}{r}2\\ \underline{\times 1}\\ 2\end{array}$ | $\begin{array}{r}2\\ \underline{\times 0}\\ 0\end{array}$ | $\begin{array}{r}2\\ \underline{-1}\\ -2\end{array}$ | $\begin{array}{r}2\\ \underline{-2}\\ -4\end{array}$ | $\begin{array}{r}2\\ \underline{-3}\\ -6\end{array}$ | $\begin{array}{r}2\\ \underline{-4}\\ -8\end{array}$ | $\begin{array}{r}2\\ \underline{-5}\\ -10\end{array}$ | $\begin{array}{r}2\\ \underline{-6}\\ -12\end{array}$ | $\begin{array}{r}2\\ \underline{-7}\\ -14\end{array}$ |

Let us establish a similar pattern with a negative multiplicand.

-3	-3	-3	-3	-3	-3	-3	-3	-3	-3	-3
5	4	3	2	1	0	-1	-3	-4	-5	-6
-15	-12	-9	-6	-3	0	3	6	9	12	15

Focus on the first five multiplications. Notice that as the multiplier decreases by 1, the product increases by 3. (You can always check the accuracy of your calculations when you get to the multiplicative identity which is 1, and when 0 multiplied by any number is 0.) Now focus on the last six multiplications. You will notice that as the multiplier decreases by 1, the product increases by 3. Also note the change in the sign of the product when two negative numbers are multiplied. This can be seen by examining the products.

Rules for Multiplication of Integers

The product of two numbers that have like signs is always positive. The product of numbers that have unlike signs is negative.

Each number has two square roots. The square roots of 9 are 3 and -3 since $3 \times 3 = 9$ and -3×-3 is also equal to 9. This is true for fractions as well. The square roots of $\frac{4}{25}$ are $\frac{2}{5}$ and $-\frac{2}{5}$ since $\frac{2}{5} \times \frac{2}{5} = \frac{4}{25}$ and $-\frac{2}{5} \times -\frac{2}{5} = \frac{4}{25}$. It is also true for Irrational numbers. The square roots of 2 that are written as $\sqrt{2} = 1.414$ and -1.414.

The Absolute Value of a Number

Associated with each element in the set of Integers, there is a number called its absolute value. Therefore, 4 and -4 each have an absolute value just as the vectors, 4 to the right and 4 to the left have length 4. The symbol used to indicate the absolute value of a number is $|\ |$. By definition, the absolute value of $x = x$ if $x \geq 0$, and the absolute value of x is $-x$ if $x < 0$. This may appear as though $-x$ is negative but it is not if x is less than 0. The absolute value of $|3| = 3$ and $|-3| = -(-3)$. The latter can be justified by knowing that $|n| = n$ if $n > 0$ and $|n| = -n$ if $n < 0$. $|3| = 3$ and $|-3| = -(-3) = 3$.

Exercise 42

1. Multiply each of the following:

5	4	3	2	1	0	-1	-2	-3	-4
5	5	5	5	5	5	5	5	5	5

2. Multiply each of the following and write a comment regarding changes in signs:

5	4	3	2	1	0	-1	-2	-3	-4	-5
-4	-4	-4	-4	-4	-4	-4	-4	-4	-4	-4

3. Multiply each of the following and write a comment regarding changes in signs:

-8	-8	-8	-8	-8	-8	-8	-8	-8	-8
$\underline{5}$	$\underline{4}$	$\underline{3}$	$\underline{2}$	$\underline{1}$	$\underline{0}$	$\underline{-1}$	$\underline{-2}$	$\underline{-3}$	$\underline{-4}$

4. Multiply each of the following and write a comment regarding changes in signs:

5	4	3	2	1	0	-1	-2	-3	-4
$\underline{-3}$	$\underline{-3}$	$\underline{-3}$	$\underline{-3}$	$\underline{-3}$	$\underline{-3}$	$\underline{-3}$	$\underline{-3}$	$\underline{-3}$	$\underline{-3}$

5. Multiply each of the following and write a comment regarding changes in signs:

-5	-4	-3	-2	-1	0	1	2	3	4
$\underline{-4}$	$\underline{-4}$	$\underline{-4}$	$\underline{-4}$	$\underline{-4}$	$\underline{-4}$	$\underline{-4}$	$\underline{-4}$	$\underline{-4}$	$\underline{-4}$

Division of Integers

The Integers are not closed with respect to division. That is, you cannot always divide two Integers and obtain an Integer as the quotient. (This will happen only when 0 is the remainder.) There are many examples in which division is possible. For instance, $35 \div 5 = 7$ because $7 \times 5 = 35$. However, if we wish to divide 3 by 5, there is no Integer that will result. One counter–example is all that is needed to show that an operation is not always possible.

Zero divided by a non-zero number gives a quotient of zero. $0 \div 6 = 0$. Division of a non-zero number by zero is undefined. $6 \div 0 = ?$ What number multiplied by 0 will give you 6? Any number multiplied by 0 is 0. Any number divided by 0 is indeterminate.

1 is the identity element for division in the same way that 1 is the multiplicative identity in the Natural numbers. Any number divided by 1 remains unchanged. For example, $5 \div 1 = 5: -3 \div 1 = -3$.

In some cases, we will divide a fraction by 1 in the form of $\frac{2}{2}$, $\frac{3}{3}$ or $\frac{4}{4}$ and so on.

Each of these fractions is equal to 1.

Rules for Division of Integers

Since division is the reverse operation of multiplication, the same rules for signs apply. (Remember that division within the set of Integers is defined if and only if the remainder is 0.) A positive number divided by a positive number is positive.

Example: $12 \div 3 = 4$ because $4 \times 3 = 12$. A negative number divided by a positive number is negative. Example: $-12 \div 3 = -4$ because $(-4) \times 3 = -12$. A positive number divided by a negative number is negative. Example: $12 \div -3 = (-4)$ because $(-4) \times (-3) = 12$. A negative number divided by a negative number is positive. Example: $(-12) \div (-3) = 4$ because $4 \times (-3) = -12$.

Exercise 43

1. Write the quotient of each of the following:

a) $16 \div -4 =$ b) $-18 \div 6 =$ c) $-12 \div 6 =$ d) $-7 \div 1 =$

e) $0 \div 1 =$ f) $-15 \div -5 =$ g) $-3 \div 1 =$ h) $3 \div -3 =$

The Set of Rational Numbers

We started with the Natural numbers (positive Whole numbers) and saw that the only operations that were always possible were addition and multiplication. Then we added the negative Whole numbers and zero to form the set of Integers. We found that addition, multiplication and subtraction were always possible, but division was not always possible. Therefore, we need more numbers in our number system. We will now add the set of fractions to the number system. The set of Rational numbers (from the word ratio) consists of the Natural numbers (positive Whole numbers), the Integers (positive Whole numbers, negative Whole numbers and zero) and all numbers that can be written in the form of $\frac{a}{b}$ where a and b are Integers and $b \neq 0$.

This new set of numbers is called the set of Rational numbers – designated Ra.

Notice that N is a subset of I and I is a subset of Ra. Therefore, N is also a subset of Ra. (Transitivity property.)

Rational numbers are those that we refer to as common fractions. There are many other rational numbers between any two such numbers. For example, on the following number line, there is a mid-point that is $\frac{1}{2}$.   0   ½   1 This number is found by adding $0 + 1$ and then dividing by 2. Between $\frac{1}{2}$ and 1 there is a mid-point that is $\frac{3}{4}$. Between $\frac{3}{4}$ and $\frac{1}{2}$ there is a mid-point that is $\frac{5}{8}$. The process of finding the mid-point between any two numbers can go on forever. Change $\frac{1}{2}$ to $\frac{1}{3}$ and find the $\frac{1}{3}$ point between any two numbers. Then you can change to $\frac{1}{4}$, $\frac{1}{5}$, $\frac{1}{6}$ and so on.

The major point is that there is an indefinite number of numbers between any two points on the Rational number line. There is no end to the number of Rational numbers that can be placed on the number line. That is, between any two Rational numbers, there exists at least one other Rational number. We convey this notion by saying that the number line is dense when using the set of Rational numbers.

However, it should be noted that there is not a one-to-one correspondence between all points on the number line and the set of Rational numbers. (This is to come later.) A one-to-one correspondence, in this case, means that every point on the number line has a number assigned to it and every number has a point on the line.

Terminating and Recurring Decimals

All fractions in the form of $\frac{a}{b}$ (where $b \neq 0$) are either terminating decimal numbers or recurring decimal numbers.

Example: $\frac{4}{5} = 0.8$, $\frac{1}{4} = 0.25$, $\frac{1}{2} = 0.5$ etc.

The results are found by dividing the numerator by the denominator and they are terminating decimal fractions because when the numerator is divided by the denominator, the division will come to an end, i.e. the remainder will be 0.

Examples of recurring decimal fractions are $\frac{1}{3} = 0.333333\ldots$ which is $0.\dot{3}$ (obtained by dividing 1 by 3 and $\frac{1}{6}$ is equal to $0.166666666\ldots$ which is written as 0 $0.1\dot{6}$. (This was obtained by dividing 1 by 6.) Note that $\frac{23}{99} = .232323\ldots = 0.\dot{2}\dot{3}$. (This was obtained by dividing 23 by 99.)

Notice the dot above some numbers. If one digit recurs, place a dot over that digit. If two digits recur, put a dot over each digit. If more than two digits recur, put a dot over the first and the last digit of those digits that do recur.

The Rational numbers are closed with respect to addition, subtraction, multiplication and division.

The Rational number line can exhibit many equivalent fractions that are coordinated to one point. For example:

$$\longleftrightarrow$$
1/2
2/4
3/6 and so on

The Multiplicative Inverse

For every Rational number $\frac{a}{b}$ (where $a \neq 0$ and $b \neq 0$) there exists another Rational number $\frac{b}{a}$ such that the product of these two numbers is equal to 1, and 1 is called the multiplicative identity. For example, the multiplicative inverse of $\frac{3}{5}$ is $\frac{5}{3}$ because $\frac{3}{5} \times \frac{5}{3} = 1$. Similarly, $-\frac{2}{3}$ has a multiplicative inverse, $-\frac{3}{2}$ because $-\frac{2}{3} \times -\frac{3}{2} = 1$.

Properties of the Set of Rational Numbers

The set of Rational numbers is closed with respect to addition, subtraction, multiplication, and division. That is, if we perform any of the four operations on two Rational numbers, the result will be a Rational number.

The set of Rational numbers has all of the properties of the set of Integers plus it has a multiplicative inverse for each Rational number. In addition, the set of Rational numbers is dense. That is, between any two Rational numbers, there is at least one number that can be placed on the number line.

Operations Using Rational Numbers

The Meaning of a Fraction

A fraction is an equal part of a whole. Or, if a whole has been separated into equal parts, each of these equal parts is a fraction of the whole.

If the whole is divided into 10 equal parts, the number 10 becomes the denominator of the fraction. The denominator indicates the number of equal parts into which the whole is divided.

If we shade 3 of the equal parts, the number 3 becomes the numerator. The numerator indicates the number of equal parts under consideration.

Therefore, the fraction above is the shaded area which is $\frac{3}{10}$. In this fraction, the denominator 10 tells us how many equal parts that the whole has been divided into and the 3 tells us how many of these equal parts are being used. The number of parts that are not shaded is 7. Therefore the non-shaded portion is $\frac{7}{10}$. Note that the sum of the shaded parts and the non-shaded parts must be equal to 1 which is the unit that we separated into 10 equal parts. $\frac{3}{10} + \frac{7}{10} = \frac{10}{10} = 1$.

In the following diagram, 5 equal parts have been shaded and therefore, the fraction shaded is $\frac{5}{10}$. There are 5 equal parts that are not shaded. Therefore, the non-shaded parts are $\frac{5}{10}$.

$\frac{1}{10}$	$\frac{1}{10}$	$\frac{1}{10}$	$\frac{1}{10}$	$\frac{1}{10}$	$\frac{1}{10}$	$\frac{1}{10}$	$\frac{1}{10}$	$\frac{1}{10}$	$\frac{1}{10}$

$\frac{5}{10} + \frac{5}{10} = \frac{10}{10}$ or 1.

Note that the sum of the part shaded and the part not shaded is equal to 1.

The unit that is being divided may be any shape.

 The circle has been divided into 4 equal parts and 3 of these parts have been shaded. The fraction of the shape that has been shaded is $\frac{3}{4}$.

One part has not been shaded and this part is $\frac{1}{4}$ of the whole.

$\frac{3}{4} + \frac{1}{4} = \frac{4}{4}$ or 1.

Fractions may be displayed by using objects: For example, if we have colored markers:

B	R	B	G	B	G	G	B	G	R	G	R

We must first count the number of markers. There are 12 markers. How many of these are blue? The answer is 4. What fraction of the markers is blue? The answer is $\frac{4}{12}$. How many markers are red? The answer is 3. What fraction of the markers is red? The answer is $\frac{3}{12}$. How many markers are green? The answer is 5. What fraction of the markers is green? The answer is $\frac{5}{12}$. Note that the sum of

$\frac{4}{12} + \frac{3}{12} + \frac{5}{12} = \frac{12}{12}$ or 1.

Equivalent Fractions

In the following diagram, five parts have been shaded and therefore, the shaded part is $\frac{5}{10}$ of the whole.

$\frac{1}{10}$	$\frac{1}{10}$	$\frac{1}{10}$	$\frac{1}{10}$	$\frac{1}{10}$	$\frac{1}{10}$	$\frac{1}{10}$	$\frac{1}{10}$	$\frac{1}{10}$	$\frac{1}{10}$

The following whole is equal to the above whole, but it has been divided into 2 equal parts.

Notice that the two shaded parts are equal. Therefore, $\frac{5}{10} = \frac{1}{2}$. These are called equivalent fractions.

127

It should be noted that $\frac{1}{2}$ x $\frac{5}{5}$ = $\frac{5}{10}$. We have multiplied $\frac{1}{2}$ by $\frac{5}{5}$ (which is equal to 1). Any number multiplied by 1 remains unchanged since 1 is the multiplicative identity.

In the same way, $\frac{5}{10}$ ÷ $\frac{5}{5}$ = $\frac{1}{2}$. We have divided $\frac{5}{10}$ by $\frac{5}{5}$ which is equal to 1. Any number divided by 1 remains unchanged. 1 is the identity element with respect to division in the set of Integers.

Equivalent fractions can be generated by multiplying (or dividing) a fraction by 1 in the form of $\frac{n}{n}$ where n is an Integer and n ≠ 0. For example, $\frac{2}{3}$ = $\frac{2}{3}$ x $\frac{2}{2}$ = $\frac{4}{6}$ and $\frac{2}{3}$ x $\frac{3}{3}$ = $\frac{6}{9}$.

Proper and Improper Fractions

A proper fraction is a fraction in which the numerator is less than the denominator. All proper fractions are less than 1. $\frac{2}{3}$, $\frac{10}{24}$, $\frac{3}{4}$, $\frac{6}{8}$ are some examples of proper fractions.

An improper fraction is a fraction in which the numerator is greater than the denominator. All positive improper fractions are greater than 1. $\frac{7}{5}$, $\frac{8}{3}$, $\frac{9}{5}$ are some examples of improper fractions.

The following diagram will show why an improper fraction, for example, $\frac{8}{6}$ is greater than 1.

$\frac{1}{6}$	$\frac{1}{6}$	$\frac{1}{6}$	$\frac{1}{6}$	$\frac{1}{6}$	$\frac{1}{6}$
$\frac{1}{6}$	$\frac{1}{6}$	$\frac{1}{6}$	$\frac{1}{6}$	$\frac{1}{6}$	$\frac{1}{6}$

In the top row, there are 6 x $\frac{1}{6}$ or $\frac{6}{6}$ parts shaded. This is equal to 1. In the bottom row, there are 2 x $\frac{1}{6}$ or $\frac{2}{6}$ parts shaded. Therefore, the total number of equal parts shaded is $\frac{8}{6}$ which are 2 x $\frac{1}{6}$ or $\frac{2}{6}$ and 6 x $\frac{1}{6}$ parts shaded. Therefore, the total number of equal parts shaded is $\frac{8}{6}$ which is an improper fraction and is greater than 1. In fact, $\frac{8}{6}$ = $\frac{6}{6}$ + $\frac{2}{6}$ = 1 + $\frac{2}{6}$ = $1\frac{2}{6}$.

Improper fractions can be changed to mixed numbers (numbers that contain an Integer and a fraction) by dividing the numerator by the denominator. The Integer

128

that results is the whole number and the remainder resulting from the division becomes the numerator of the fraction.

For example, $\frac{17}{5} = 3\frac{2}{5}$. $17 \div 5 = 3$ with a remainder of 2. 2 becomes the numerator and 5 is the denominator of the fraction. Note that $(5 \times 3) + 2 = 15 + 2$ or 17. Therefore, the improper fraction of $\frac{17}{5}$ has been changed to $3\frac{2}{5}$.

Reducing Fractions

When a fraction is reduced it has no factors common to the numerator and the denominator. Fractions may be reduced as follows:

Example 1: Reduce $\frac{3}{12}$

We note that the numerator 3 is divisible by 3 and the denominator 12 is divisible by 3. If we divide both the numerator and the denominator by 3, we are dividing by $\frac{3}{3}$ which is 1. Any number divided by 1 remains unchanged. Therefore, $\frac{3}{12} = \frac{1}{4}$.

When there are no factors (other than 1) common to the numerator and the denominator, the fraction is said to be reduced to its lowest terms.

Example 2: When we are asked to reduce a fraction to its lowest terms, it means that no other common factor except 1 is contained in both the numerator and the denominator. If we wish to reduce $\frac{16}{24}$, we may recognize that 2 is a factor of both the numerator and the denominator. Dividing both by 2, we have the fraction $\frac{8}{12}$. We can still divide the numerator and denominator by 2 and we have $\frac{4}{6}$ and again 2 is common and we finally have $\frac{2}{3}$ which does not have a factor (other than 1) common to the numerator and the denominator. Therefore, we say that $\frac{16}{24}$ reduced to its lowest terms is $\frac{2}{3}$. This is a long process to determine the desired result. When we wish to reduce a fraction to its lowest terms, we should determine the largest factor that is common to the numerator and the denominator. In this case, 8 is the largest such factor. If we had recognized this, we could have reduced $\frac{16}{24}$ to the lowest terms by dividing the numerator and the denominator by 1 in the form of $\frac{8}{8}$ to get $\frac{2}{3}$.

Not all fractions must be reduced to their lowest terms. For example, if a person was playing cards and wanted to know the probability of being dealt an ace, it would be better to use the probability $\frac{4}{52}$ than $\frac{1}{13}$ because the first fraction tells us that there are 52 cards in the pack and the probability of being dealt an ace is 4 of these.

Exercise 44

1. Draw a rectangle. Divide the rectangle into 4 equal parts and shade 2 of these parts. What fraction of the rectangle has been shaded?

2. Draw a rectangle the same size as above. Divide the rectangle into 4 equal parts and shade 3 of these parts. What fraction of the rectangle has been shaded?

Is the shaded area of this rectangle greater than, equal to, or less than the shaded area of the rectangle in Number 1?

3. Use the following diagram to answer the questions:

W	B	G	B	W	B	G	G	W	W	B	G

a) How many items are there in the set?

b) What fraction of the markers is colored white?

c) What fraction of the markers is colored blue?

d) What fraction of the markers is colored green?

e) What is the sum of the answers of b), c) and d)?

4. Write five fractions equivalent to each of the following:

a) $\frac{2}{3}$ =   =   =   =   =

b) $\frac{4}{5}$ =   =   =   =   =

c) $\frac{5}{7}$ =   =   =   =   =

d) $\frac{4}{9}$ =   =   =   =   =

e) $\frac{7}{8}$ =   =   =   =   =

5. Write a simple method for generating equivalent fractions.

List six equivalent fractions.

6. How many equivalent fractions are there to $\frac{1}{2}$?

List six of these.

7. Write P for proper and I for improper for each of the following:

a) $\frac{2}{3}$ b) $\frac{3}{5}$ c) $\frac{10}{6}$ d) $\frac{12}{13}$ e) $\frac{15}{14}$ f) $\frac{9}{11}$ g) $\frac{9}{8}$

8. Reduce each of the following fractions to the lowest terms:

a) $\frac{10}{15}$ =   b) $\frac{24}{32}$ =   c) $\frac{15}{25}$ =

d) $\frac{32}{64}$ =   e) $\frac{17}{51}$ =   f) $\frac{25}{75}$ =

9.   List two situations in which it is better not to reduce a fraction to its lowest terms.

Addition of Proper Fractions

When the denominators are the same, the sum can be determined by adding the numerators. If we wish to add $\frac{1}{6}$ + $\frac{2}{6}$, we add the numerators since the denominators (the parts being added) are the same. $\frac{1}{6}$ + $\frac{2}{6}$ = $\frac{3}{6}$.

When the denominators are not the same, either or both of the fractions must be changed to equivalent fractions that have the same denominator. We must look for the least number into which the two denominators will divide. This is called the Lowest Common Denominator or L.C.D.

Example 1: add $\frac{1}{2}$ + $\frac{2}{3}$.

It is difficult to add these two fractions in their present form. We must find the least common denominator, that is, the least number into which both 2 and 3 will divide. This number is 6.

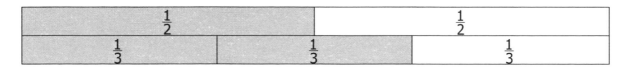

Therefore, we must change the fractions to their equivalent forms in which each of the denominators is 6.

$\frac{1}{2}$			$\frac{1}{2}$		
$\frac{1}{6}$	$\frac{1}{6}$	$\frac{1}{6}$	$\frac{1}{6}$	$\frac{1}{6}$	$\frac{1}{6}$
$\frac{1}{3}$		$\frac{1}{3}$		$\frac{1}{3}$	
$\frac{1}{6}$	$\frac{1}{6}$	$\frac{1}{6}$	$\frac{1}{6}$	$\frac{1}{6}$	$\frac{1}{6}$

We note in the above diagram that $\frac{1}{2}$ is equal to $3 \times \frac{1}{6}$ or $\frac{3}{6}$ and $\frac{2}{3}$ is equal to $4 \times \frac{1}{6}$ or $\frac{4}{6}$. Now we can add $\frac{3}{6} + \frac{4}{6}$ to get $\frac{7}{6}$. Therefore, $\frac{1}{2} + \frac{2}{3} = \frac{7}{6}$.

The diagram above illustrates the process of changing fractions with unlike denominators to equivalent fractions with like denominators. However, we do not want to draw diagrams to add fractions. Therefore, we will proceed as follows:

Example 2: Add $\frac{2}{3} + \frac{1}{5}$. The least number into which 3 and 5 will divide is 15. Therefore, we will change each fraction to its equivalent form in which 15 is the denominator.

$\frac{2}{3} = \frac{10}{15}$ because $\frac{2}{3} \times \frac{5}{5} = \frac{10}{15}$ and $\frac{1}{5} = \frac{3}{15}$ because $\frac{1}{5} \times \frac{3}{3} = \frac{3}{15}$.
And $\frac{10}{15} + \frac{3}{15} = \frac{13}{15}$.

Another way most often used is to determine the least common denominator (in this case, 15) and change each fraction to an equivalent fraction with the same denominator. Divide 15 by 3 and multiply by the numerator (in this case 2) to obtain $\frac{10}{15}$. Divide 15 by 5 and multiply by the numerator (in this case 1).

Now we have $\frac{10}{15} + \frac{3}{15}$ and this is equal to $\frac{13}{15}$.

We can simplify the addition above by determining the lowest common denominator, 15. Let this be the denominator $\frac{}{15}$. Then we will divide 15 by 3 and then multiply by 2 to obtain 10. Now we have $\frac{10}{15}$. We will divide 15 by 5 and multiply by 1 to obtain 3. We will place the numerator over the same denominator to obtain $\frac{10+3}{15}$ and this is $\frac{13}{15}$.

132

Example 3: Sometimes it is not easy to determine the lowest common denominator. We can make factor trees using each denominator. A factor tree determines the factors of the denominators.

Find the common denominator for $\frac{1}{8}$ and $\frac{1}{12}$. List the factors of each denominator.

Therefore, the lowest common denominator is 4 x 2 x 3 or 24. That is, 24 is the lowest number into which 8 and 12 will divide. Notice that 4 x 3 x 2 was used. The second 4 was not used because there would be 2 factors of 4 which is already a factor of 8.

Example 4: Find the lowest common denominator of $\frac{1}{15}$ and $\frac{1}{20}$.

Therefore, the lowest common denominator of $\frac{1}{15}$ and $\frac{1}{20}$ is 5 x 3 x 4 or 60. Note that factors that are repeated in each number are used only once.

If there are no common factors in the denominator, then the lowest common denominator is the product of the denominators.

Example 5: Add $\frac{1}{2} + \frac{1}{3}$. There are no factors common to each denominator and therefore, the lowest common denominator is 2 x 3 or 6. $\frac{1}{2} = \frac{3}{6}$ and $\frac{1}{3} = \frac{2}{6}$ and $\frac{3}{6} + \frac{2}{6} = \frac{5}{6}$.

A shorter way of adding the above fractions is to determine the Lowest Common Denominator (which is 6) and then divide the denominator of the first fraction and multiply by the numerator. Repeat the same process for the second fraction. The problem now becomes $\frac{3+2}{6}$ or $\frac{5}{6}$.

Mixed Numbers

A mixed number consists of a whole number and a fraction. For example, $2\frac{1}{3}$ is a mixed number in which 2 is the whole number and $\frac{1}{3}$ is the fraction.

$1\frac{4}{5}$ is illustrated in the following diagram.

$\frac{1}{5}$	$\frac{1}{5}$	$\frac{1}{5}$	$\frac{1}{5}$	$\frac{1}{5}$

$\frac{1}{5}$	$\frac{1}{5}$	$\frac{1}{5}$	$\frac{1}{5}$	$\frac{1}{5}$

The top bar shows 1 in the form of 5 x $\frac{1}{5}$. The lower bar shows four $\frac{1}{5}$'s or $\frac{4}{5}$.

Therefore, $1\frac{4}{5} = \frac{5}{5} + \frac{4}{5}$ or $\frac{9}{5}$. Conversely, by observing the diagram, we see that

$\frac{9}{5} = 1\frac{4}{5}$.

Example 1: Change $3\frac{3}{4}$ to an improper fraction.

$\frac{1}{4}$	$\frac{1}{4}$	$\frac{1}{4}$	$\frac{1}{4}$
$\frac{1}{4}$	$\frac{1}{4}$	$\frac{1}{4}$	$\frac{1}{4}$
$\frac{1}{4}$	$\frac{1}{4}$	$\frac{1}{4}$	$\frac{1}{4}$
$\frac{1}{4}$	$\frac{1}{4}$	$\frac{1}{4}$	$\frac{1}{4}$

Each of the top three bars represents 1 divided into 4 equal parts. Therefore, in the top three bars there are 12 x $\frac{1}{4}$ or $\frac{12}{4}$. 3 x $\frac{1}{4}$ have been shaded in the lower bar.

Therefore, $3\frac{3}{4} = \frac{12}{4} + \frac{3}{4}$ or $\frac{15}{4}$.

Once a clear understanding of the above method for changing a mixed number to an improper fraction has been achieved, it is easy to see that a shortcut is possible. To change $3\frac{3}{4}$ to an improper fraction, multiply the whole number by the denominator and then add the numerator. Note that in the above example, there are 3 rows each containing four $\frac{1}{4}$'s and this is why we multiply 4 x 3. In addition, there are three $\frac{1}{4}$'s in the fourth row and this is why they must be added to 4 x 3. Therefore we have 4 x 3 + 3 which is 15 and this tells us how many $\frac{1}{4}$'s we have. Therefore, $3\frac{3}{4} = \frac{15}{4}$.

In the example above, $3\frac{3}{4} = (4 \times 3) + 3$ or 15. Therefore, the improper fraction is $\frac{15}{4}$.

Changing an improper fraction to a mixed number is illustrated by the following diagram. Change $\frac{14}{5}$ to a mixed number.

$\frac{1}{5}$	$\frac{1}{5}$	$\frac{1}{5}$	$\frac{1}{5}$	$\frac{1}{5}$
$\frac{1}{5}$	$\frac{1}{5}$	$\frac{1}{5}$	$\frac{1}{5}$	$\frac{1}{5}$
$\frac{1}{5}$	$\frac{1}{5}$	$\frac{1}{5}$	$\frac{1}{5}$	$\frac{1}{5}$

There are five $\frac{1}{5}$'s in the top row and these are equal to 1. There are five $\frac{1}{5}$'s in the second row and these are equal to 1. There are four $\frac{1}{5}$'s in the third row. Therefore, $\frac{14}{5}$ has been separated into (2 x 1) + (4 x $\frac{1}{5}$) which equals $2\frac{4}{5}$.

By observing what has been done, it is seen that an improper fraction can be changed to a mixed number by dividing the numerator by the denominator. The number of multiples of the denominator that the numerator contains is the whole number part of the mixed number and the remainder becomes the numerator of the fraction. The denominator remains the same.

Therefore, $\frac{14}{5}$ = 14 ÷ 5 which is 2 and the remainder is 4. Therefore, $\frac{14}{5}$ = $2\frac{4}{5}$. This can be checked by multiplying 2 x 5 and adding 4. 2 x 5 = 10. 10 + 4 = 14. Therefore, the improper fraction is $\frac{14}{5}$.

Addition of Improper Fractions

The easiest way to add improper fractions is to change them to mixed numbers. For example, if we wish to add $\frac{6}{5}$ + $\frac{5}{4}$ we can change $\frac{6}{5}$ to $1\frac{1}{5}$ and we can change $\frac{5}{4}$ to $1\frac{1}{4}$. By adding the whole numbers, we obtain 1 + 1 or 2. Then, by adding the fractions $\frac{1}{5}$ + $\frac{1}{4}$ we obtain $\frac{4+5}{20}$ or $\frac{9}{20}$. Therefore, the sum of $\frac{6}{5}$ + $\frac{5}{4}$ is equal to $2\frac{9}{20}$.

Subtraction of Fractions
The only difference encountered when fractions are subtracted is that the operation of subtraction replaces the operation of addition.

Example: Subtract $\frac{4}{5}$ − $\frac{1}{3}$.

The lowest common denominator is 15. $\frac{4}{5} = \frac{12}{15}$ and $\frac{1}{3} = \frac{5}{15}$. Therefore,

$\frac{4}{5} - \frac{1}{3} = \frac{12}{15} - \frac{5}{15} = \frac{7}{15}$ or $\frac{12-5}{15} = \frac{7}{15}$.

Addition of Mixed Numbers

There are two ways in which mixed numbers can be added (or subtracted):

Method 1. Add the whole numbers and then add the fractions. Then combine the results.

Example 1: Add $4\frac{2}{5}+3\frac{1}{4}$.

Step 1. Add $4 + 3 = 7$

Step 2. Add $\frac{2}{5}+\frac{1}{4} = \frac{8+5}{20}$ or $\frac{13}{20}$

Step 3. Add $7 + \frac{13}{20} = 7\frac{13}{20}$

Method 2. Change each mixed number to an improper fraction and then add (or subtract).

Step 1. $4\frac{2}{5} = \frac{22}{5}$ and $3\frac{1}{4} = \frac{13}{4}$

Step 2. $\frac{22}{5} + \frac{13}{4} = \frac{88}{20} + \frac{65}{20} = \frac{153}{20} = 7\frac{13}{20}$

The above method may result in operating with larger numbers.

Example 2: Subtract $3\frac{1}{2}-1\frac{1}{4}$.

$3 - 1 = 2$ and $\frac{1}{2} - \frac{1}{4} = \frac{2}{4} - \frac{1}{4} = \frac{1}{4}$. Therefore, $3\frac{1}{2}-1\frac{1}{4}=2\frac{1}{4}$.

or, $\frac{7}{2} - \frac{5}{4} = \frac{14}{4} - \frac{5}{4} = \frac{9}{4} = 2\frac{1}{4}$.

Extending Addition and Subtraction to More than Two Terms

The same steps are followed for addition of more than two terms.

Example 1: Add $4\frac{1}{3} + 2\frac{5}{6} + 3\frac{1}{12}$.

$4 + 2 + 3 = 9$ and $\frac{1}{3} + \frac{5}{6} + \frac{1}{12} = \frac{4 + 10 + 1}{12} = \frac{15}{12} = \frac{5}{4} = 1\frac{1}{4}$. $9 + 1\frac{1}{4} = 10\frac{1}{4}$

Example 2: Subtract $5\frac{2}{3} - 2\frac{1}{2} - 1\frac{1}{6}$.

$5 - 2 - 1 = 2$ and $\frac{2}{3} - \frac{1}{2} - \frac{1}{6} = \frac{4}{6} - \frac{3}{6} - \frac{1}{6} = 0$. Therefore, the difference is 2.

Example 3: Simplify the following: $3\frac{1}{5} + \left(2\frac{1}{3} + 1\frac{7}{15}\right)$. The number within the parentheses must be calculated first and then this number is added to $3\frac{1}{5}$.

$2\frac{1}{3} + 1\frac{7}{15} = 2 + 1$ or 3. $\quad \frac{1}{3} + \frac{7}{15} = \frac{5+7}{15} = \frac{12}{15} = \frac{4}{5}$. $\quad 3 + \frac{4}{5} = 3\frac{4}{5}$.

$\frac{1}{5} + \frac{4}{5} = \frac{5}{5}$ or 1. $\quad 6 + 1 = 7$

Exercise 45

1. Find the lowest common denominator for each of the following:

a) $\frac{1}{3} + \frac{5}{12} =$

    L.C.D. =

b) $\frac{3}{4} + \frac{2}{5} =$

    L.C.D. =

c) $\frac{2}{7} + \frac{1}{5} =$

    L.C.D.=

d) $\frac{3}{8} - \frac{5}{12} =$

    L.C.D. =

e) $\frac{2}{3} - \frac{1}{4} =$

    L.C.D =

f) $\frac{2}{9} - \frac{1}{11} =$

    L.C.D =

2. Add each of the following and reduce to lowest terms:

a) $\frac{1}{3} + \frac{1}{5} =$

b) $\frac{1}{6} + \frac{1}{12} =$

c) $\frac{1}{8} + \frac{2}{7} =$

d) $\frac{4}{15} + \frac{2}{5} =$

e) $\frac{2}{9} + \frac{4}{27} =$

f) $\frac{5}{9} + \frac{4}{5} -$

g) $\frac{2}{3} + \frac{4}{15} =$

h) $\frac{3}{8} + \frac{1}{3} =$

i) $\frac{3}{4} + \frac{2}{3} =$

j) $\frac{5}{3} + \frac{5}{8} =$

k) $\frac{5}{6} + \frac{4}{5} =$

l) $\frac{2}{7} + \frac{5}{8} =$

3. Subtract each of the following:

a) $\frac{1}{3} - \frac{1}{4} =$

b) $\frac{3}{5} - \frac{1}{4} =$

c) $\frac{5}{8} - \frac{2}{7} =$

4. Change each of the following to a mixed number:

a) $\frac{9}{4} =$

b) $\frac{7}{2} =$

c) $\frac{10}{3} =$

d) $\frac{21}{5} =$

e) $\frac{19}{3} =$

f) $\frac{25}{4} =$

5. Change each of the following to improper fractions:

a) $3\frac{2}{5} =$

b) $2\frac{1}{7} =$

c) $5\frac{2}{3} =$

d) $7\frac{3}{4} =$

e) $4\frac{1}{8} =$

f) $6\frac{2}{9} =$

6. Find the sum or difference of each of the following using the easiest possible way:

a) $4\frac{1}{8} + 5\frac{4}{5} =$

b) $2\frac{3}{7} + 1\frac{2}{3} =$

c) $4\frac{3}{8} + 3\frac{1}{4} =$

d) $3\frac{5}{6} - 3\frac{2}{3} =$

e) $5\frac{2}{3} + 4\frac{3}{5} =$

f) $3\frac{3}{8} + 3\frac{3}{4} =$

g) $6\frac{3}{10} - 4\frac{4}{5} =$

h) $7\frac{5}{6} + 4\frac{5}{12} =$

i) $5\frac{5}{9} - 3\frac{2}{3} =$

7. Perform the operations indicated in each of the following and reduce to lowest terms:

a) $\frac{3}{5} + \frac{5}{6} + \frac{4}{15} =$

b) $\frac{2}{3} + \frac{5}{12} - \frac{5}{6} =$

c) $\frac{3}{4} + \frac{5}{8} - \frac{3}{16} =$

138

d) $4\frac{2}{3} + 3\frac{3}{8} + 4\frac{5}{12} =$

e) $(2\frac{1}{5} - 2\frac{1}{5}) - 3\frac{7}{15} =$

f) $(5\frac{2}{9} + 4\frac{2}{3}) - 3\frac{5}{6} =$

g) $5\frac{4}{5} + (2\frac{3}{10} - 1\frac{4}{5}) =$

8. Paul had a piece of wood that was 36 cm long. He divided it into 12 equal parts. He cut off 3 of these parts. Then he cut off 4 of these parts. What was the length of the piece of wood remaining and what fraction of the original piece did he cut off?

length remaining   fraction remaining

9. Maria was knitting a sweater. On Monday she used $\frac{1}{3}$ of the wool. On Tuesday she used $\frac{1}{6}$ of the remaining wool. On Wednesday she used $\frac{1}{2}$ of the remaining wool. How much of the wool was used and what fraction of the wool was not used?

fraction of the wool used   fraction remaining

10. George had a box of nails. He used $\frac{1}{6}$ of them to repair a chair. He then used $\frac{1}{6}$ of the remainder to repair a mirror. He then used $\frac{1}{6}$ of the remaining nails to repair a table. What fraction of the nails was used and what fraction of the nails was not used?

fraction of nails used   fraction remaining

11. Joan ate $\frac{1}{6}$ of a box of chocolates during the morning, $\frac{1}{3}$ during the afternoon, and $\frac{1}{2}$ of the remaining chocolates during the evening. What fraction of the chocolates did she eat and what fraction of the chocolates did she not eat?

fraction eaten   fraction not eaten

12. Peter said that when he cut a pizza for his family, he cut $\frac{1}{5}$ for his son, $\frac{2}{5}$ for his wife and $\frac{2}{3}$ for him. If you were the owner of a pizza store, would you hire Peter to cut pizzas?   Explain

13. Rose used $\frac{2}{7}$ of a can of flour and then used $\frac{2}{5}$ of another can of flour of the same size. What fraction of a can of flour did Rose use?

14. Use the method of changing to equivalent fractions to add the following.
$\frac{2}{3} + \frac{3}{4} + \frac{1}{6} + \frac{5}{12} =$

15. John bought $3\frac{1}{2}$ kg of carrots and his wife bought $2\frac{3}{4}$ kg. How many kg of carrots were bought?

16. Phillip worked $2\frac{1}{2}$ hours on his boat on Monday, $3\frac{3}{4}$ hours on Tuesday, and $4\frac{2}{3}$ hours on Wednesday. How many hours did Phillip work on his boat during these three days?

The Comparison of Fractions

The following guidelines will help in the comparison of fractions.

1. The numerators of the fractions are the same, 1.

As the denominator becomes larger, the fraction becomes smaller.

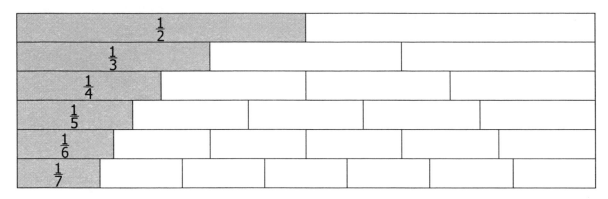

2. $\frac{1}{2} > \frac{1}{3} > \frac{1}{4} > \frac{1}{5} > \frac{1}{6} > \frac{1}{7}$

3. If the numerators are different and the denominators are the same, then the two numerators can be compared. $\frac{1}{4} < \frac{3}{4}$ because 1 is less than 3: $\frac{6}{10} > \frac{4}{10}$ because 6 is greater than 4.

4. If the denominators are not the same and if not all numerators are 1, the fractions must be changed to equivalent fractions having the same denominator in order to determine which fraction is the greater.

Compare $\frac{2}{3}$ and $\frac{4}{5}$. The lowest common denominator is 15. $\frac{2}{3} = \frac{10}{15}$ and $\frac{4}{5} = \frac{12}{15}$.

Therefore, $\frac{4}{5}$ is greater than $\frac{2}{3}$.

6. Mixed numbers may be compared by comparing the whole number parts of the numbers. For example, $4\frac{2}{3} > 3\frac{3}{5}$ because 4 > 3.

7. Improper fractions should be changed to mixed numbers before they are compared. If the whole number part of one fraction is greater than the whole number part of the other fraction, then we know that the fraction with the greater whole number is greater than the other mixed number. If the whole number parts of the two fractions are the same, then we must compare the fraction parts of the two numbers to determine which fraction is greater.

Exercise 46

1. Compare each of the following and insert >, <, = between them. Solve these mentally.

a) $\frac{1}{6}$ $\frac{1}{5}$ b) $\frac{1}{3}$ $\frac{1}{2}$ c) $\frac{1}{5}$ $\frac{1}{3}$ d) $\frac{1}{9}$ $\frac{1}{10}$

e) $\frac{1}{10}$ $\frac{3}{5}$ f) $\frac{8}{5}$ $\frac{6}{5}$ g) $\frac{5}{3}$ $\frac{7}{3}$ h) $\frac{10}{9}$ $\frac{8}{9}$

i) $\frac{2}{3}$ $\frac{3}{5}$ j) $\frac{3}{4}$ $\frac{9}{12}$ k) $\frac{3}{5}$ $\frac{1}{2}$ l) $\frac{3}{4}$ $\frac{2}{3}$

m) $4\frac{4}{5}$ $4\frac{3}{5}$ n) $3\frac{1}{3}$ $4\frac{2}{3}$ o) $5\frac{5}{6}$ $5\frac{7}{12}$ p) $3\frac{1}{2}$ $5\frac{2}{3}$

q) $3\frac{1}{4}$ $4\frac{2}{5}$ r) $2\frac{3}{8}$ $2\frac{5}{8}$ s) $3\frac{1}{4}$ $3\frac{4}{16}$ t) $5\frac{1}{7}$ $4\frac{3}{7}$

2. Angela answered 15 out of 20 questions correctly on an exam. Patricia answered 18 out of 24 correctly. Who answered the larger fraction of questions correctly?

Explain

3. Celia wanted her mother to cut a pizza in three equal parts and she wanted one of these parts. Betty wanted the pizza cut in six equal parts so that she could have two of these parts. Who would get the greater amount of pizza?

4. Henry worked for $7\frac{1}{2}$ hours: Jim worked for $8\frac{3}{4}$ hours: Paul worked for $7\frac{3}{4}$ hours: Steve worked for $8\frac{7}{8}$ hours; and Roger worked for $8\frac{1}{2}$ hours. List the number of hours worked from the greatest to the least.

Multiplication of Fractions

Fractions (in the form of $\frac{a}{b}$ where a and b are Integers and b is not equal to zero) are multiplied by multiplying the numerators and then multiplying the denominators.

Example 1: $\frac{4}{5} \times \frac{3}{7} = \frac{4 \times 3}{5 \times 7}$ or $\frac{12}{35}$.

Normally, fractions are reduced before being multiplied.

142

Example 2: $\frac{3}{12}$ x $\frac{5}{15}$ by the above method is $\frac{3 \times 5}{12 \times 15}$ or $\frac{15}{180}$ or $\frac{1}{12}$. The multiplication becomes easier if we reduce each fraction before multiplying. $\frac{3}{12} = \frac{1}{4}$ and $\frac{5}{15} = \frac{1}{3}$. Therefore, $\frac{1}{4}$ x $\frac{1}{3} = \frac{1}{12}$.

Example 3: If the numbers to be multiplied are mixed numbers, we can change all mixed numbers to improper fractions and multiply as above.

Multiply $3\frac{2}{5}$ x $2\frac{2}{3}$ x $4\frac{1}{2}$.

$3\frac{2}{5} = \frac{17}{5}$, $2\frac{2}{3} = \frac{8}{3}$, and $4\frac{1}{2} = \frac{9}{2}$. Now, $\frac{17}{5}$ x $\frac{8}{3}$ x $\frac{9}{2} = \frac{1224}{30}$. This fraction can be reduced to $\frac{204}{5}$ and this is equal to $40\frac{4}{5}$.

Or, we could have reduced when the numbers were expressed as improper fractions.

$\frac{17}{5}$ x $\frac{8}{3}$ x $\frac{9}{2}$ becomes $\frac{17}{5}$ x $\frac{4}{1}$ x $\frac{3}{1} = \frac{204}{5}$ or $40\frac{4}{5}$.

The Use of the Word "of"

The word "of" indicates multiplication. For example, if the following question is asked: What is $\frac{2}{5}$ of 40? The result is obtained as follows: $\frac{2}{5}$ x 40 = 16.

Example: Increase 40 by $\frac{1}{5}$. We can do this in two different ways.

Method 1: $\frac{1}{5}$ of 40 means $\frac{1}{5}$ x 40 = 8. Add 8 to 40 to obtain 48.

Method 2: Let 40 be $\frac{5}{5}$. Since we want to increase by $\frac{1}{5}$, we want to calculate $\frac{6}{5}$ of 40. $\frac{6}{5}$ x 40 = 48.

The same procedures should be followed for decreasing a number. If we wish to decrease 40 by $\frac{1}{5}$, we multiply 40 by $\frac{1}{5}$ and subtract. 40 x $\frac{1}{5}$ = 8 and 40 − 8 = 32. Using the second method, we will find $\frac{4}{5}$ of 40. $\frac{4}{5}$ x 40 = 32.

Exercise 47

1. Multiply each of the following and reduce to lowest terms or reduce the fractions, if possible and then multiply:

a) $\frac{3}{5}$ x $\frac{2}{7}$ =

b) $\frac{3}{4}$ x $\frac{2}{9}$ =

c) $\frac{5}{6}$ x $\frac{7}{8}$ =

d) $\frac{2}{3}$ x $\frac{6}{9}$ =

e) $\frac{3}{8}$ x $\frac{4}{5}$ =

f) $\frac{7}{12}$ x $\frac{3}{5}$ =

g) $3\frac{2}{5} \times 4\frac{1}{6} =$ h) $2\frac{1}{7} \times 3\frac{2}{3} =$ i) $5\frac{4}{5} \times 3\frac{1}{3} =$

j) $4\frac{3}{5} \times 2\frac{3}{6} =$

2. Jim has $\frac{3}{4}$ of a loaf of bread. Harry has $\frac{1}{2}$ as much bread as Jim has. How much bread does Harry have?

3. Lisa cut a poster board in half. She then cut 1 of these pieces in $\frac{1}{2}$. She discarded all but one piece and then cut this piece in $\frac{1}{4}$ s. She discarded all but one of these pieces. What fraction of the poster board does she now have?

4. A rectangle was divided into $\frac{1}{3}$ s. One of these $\frac{1}{3}$ s was divided into $\frac{1}{4}$ s. What fraction of the whole is one of these $\frac{1}{4}$ s?

5. Ron had $4\frac{1}{2}$ cans of nails. Jim had $2\frac{1}{3}$ times as many. How many cans of nails did Jim have?

6. Ruth put $2\frac{3}{4}$ cups of orange juice in a punch. She then added twice as much cranberry juice. She then added $3\frac{1}{3}$ times as much ginger ale as there was liquid in the punch. How many cups of punch were made? (Use a calculator.)

7. A regular bus ticket costs $2.00. A senior's ticket costs $\frac{3}{4}$ of the regular cost and a student ticket costs $\frac{4}{5}$ of the regular cost.
What is the cost of a senior ticket?   What is the cost of a student ticket?

8. Joe bought carrots in packages that weighed $\frac{3}{4}$ kg. He bought 8 packages. How many kilograms of carrots did Joe buy?

9. Sarah's weight is 72 kg. Her sister weighs $\frac{7}{8}$ as much as Sarah. How many kg does her sister weigh?

10. Jennifer had $3\frac{2}{3}$ cups of punch. $\frac{1}{2}$ of the punch was ginger ale. How many cups of the punch were not ginger ale?

11. Robert weighed $82\frac{1}{2}$ kg. Bill weighed $\frac{1}{3}$ less than Robert, and Charles weighed $\frac{1}{3}$ more than Robert. What is the average weight of the three men? What would the average weight of the three men have been if Charles weighed $\frac{1}{3}$ more than Bill. (Use a calculator.)

average weight   average weight when Charles weighed more

12. Hazel baked 60 squares. $\frac{1}{3}$ of the squares were chocolate, $\frac{1}{4}$ were caramel, and the rest were lemon flavored. How many squares were lemon flavored?

Division of Fractions

Division of fractions may be more easily understood by asking questions such as, "How many fives are there in 15? $15 \div 5 = 3$ because $3 \times 5 = 15$. If we have 15 objects we would want to know how many sets of 5 there are, we separate the 15 objects into groups of 5 and we see that there are 3 groups of 5. The same thinking for division of whole numbers should be applied to division of fractions.
$15 \div 5$ is asking the question, "How many fives are there in 15?"

In the same manner, we ask how many $\frac{1}{3}$'s are there in a whole? This operation may be illustrated by dividing a shape into three equal parts. Cut the second row into the three equal parts. It is easily seen that three $\frac{1}{3}$'s equals the whole (or 1). Therefore, $1 \div \frac{1}{3} = 3$. Note that this is similar to saying that $1 \div \frac{1}{3}$ is the same as $1 \times \frac{3}{1}$ or 3. In other words, when we write $1 \div \frac{1}{3}$ we are asking how many $\frac{1}{3}$'s are there in 1. The answer is that there are three $\frac{1}{3}$'s in 1.

1		
$\frac{1}{3}$	$\frac{1}{3}$	$\frac{1}{3}$

The same process is used for: $\frac{3}{5} \div \frac{2}{3} = \frac{3}{5} \times \frac{3}{2} = \frac{9}{10}$.

A more generalized understanding of why the divisor is inverted and the two fractions are then multiplied is as follows.

Example 1: $\frac{3}{5} \div \frac{2}{3} = ?$

$$\frac{3}{5} \div \frac{2}{3} = \frac{\frac{3}{5}}{\frac{2}{3}}$$

Write the division as a complex fraction. $\dfrac{\frac{3}{5}}{\frac{3}{2}}$

$$= \frac{\frac{3}{5} \times \boxed{\frac{3}{2}}}{\frac{2}{3} \times \boxed{\frac{3}{2}}}$$

Multiply the numerator and the denominator by $\frac{3}{2}$ and this is equal to 1 and therefore, we have not changed the fraction.

146

Note also that $\frac{2}{3} \times \frac{3}{2}$ is also equal to 1.

Therefore, $\frac{3}{5} \times \frac{3}{2} = \frac{9}{10}$.

The reason that $\frac{3}{2}$ was used is that it changes the complex fraction to an ordinary fraction by making the denominator of the complex fraction equal to 1. Note also that, as a result, the operation has been changed from division to multiplication.

We can see from the above that to divide one fraction by another, use the multiplicative inverse of the divisor and multiply. For example $\frac{3}{7} \div \frac{2}{5} = \frac{3}{7} \times \frac{5}{2} = \frac{15}{14}$ or $1\frac{1}{14}$. The multiplicative inverse of a fraction is that fraction inverted. For example, the multiplicative inverse of $\frac{5}{3}$ is $\frac{3}{5}$.

If mixed numbers are used, change the mixed numbers to improper fractions and proceed as above.

Example 2: $4\frac{2}{5} \div 2\frac{5}{6} = \frac{22}{5} \div \frac{17}{6} = \frac{22}{5} \times \frac{6}{17} = \frac{132}{85} = 1\frac{47}{85}$.

Exercise 48

1. Perform the following divisions and reduce to lowest terms.

a) $\frac{2}{3} \div \frac{4}{5} =$

b) $\frac{1}{6} \div \frac{1}{4} =$

c) $\frac{2}{7} \div \frac{1}{7} =$

d) $\frac{4}{3} \div \frac{2}{5} =$

e) $\frac{5}{8} \div \frac{2}{5} =$

f) $\frac{4}{9} \div \frac{3}{10} =$

g) $2\frac{1}{3} \div 4\frac{1}{2} =$

h) $3\frac{2}{5} \div 2\frac{1}{7} =$

i) $5\frac{1}{4} \div 2\frac{2}{5} =$

2. John bought $2\frac{1}{2}$ boxes of candy. He wanted to share them equally among 5 of his friends. What fraction of a box did each receive?

3. A teaspoon is equal to 5 ml. A tablespoon is three times the size of a teaspoon. Sheila had 6 tablespoons of sugar that she divided into 8 equal parts. How many ml were there in each part?

4. Tom was building a staircase and he wanted to put a backing for each step. He had a piece of wood that was $50\frac{3}{10}$ cm long. The distance between the steps was $16\frac{3}{4}$ cm. What is the maximum number of steps that can be built?

5. Gina had a piece of ribbon that was $26\frac{2}{3}$ cm long. She required pieces that were $7\frac{1}{10}$ cm long. How many pieces of ribbon can Gina cut?

6. If 6 liters of milk have to be placed in milk cups that contain $\frac{2}{3}$ of a liter, how many milk cups are required?

7. Increase 60 by $\frac{1}{5}$

8. Decrease 80 by $\frac{1}{4}$

9. Increase 80 by $\frac{1}{4}$

10. Decrease 100 by $\frac{2}{5}$

148

The Set of Real Numbers

It was stated that any Rational number may be changed to a decimal number that is a terminating or recurring decimal number. (Remember $\frac{1}{4}$ = 0.25 and $\frac{1}{3}$ = 0.$\dot{3}$.)

There are other numbers that when represented in their decimal form are not terminating and they are not recurring decimals. A number such as $\sqrt{2}$ is neither terminating nor recurring. The positive square root of 2 is 1.4142. . . and the positive square root of 3 is 1.7321. . . No matter how many times the square root algorithm is applied to such numbers, the process will never stop and the decimal numbers will never repeat in the same sequence.

It should be noted that $\sqrt{2}$ has two square roots: 1.4142 . . . and − 1.4142 . . . Remember that − 3 x − 3 = + 9.

Non-terminating, non-recurring decimal numbers are called Irrational numbers. (That is, they cannot be written as a Rational number in the form of $\frac{a}{b}$ where a and b are Integers and b ≠ 0.) We have already seen one Irrational number when the area of a circle was determined to be π r². π is an Irrational number that is equal to 3.14159. . . or approximately 3.14.

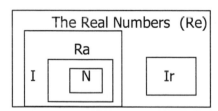

Rational numbers are terminating or recurring decimal fractions. Irrational numbers are non-terminating non-recurring decimal fractions. The set of Real numbers is the union of the Rational numbers and the Irrational numbers. The set of Real numbers has a one–to–one correspondence with all points on the number line. That is, all points on the number line have a specific Real number and all Real numbers have a point on the number line. The number line is now continuous.

Exercise 49

1. List the property of the number system that is exhibited by each of the following:

a) 7 + 6 = 6 + 7

b) if ab = cb, then a = c

c) 8 + (− 8) = 0

d) 5(6 + 4) = 5 x 6 + 5 x 4

e) 1 x 7 = 7

f) (7 + 5) + 6 = 7 + (5 + 6)

g) a > b or a < b or a = b

2. Give an example of each of the following:

a) the distributive property of multiplication with respect to subtraction

b) the existence of an additive identity

c) the associative property of multiplication

d) the existence of the cancellation property for subtraction

e) the property of transitivity

3. Answer each of the following:

a) Are all Natural numbers Integers?

b) Are all Integers Natural Numbers?

c) Give an example of a fraction that is a non-terminating, non-recurring decimal.

d) Give an example of a fraction that is a terminating decimal

e) Is π a Real number?

f) What type of a number is π?

SELF-ASSESSMENT of the ATTAINMENT of the OBJECTIVES

	5	4	3	2	1
- define a Natural number					
- tell what is meant by a set being closed					
- tell what is meant by the communicative property					
- give an example of the associative property					
- give an example of the distributive property					
- give an example using the identity element for multiplication					
- tell what is meant by a set being ordered					
- list an example of the property of transitivity					
- name the operations that can be performed using the Natural numbers only					
- define the set of Integers					
- what new operation is possible using the set of Integers?					

- demonstrate that the set of Natural numbers is a subset of the set of Integers
- demonstrate the use of the additive identity in the set of Integers
- demonstrate that each Integer has an additive inverse
- define a vector
- demonstrate the ability to use vector addition
- add Integers
- subtract Integers
- multiply Integers
- divide Integers
- demonstrate the ability to subtract Integers using vectors
- define subtraction
- demonstrate that any number multiplied by 0 is 0
- define the absolute value of a number
- define the set of Rational numbers
- give an example of a fraction that is a terminating decimal fraction
- give an example of a fraction that is a non–terminating decimal fraction
- give an example of a recurring decimal fraction
- give an example using the multiplicative inverse of a Rational number
- explain what is meant by saying that the set of Rational numbers is dense
- indicate what new operation is possible when the set of Rational numbers is added to the set of Integers
- list four fractions that are equivalent to a given fraction
- define a proper fraction
- demonstrate the ability to add, subtract, multiply and divide proper fractions
- demonstrate the ability to add, subtract, multiply and divide improper fractions
- demonstrate the ability to add, subtract, multiply and divide mixed numbers
- define an improper fraction
- demonstrate the ability to reduce fractions to their lowest terms
- define a Rational number
- demonstrate the ability to find the Lowest Common Denominator
- define the set of Real numbers
- list an example of an Irrational number
- solve problems using the various sets of numbers

Score   /215   Date _____

Section IV—The Number System from the Natural Numbers to the Real Numbers
Post—Test IV

Answers can be found at the back of the book.

1. Write an example of the commutative property of addition.

2. What number is the multiplicative identity?

3. Give an example of the associative property of multiplication.

4. Give an example of the distributive property of multiplication with respect to addition.

5. Give an example of the cancellation property of multiplication.

6. What new operation always becomes possible when we add the negative whole numbers and zero to the positive whole numbers?

7. What is the additive identity in this new set of numbers?

8. Add each row and place the result in each box in column (a). Then add each column and place the result in each box in row (b). Then add column (a) and row (b).

						(a)
	4	− 5	6	− 2	− 3	
	− 3	2	− 1	4	6	
	− 7	0	− 2	− 3	− 2	
	− 4	3	3	6	3	
	3	5	− 4	2	− 1	
(b)						

9. Add each of the following:

a) − 7
  − 5

b) 7
  − 5

c) − 7
  − 5

d) 7
  − 5

10. Multiply each of the following:

a) − 7
  − 8

b) 7
  8

c) 7
  − 8

d) − 7
  8

11. What is the additive inverse of -5?

12. Subtract each of the following:

a) $-5 - 4 =$ b) $4 - (-5) =$ c) $-7 + 7 =$ d) $7 - (-3) =$

13. Divide each of the following:

a) $16 \div -4 =$ b) $-16 \div 4 =$ c) $-16 \div -4 =$ d) $3 \div -3 =$

14. Determine whether each of the following is a terminating or a recurring decimal fraction

a) $\frac{2}{3}$ is b) $\frac{3}{5}$ is

15. Perform the following division: $6 \div 0 =$

Explain

16. Calculate each of the following:

a) $\frac{3}{5} + \frac{3}{5} =$ b) $\frac{1}{4} - \frac{1}{6} =$ c) $\frac{3}{7} + \frac{1}{21} =$

d) $\frac{3}{8} - \frac{1}{4} =$ e) $3\frac{1}{4} + 2\frac{5}{6} =$ f) $4\frac{4}{5} - 3\frac{1}{10} =$

g) $5\frac{3}{8} - 4\frac{3}{4} =$ h) $\frac{5}{3} \times \frac{4}{7} =$ i) $2\frac{3}{5} \times 4\frac{3}{4} =$

j) $3\frac{2}{5} \times 3\frac{2}{5} =$ k) $\frac{5}{6} \div \frac{2}{3} =$ l) $\frac{3}{7} \div \frac{4}{5} =$

m) $2\frac{2}{5} \div 4\frac{1}{3} =$

17. Calculate each of the following.

a) increase 60 by $\frac{1}{4}$

b) decrease 45 by $\frac{2}{9}$

c) increase 27 by $\frac{1}{3}$

d) decrease 36 by $\frac{2}{3}$

18. What new operation is possible when we increase the set of Integers to include the set of rational numbers?

Score _____   Date _____

154

Section V – Decimal Fractions, Percent, The Solution of Equations, Ratios
Pre–Test V

Answers to the Pre–Test can be found at the back of the book.

1. a) Increase 40 by 0.3   b) Increase 40 by $\frac{3}{10}$ c) Increase 40 by 30%

d) Decrease 36 by 0.4   e) Decrease 100 by 20%   f) Decrease 30 by 80%

2. Change each of the following to decimal fractions:

a) $\frac{2}{3}$ =   b) $\frac{7}{10}$ =   c) $\frac{1}{2}$ =   d) $\frac{1}{8}$ =

3. Change each of the following to proper fractions.
a) 0.35 =   b) 0.01 =   c) 0.63 =   d) 0.99 =

4. John earned $36,000 a year. The company offered each employee a bonus of 0.2 of his/her salary. How much money did John earn as a bonus?

5. Mary was offered a 3% increase on her salary of $27,000. What is her new salary?

6. Perform the following operations.

a) 2. 6
   + 5. 7

b) 6. 8
   − 2. 5

c) 2. 4
   x 3. 2

d) $0.133\overline{)0.338}$

155

7. Jack had a bucket of apples. He used 55% of the apples to make pies. What fraction of the apples was not used?

8. Shade the area according to the percent indicated.

a) 35%

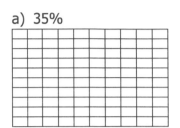

b) 40%

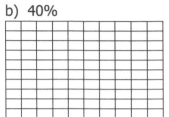

c) 60%

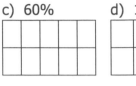

d) 10%

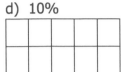

9. Change 24% to a decimal fraction and to a proper fraction.

decimal fraction   proper fraction

10. What is 10% of 15?

11. Harold spent 35% of $200. James spent 45% of $150. Who spent more money and by how much?

12. The selling price of a tool was $125. The salesman offered a discount of 20%. At what price was the tool sold?

13. a) Increase 75 by 20%   b) Decrease 250 by 24%

14. A house was listed at $230,000. The buyer received a 5% discount for paying immediately. The buyer then had to pay 12% taxes on the amount paid. What was the total amount paid?

15. What percent is 5 of 35?

16. If 250 ml of water are added to 400 ml of water, what is the percent of increase?

17. By what percent must you decrease 3,000 to get 2,000?

18. Solve each of the following:

a) $4n + 5 = 2n + 9$

b) $\dfrac{3}{4p} + \dfrac{1}{2} = \dfrac{5}{8}$

c) $\dfrac{2}{3} = \dfrac{x}{8}$

19. If it takes 2 kg of soybeans to make 5 kg of tofu, how much tofu is made from 100 kg of soybeans?

Score _____   Date _____

157

Unit 10 – Decimal Fractions

OBJECTIVES

- change fractions to their decimal form
- change decimal numbers to proper or improper fractions
- change denominators to tenths and hundredths
- identify fractions that are terminating decimal numbers
- identify fractions that are non–terminating, non–recurring decimal numbers
- increase amounts using decimal fractions
- decrease amounts using decimal fractions
- perform additions, subtractions, multiplications, and divisions using decimal numbers
- solve problems using decimal fractions

Operations using fractions were included in Unit 9 under Rational numbers. There is another way of expressing fractions by changing them to decimal numbers. Notice the diagram below. The top part of the diagram is 1 unit. The bottom part of the diagram has been divided into 10 equal parts. Each shaded part may be written as a proper fraction $\frac{1}{10}$ or as .1 or 0.1 and is read "one tenth".

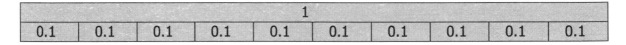

1									
0.1	0.1	0.1	0.1	0.1	0.1	0.1	0.1	0.1	0.1

The first two parts in the shaded area are written as 0.2 in the decimal form and this is read 'two tenths'.

The first number after the decimal point refers to the number of tenths in the number. For example, seven tenths is written as 0.7, five tenths is written as 0.5. In a similar manner, a unit may be divided into one hundred equal parts and each of these is called a hundredth. The part that is shaded in each diagram below is $\frac{25}{100}$ and this is written in decimal form as 0.25 and is read "twenty-five one hundredths".

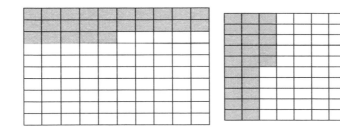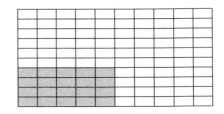

A unit may be divided into one thousand equal parts. Each of these parts is called a thousandth. For example, $\frac{325}{1000} = 0.325$.

This is read "three hundred and twenty-five one thousandths".

158

It is important to notice that any number written as a fraction in the form of $\frac{a}{b}$ where a and b are Integers and b is not equal to zero, may be written as a decimal fraction.

If the denominator is not written in tenths, or in hundredths, or in thousandths, then one of two options is available.

1. Change the denominator of the fraction to tenths. For example, $\frac{3}{5}$ is written in its equivalent form as $\frac{6}{10}$ which written in its decimal form is 0.6 and is read "six tenths".

2. When the fraction cannot easily be changed to one in which the denominator is 10, then look for an equivalent fraction in which the denominator is 100. For example, $\frac{1}{4}$ cannot be changed to an equivalent fraction in which 10 is the denominator. However, it can be changed to a fraction in which the denominator is 100. $\frac{1}{4} = \frac{25}{100}$.

Now we can write $\frac{25}{100}$ as 0.25 and this is read "twenty-five one hundredths".

You can see that any zeros after the last non-zero digit will not alter the fraction since $\frac{3}{10} = \frac{30}{100} = \frac{300}{1000}$, etc. or, 0.3 = 0.30 = 0.300. These are all equivalent fractions.

Another way of changing $\frac{3}{4}$ to a decimal fraction is to divide the numerator by the denominator. When the remainder is 0, the fraction terminates (ends).

$$
\begin{array}{r}
0.75 \\
4\overline{)3.00} \\
\underline{2\ 8} \\
2\ 0 \\
\underline{2\ 0} \\
0
\end{array}
$$

Therefore, $\frac{3}{4} = 0.75$.

Sometimes, the quotient will be a recurring decimal fraction. For example, $\frac{1}{3}$ can be changed to a decimal fraction by dividing the numerator by the denominator.

Sometimes, the quotient will recur. In the example below, we are changing $\frac{1}{3}$ to a decimal fraction by dividing the numerator by the denominator. Notice that the remainder is 1, the number with which we started. Therefore, for each successive division, the quotient will be 3 and the remainder will be 1.

$$
\frac{1}{3} = \begin{array}{r}
0.3 \\
3\overline{)1.0} \\
\underline{9} \\
1
\end{array}
$$

$\frac{1}{3}$ = .3333... or 0.$\dot{3}$ (read three tenths recurring). Or, it can be written as 0.$\ddot{3}$ (read thirty-three one hundredths recurring).

Notice that the remainder in this division will always be 1. Therefore, 3 will have to be divided into 10 each time a division is made. The quotient, .3333 . . . is called a recurring decimal and is written as .$\dot{3}$ which is read as "three tenths recurring". A bar over the number – or dots over the number – are ways of indicating recurring decimal fractions and each means that part (or all) of the decimal fraction recurs.

Another example of a fraction that is a recurring decimal fraction is $\frac{1}{7}$ which is seen by dividing 1 by 7, the quotient that results will be 0 .142857 and then these 6 digits will repeat.

Note the following division:

```
     0.1 4 2 8 5 7
   7)1.0              1 + 7 = 0
      7               0 ÷ 7 = .1 with a remainder of 3
      3 0             add 0
      2 8             30 ÷ 7 = 4 with a remainder of 2
        2 0           add 0
        1 4           20 ÷ 7 = 2 with a remainder of 6
          6 0         add 0
          5 6         60 ÷ 7 = 8 with a remainder of 4
            4 0       add 0
            3 5       40 ÷ 7 = 5 with a remainder of 5
              5 0     add 0
              4 9     50 ÷ 7 = 7 with a remainder of 1
                1     We are now back to where we started.
```

If the process continued, it will repeat itself. Therefore, we say that $\frac{1}{7}$ is equal to $0.\overline{142857}$ or $0.\dot{1}4285\dot{7}$ and this is read "one hundred forty-two thousand eight hundred fifty-seven millionths recurring".

It should be noted that the dots are placed over the first and last digits of a recurring number of more than one digit.

However, numbers of this magnitude are usually "rounded off" to three decimal places. The general rule for rounding off numbers is that if the number following the digit in the place value to be rounded off is 5 or greater, then the preceding number is increased by 1. In this case, 8 is greater than 5, and therefore, the number rounded off is 0.143. If a number is to be rounded off to three decimal places and the digit in the ten thousandths place is less than 5, then the digit in the thousandth place remains unchanged. For example, 0.1643 when rounded off will be 0.164. However, 0.1647 would be changed to 0.165.

160

Increasing and Decreasing Amounts Using Decimal Fractions

Example 1: If we wish to increase 50 by 0.1, we may proceed in any of the following ways:

Method 1: We can say that 0.1 is one tenth. One tenth of 50 is equal to 5, that is $\frac{1}{10}$ x 50 = 5. 5 is added to 50 to increase the number. Therefore, 55 is 0.1 greater than 50.

Method 2: We can say that 50 = 1. To this we add 0.1. Now 1.1 is $\frac{11}{10}$ and $\frac{11}{10}$ x 50 = 55.

Example 2: If we wish to decrease a number, we may use either of the two methods.

Method 1:   If we wish to decrease 100 by 0.2, we may change 0.2 to $\frac{2}{10}$.

Now, $\frac{2}{10}$ x 100 is equal to 20. 100 − 20 = 80.

Method 2: We can say that 100 = $\frac{10}{10}$. We decrease $\frac{10}{10}$ by $\frac{2}{10}$ to obtain $\frac{8}{10}$ and $\frac{8}{10}$ x 100 = 80.

Notice that in each instance, the number to be increased or decreased is 1 in the form of $\frac{10}{10}$, in the form of $\frac{100}{100}$, or in the form of $\frac{1000}{1000}$.

Exercise 50

1. Shade the fraction indicated and write the fraction in its decimal form.

a) $\frac{4}{5}$ =

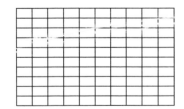

b) $\frac{3}{4}$ =

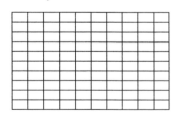

c) $\frac{1}{2}$ =

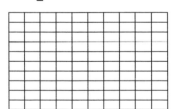

d) $\frac{1}{2}$ =   e) $\frac{3}{4}$ =   f) $\frac{9}{10}$ =

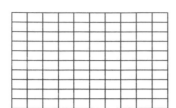
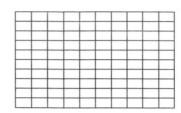
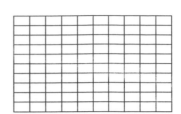

2. Change each of the following to decimal fractions.

a) $\frac{2}{5}$ =   b) $\frac{2}{3}$ =   c) $\frac{3}{5}$ =

d) $\frac{7}{10}$ =   e) $\frac{1}{4}$ =   f) $\frac{2}{4}$ =

3. Change each of the following to proper fractions and reduce each to lowest terms:

a) 0.35 =   or   b) 0.75 =   or   c) 0.63 =   or

d) 0.42 =   or   e) 0.60 =   or   f) 0.99 =   or

4. Peter had a garden that measured 30 m by 40 m. He wanted to increase the area by 0.25. By how many meters must he increase the dimensions of the garden? What is the new area?

dimensions   new area

5. John earned $36,000 a year. The company offered each employee a bonus of 0.2 of his/her annual earnings. How much money did John earn as a bonus?

6. By how much would the garden in number 4 have been decreased if Peter had wanted to decrease the area by 0.25?

7. Why is there no "ones place" to the right of the decimal point?

Decimal Numbers Using Whole Numbers and Fractions

The number 3.6 means that there are 3 ones (whole numbers) and 6 tenths. This may be represented as:

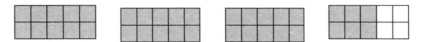

Note that $\frac{36}{10}$ is equal to 3.6. Therefore, 3.6 is the same as $3\frac{6}{10}$ and both are read "three and six tenths".

The method used to add decimal numbers that have whole numbers and decimal fractions is to add the fractions and if the sum of the tenths is greater than ten, change it to a mixed number and add the number of tens to the column containing the ones. If there are hundredths or thousandths in the fraction parts of the numbers, add these separately and then add the whole number parts.

Example 1: Add 3.4 + 5.3. Add the tenths, and then add the ones.

$$\begin{array}{r} 3.4 \\ + \ 5.3 \\ \hline = 8.7 \end{array}$$

Example 2: Add 2.7 + 3.6

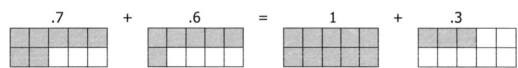

$$.7 \quad + \quad .6 \quad = \quad 1 \quad + \quad .3$$

Note that .7 + .6 = 1.3 and this is equal to 1 + .3 or 1.3. Note that the unit 1 has been added to the sum of 2 + 3. Therefore, 2.7 + 3.6 = 2 + 3 + 1 + .3 = 6.3. The operations of addition and subtraction follow the same methods.

Example 3: Subtract 5.7 − 3.6.

$$\begin{array}{r} 5.7 \\ \underline{3.6} \\ 2.1 \end{array}$$

Example 4: Subtract 6.3 − 4.5. In this case, we cannot subtract .5 from .3. Therefore, we must change 6.3 into 5 and 13 tenths. 13 tenths − 5 tenths = 8 tenths. The subtraction is as follows:

6.3 → 5.13
4.5 → 4. 5
$\quad\quad$ 1. 8

Check by adding the difference to the number that was subtracted.

Example 5: Multiply 3.6 x 5.4.

```
   3 6      tenths by tenths will be multiplied so the product will be hundreds.
   5 4      Then disregard the decimal point.
 1 4 4      4 x 6 = 24 which is 2 tens and 4 ones.  4 x 3 tens = 12 tens + 2 = 14
 1 8 0      tens
 1 9 4 4    5 tens x 6 ones = 30 tens or 3 hundreds: 5 tens x 3 tens = 15 hundred
            3 hundreds + 15 hundreds = 18 hundreds or 8 hundreds and 1
            thousand.
```

The product is 1944. But tenths were multiplied by tenths and therefore the product must be expressed in hundredths. Therefore, 3.6 x 5.4 = 19.44.

Some people omit the decimal point and multiply 36 by 22. Then they consider the fact that they multiplied a number of tenths by another number of tenths. Therefore, the product must contain hundredths. Multiplying the numbers and then counting the number of digits to the right of each decimal point in the multiplicand and in the multiplier may shorten this method. Then insert a decimal point in the product. It is important to know why the decimal places are counted.

It is useful to check the problem before proceeding. In Example 5, the whole number parts of the numbers are 3 and 5. Therefore, the product will be a two-digit number and this may help you to place the decimal point in the correct place.

Example 6: Divide 24.85 by 3.5.

Multiply the divisor by 10 to eliminate the decimal fraction. Since 10 multiplied the divisor, 10 also must multiply the dividend. Therefore, the divisor and the dividend have been multiplied by 10 and the fraction has been multiplied by $\frac{10}{10}$ or 1.

```
           7.1
3 5) 2 4 8 .5
     2 4 5
         3 5
         3 5
```

In the above example, hundredths have been divided by tenths. Therefore, the quotient must be expressed in tenths. Therefore, 24.85 ÷ 3.5 = 7.1.

Multiplying the quotient by the divisor is a check of division. 3.5 x 7.1 = 24.85.
The same methods apply for operations using more than tenths and hundredths.

Example 7: 4.65 x 5.37 = 24.9705. This number is read "twenty-four and nine thousand seven hundred and five ten thousandths".

Example 8: 24.9705 ÷ 5.37 = 4.65. (Use a calculator to verify these operations.)

164

Exercise 51

1. Shade the amount shown in each of the following:

a) 3. 8

b) 2.6

c) 3. 5

d) 3. 7

e) 1. 6

f) 2. 3 0

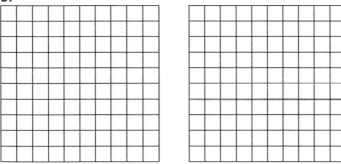

g) 1.75

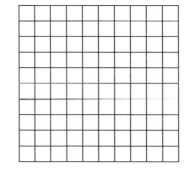

h) 2.76

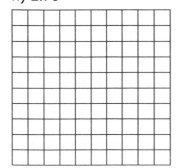
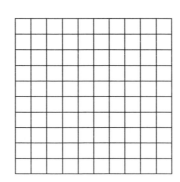
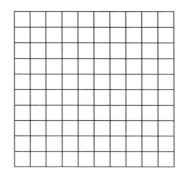

2. Add each of the following:

a) 0.7
   0.4

b) 0.6
   0.8

c) 1.4
   2.5

d) 3. 5
   2.7

e) 4.1
   5.9

f) 5.8
   6.4

g) 3.7
   8.3

h) 0.1
   0.2

i) 0.2
   0.4

j) 1.46
   2.64

k) 4.375
   2.646

l) 3.271
   2.459

m) 4.679
   3.452

3. Subtract each of the following:

a) 0.9
   0.6

b) 1.8
   0.9

c) 4.8
   3.9

d) 7.35
   2.63

e) 5.07
   3.29

f) 3.001
   2.111

4. Multiply each of the following:

a) 0.8
   0.5

b) 1.5
   2.7

c) 3.4
   1.6

d) 2.7
   3.8

e) 4.2
   8.1

f) 3.05
   0.35

5. Use a calculator to multiply each of the following and observe the movement of the decimal point:

a) 3.46
   0.21

b) 5.57
   1.35

c) 2.315
   1.426

d) 5.713
   2.015

6. Estimate the quotient and then divide each of the following: (use a calculator)

a) 4. 6)‾10.5 8

b) 3. 7)‾1 7.0 2

SELF-ASSESSMENT of the ATTAINMENT of the OBJECTIVES

	5	4	3	2	1
- change fractions to their decimal form					
- change decimal numbers to proper or improper fractions					
- change denominators to tenths and hundredths					
- identify fractions that are terminating decimal numbers					
- identify fractions that are non–terminating, non–recurring decimal numbers					
- increase amounts using decimal fractions					
- decrease amounts using decimal fractions					
- perform additions, subtractions, multiplications, and divisions using decimal fractions					
- solve problems involving decimal numbers					

Score   /45   Date _____

Unit 11—Using Percent

OBJECTIVES

- explain the meaning of percent
- change a percent to a common fraction
- change a percent to a decimal fraction
- change a common fraction to a percent
- change a decimal fraction to a percent
- add percents
- subtract percents
- multiply percents
- divide percents
- determine the percent of a number
- calculate percentage discounts
- calculate percentage markups
- increase a number by a certain percent
- decrease a number by a certain percent
- determine the percent of increase of a number
- determine the percent of decrease of a number
- solve problems using percent

Percent

Percent means hundredths. When we write 25%, we mean $\frac{25}{100}$ or 0.25. We know that $\frac{25}{100}$ is equal to $\frac{1}{4}$. Note that 100% means $\frac{100}{100}$ or 1. If John attained 100% on his mathematics test, he received all of the marks possible. If Harry attained 80% on his test, then he attained $\frac{80}{100}$ or 0.80. Another way of writing $\frac{80}{100}$ is $\frac{4}{5}$.

From the above, we can see that a common fraction $\frac{75}{100}$ is the same as the decimal fraction 0.75, and the same as 75%.

Each of the shaded areas following is equal to $\frac{3}{4}$ because 75% equals $\frac{75}{100}$ which is equal to $\frac{3}{4}$.

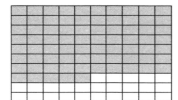 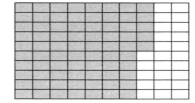 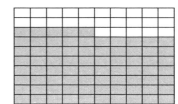

Changing from Percent to Common Fractions and from Common Fractions to Percent

To change percent to a common fraction write the percent as hundredths and reduce the fraction. For example, $25\% = \frac{25}{100} = \frac{1}{4}$.

To change a common fraction into a percent, divide the denominator into the numerator and multiply by 100. If the fraction is a terminating decimal such as $\frac{3}{4}$, the quotient will be 0.75. This is read as seventy-five one hundredths and is written as 0.75 x 100 or 75%. Or, $\frac{3}{4}$ may be changed to an equivalent fraction in which the denominator is 100. $\frac{3}{4} = \frac{75}{100} = 75\%$.

Changing a Percent to a Decimal Fraction and Changing a Decimal Fraction to a Percent

To change a percent to a decimal fraction, write the percent as a proper fraction and divide the denominator into the numerator. For example, $30\% = \frac{30}{100} = 0.30$ or 0.3.

To change a decimal fraction to a percent, read the decimal fraction in words. For example, $0.5 =$ five tenths or $\frac{5}{10}$. If necessary, this fraction may be reduced to $\frac{1}{2}$ which is 50%. Or, $0.5 = 0.50 = \frac{50}{100} = 50\%$.

Exercise 52

1. Shade the area according to the percents indicated:

a) 40%

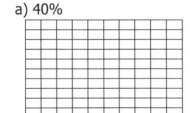

b) 65%

c) 83%

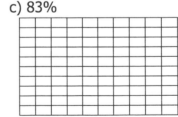

d) 33%

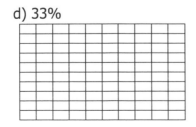

e) 75%

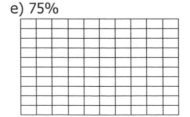

f) 46%

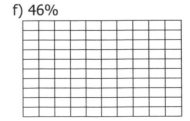

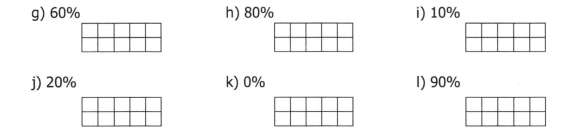

g) 60%   h) 80%   i) 10%

j) 20%   k) 0%   l) 90%

2. Janice had $300 in her purse. After she had gone shopping she had 40% of her money left. What percent of her money did she spend?
How much did she have left?

3. Bill read $\frac{4}{5}$ of his mathematics book. What percent of the book did he read?

$\frac{4}{5} = $ %

4. Jack had a bucket of apples. He used 55% of the apples to make pies. What fraction of the apples did Jack use?   Write this in two other ways.

5. Jane used 0.67 of a ball of wool. What percent of the ball was used?   Write this in another way.

6. Mary ate $\frac{1}{3}$ of a cake. Joan ate 33% of the cake, and Helen ate the remainder.

Who ate the largest piece of cake?
Explain

Operations Using Percent as a Fraction

We have seen that 75% = 0.75. Similarly, any percent may be changed to a decimal fraction. A decimal fraction (or a percent) may be changed to a common fraction. Since 75% = 0.75 which is read "seventy-five one hundredths,

$75\% = 0.75 = \frac{75}{100} = \frac{3}{4}$.

When the operations of addition, subtraction, multiplication, or division are used, the easiest way to proceed is to change the percents into decimal fractions or common fractions. Care must be taken concerning the tenths, the hundredths, and in some cases the ones digit of a number.

Example 1: Add 35% and 46%.

3 5%
4 6%
8 1 %

Or, $\frac{35}{100} + \frac{46}{100}$ is $\frac{81}{100}$ or 0.81 or 81%.

Example 2: Add 74% and 37%.

74 Ignore the decimal point and then insert it after addition.
37 = 7 + 4 = 11, that is 1 ten and 1 one.
We now have 1 + 3 + 7 in the tens column which is 11 tens or 1 hundred and 1
ten. Tenths were added to tenths and therefore, the sum will be in hundredths.
It may be instructive to note that 74% + 37% = 111% or 1.11.

Or, change the percents to common fractions.
$\frac{74}{100} + \frac{37}{100} = \frac{111}{100}$ which is 1.11.

Subtraction may be done in the same way, but "combining" may occur.

Example 3: Subtract 37% from 74%.
$\quad$ 7 4 → 6 $\;$ 14 $\qquad$ 7 units cannot be subtracted from 4 units. Therefore, we must
$\qquad\qquad\qquad\qquad$ "combine" 1 tenth which is 10 units. Now 7 units is subtracted
$\qquad\qquad\qquad\qquad$ from 14 units to obtain 7 units.
$\quad$ 3 7 → $\underline{3 \;\; 7}$ $\qquad$ 3 tenths is subtracted from 6 tenths to obtain 3 tenths.
$\qquad\quad$ 3 $\;\;$ 7 $\qquad$ Therefore, the difference is 37 meaning 37%.

Another way of subtracting 37% from 74% is to subtract 37 from 74 to obtain 37%.

Or $\frac{74}{100} - \frac{37}{100} = \frac{37}{100}$ or 37% or 0.37.

Example 4: Multiply 46% x 27%.

Change each to a fraction: $\frac{46}{100}$ x $\frac{27}{100}$ = $\frac{1242}{10000}$ which is read as one thousand two
hundred and forty-two ten thousandths.   By dividing the numerator and the
denominator by 100, we obtain $\frac{12.42}{100}$ which is 0.1242%.

Or, multiply .46 x .27 in their decimal form.

$\quad$ .4 6
$\quad$ .2 7
$\;$ 3 2 2
$\;$ 9 2
1 2 4 2 = .1242 = .1242% since we are multiplying hundredths by hundredths.

Example 5: Divide 56% ÷ 8%.
56% ÷ 8% is the same as $\frac{56}{100} ÷ \frac{8}{100}$ or $\frac{56}{100}$ x $\frac{100}{8}$ = 7.
Therefore, 56% ÷ 8% = 7%.

Example 6: Divide 80% by 15%.

$\frac{80}{100} \times \frac{100}{15} = \frac{80}{15}$ or $\frac{16}{3}$ or $5.33\dot{3}$ or $5.\dot{3}$ and this is $5.\dot{3}$ %.

Calculating the Percent of a Number

1. If we wish to calculate 30% of 90, there are three ways in which we may proceed. We can change 30% to its form as a common fraction $\frac{30}{100}$ and multiply.

$\frac{30}{100} \times 90 = 27$. Therefore, 30% of 90 is 27.

2. We can change 30% to its decimal form .30 and multiply. 90 x .30 = 27. Note the multiplication: 90 x .30. Since we multiplied by thirty one hundredths, the product must be in hundredths. Therefore, the product is 27.00 or 27. Unless you are dealing with money or are measuring to hundredths, the two zeros and the decimal point may be omitted. Therefore, 30% of 90 is 27.

3. We can say that 100% = 90. Therefore, 1% = .90 (divide each by 100). Hence, 30% = 30 x .90 = 27.00 or 27.

Exercise 53

1. Change each of the following percents to a decimal fraction and then to a proper fraction:

a) 40% =   decimal fraction   =   proper fraction

b) 25% =   decimal fraction   =   proper fraction

2. Add each of the following:

a) 29% + 41% =   b) 36% + 24% =   c) 17% + 38% =

3. Subtract each of the following:

a) 68% – 37% =   b) 54% – 28% =   c) 97% – 25% =

4. Multiply each of the following:

a) 23% x 47% =   b) 10% x 50% =   c) 19% x 45% =

5. Divide each of the following:

a) 99% ÷ 11% =   b) 45% ÷ 9% =   c) 30% ÷ 8% =

6. What is 10% of 15?

7. Which is less: 75% of 15 or 20% of 20?

8. Sarah had $500. She wanted to spend 75% of her money. Her friend suggested that she spend only $\frac{3}{4}$ of her money. Determine how much she would spend in each case. Explain

9. Harold spent 35% of $200. James spent 45% of $150. How much did each spend? Harold spent   James spent   How much more money than the other did one of them spend?

10. Ingrid was shopping for a new refrigerator. She went to four stores that had the exact same model and all were priced the same. One store offered a discount of $33\frac{1}{3}$%. Another store offered a discount of $\frac{1}{3}$. The third store offered a discount of 0.33. The fourth store offered her a deal in which she would to pay 60% of the marked price.

Which store offered the best price?   Explain

11. The selling price of a tool was $125. The store offered a discount of 20%. At what price was the tool sold?

12. A shirt costing $100 has a 40% reduction and a tie costing $50 has a 20% reduction. What percent of discount is there on the entire sale?

13. Decrease 250 by 24%. Do this in three different ways.
   Method 1   Method 2   Method 3

14. Increase 75 by 20%. Do this in three different ways.

   Method 1   Method 2   Method 3

15. Reduce the mass of 90 kg by $33\frac{1}{3}$%. Then increase the new amount by 25%. What is the weight of the new mass?

16. A ship carried 800,000 liters of oil. At the first stop, 20% of the oil was transferred to shore. How much oil did the ship have then? Solve this in two different ways.

Method 1   Method 2

17. A used car was priced at $4,000. The price was reduced by 8%. What was the new price of the car? Solve this in two different ways.

Method 1   Method 2

18. A house was listed at $230,000. The buyer received a 5% discount for paying immediately. He had to pay 12% taxes on the price he paid. What was the total amount paid?

19. What percent is 5 of 35?

20. John was playing a game on his computer. He won 6 games and lost 4 games. What was his winning percentage?

Determining the Percentage of Increase or Decrease of a Number

Example 1: Determine the percent of increase if an article was bought for $50 and sold for $75. The cost price was $50. The selling price was $75. Therefore, the profit was $25. When we wish to find the percent of profit, we base it on the original price, that is, the cost price. Therefore, the percent of increase (or profit) is $\frac{25}{50}$ or $\frac{1}{2}$ or 50%.

Example 2: If the membership fee of a golf club was $300 one year and $250 the next year, what was the percent of decrease in the membership fee?

The original membership fee was $300.   The new membership was $250.   The decrease was $50. Therefore, the percent of decrease was $\frac{50}{300} = \frac{1}{6}$ or $16\frac{2}{3}\%$.

Exercise 54

1. George wanted to sell his car for $6,450. He sold it for $5,289. What percent of discount did he give? (Use a calculator.)

2. Gertrude saved 30% on a cost of $60. How much did she save? Solve this in three different ways.

Method 1   Method 2   Method 3

3. Paul opened a retail store. In order to attract customers, he increased his cost price by 40% and this became his marked price. He then gave a discount of 40% of the marked price in order to break even. Paul is not in business any longer. Explain.

4. A retailer increased his sales from $1,500 a week to $1,800 a week. What was the percent of increase?

5. If 250 ml of water are added to 400 ml of water, what is the percent of increase?

6. Norman had 50 liters of gas in his tank. He used 10 liters on Monday and 12 liters on Tuesday. What percent of gas remained in the tank?

7. John invested $1,000. At the end of the year, his investment was worth $1,040. What percent of profit did John make on his investment?

8. Margaret had $1,000. She spent $200 and then she spent $\frac{1}{4}$ of the remaining money. What percent of her original money does Margaret have now?

9. An emergency clinic treated 1,500 people for the flu in one year. During the next year, only 1,200 people were treated. What was the percent of decrease? Solve this in three different ways.

Method 1   Method 2   Method 3

10. Your department budget increased from $300,000 to $500,000 from one year to the next. What was the percent of increase?

11. A store gave discounts of 20% and then 10%. Is this the same as giving a discount of 30%?   Use $100 as the amount.
Explain

12. By what percent must you increase $2,000 in order to have $3,000?

13. By what percent must you decrease $3,000 in order to have $2,000?

14. The membership fee of a golf club was $300. The membership fee increased by 40% during the following year. What was the new membership fee?

SELF-ASSESSMENT of the ATTAINMENT of the OBJECTIVES

	5	4	3	2	1
- explain the meaning of percent					
- change a percent to a common fraction					
- change a percent to a decimal fraction					
- change a common fraction to a percent					
- change a decimal fraction to a percent					
- add percents correctly					
- subtract percents correctly					
- multiply percents correctly					
- divide percents correctly					
- determine the percent of a number					
- calculate percentage discounts					
- calculate percentage markups					
- increase a number by a certain percent					
- decrease a number by a certain percent					
- determine the percentage of increase of a number					
- determine the percentage of decrease of a number					
- solve problems using percent					

Score /85   Date _____

Unit 12—The Solution of Equations

OBJECTIVES

- solve linear equations by using the cancellation properties
- solve equations that contain fractions
- demonstrate that if $\frac{a}{b} = \frac{c}{d}$, then $\frac{a}{c} = \frac{b}{d}$
- demonstrate the rationale for "cross multiplication"
- solve equations in which variables are used in fractions
- solve problems using equations

Solving Equations by Using the Cancellation Properties

Equations may be solved by using the properties of cancellation.
If equals are added to equals, the sums are equal. Example: if n = 7 then
n + 3 = 7 + 3.

If equals are subtracted from equals, the differences are equal.
Example: if n + 3 = 7 then n + 3 − 4 = 7 − 4 .

If equals are multiplied by equals, the products are equal.
Example: if n = 3 then 4n = 4 x 3.

If equals are divided by equals, the quotients are equal.
Example: if 3n = 6 then 3n ÷ 3 = 6 ÷ 3.

Example 1: If n − 3 = 7, then n − 3 + 3 = 7 + 3. Note that we have added 3 to each side of the equation. If n + 0 = 10 (0 is the additive identity) then n = 10.

Notice that we can substitute the value, n = 10 in the original equation, n − 3 = 7. Substituting 10 for n, we have 10 − 3 = 7 which is a correct statement.

Example 2: If 7n + 4 = 18, then 7n + 4 − 4 = 18 − 4 (equals are subtracted from equals).

Therefore, 7n + 0 = 14 (− 4 and 4 are additive inverses) and 7n = 14 (0 is the additive identity) and n = 2 (each side is divided by 7, that is, equals have been divided by equals). Check by substituting n by 2 in the original equation.

Example 3: if $\frac{1}{2}$n = 7, then n = 14 (multiply each side of the equation by 2).

Example 4: If $\frac{5}{6}$n = 15, then $\frac{5}{6}$n x $\frac{6}{5}$ = 15 x $\frac{6}{5}$ (multiply each side by $\frac{6}{5}$) and n = 18.
$\frac{5}{6}$ x $\frac{6}{5}$ = 1, and 15 x $\frac{6}{5}$ = 18.

Example 5: If 4n = 20, then 4n ÷ 4 = 20 ÷ 4 or n = 5.

Example 6: If $\frac{2}{3}n + \frac{5}{6} = \frac{11}{12}$ (the fractions can be eliminated by multiplying each term by 12 to obtain) 8n + 10 = 11. Subtract 10 from each side. 8n = 1 and therefore, n = $\frac{1}{8}$. Divide each side by 8.

Or, $\frac{5}{6}$ can be subtracted from both sides and we now have $\frac{2}{3}n = \frac{1}{12}$. Multiply each side by $\frac{3}{2}$ and the result is n = $\frac{1}{8}$.

Solving Equations in which Both Sides are Fractions

If $\frac{a}{b} = \frac{c}{d}$, then $\frac{a}{b} \times bd = \frac{c}{d} \times bd$ (equals multiplied by equals are equal). Therefore, ad = bc. (This used to be known as cross multiplication. Most people did it but they didn't know why.)

The mathematical operation provided above is often seen in the form:

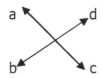

In the same way, if $\frac{a}{b} = \frac{c}{d}$ then $\frac{a}{c} = \frac{b}{d}$.

Cross multiply. ad = bc (see above).

Divide each side by cd. $\frac{ad}{cd} = \frac{bc}{cd} \rightarrow \frac{a}{c} = \frac{b}{d}$ (reduce fractions).

Example 1: if $\frac{n}{3} = \frac{1}{2}$, then 2n = 3 (multiply each side by 3 x 2 or 6 or cross multiply).

n = $\frac{3}{2}$ (divide each side by 2).

Or, using the above, if $\frac{a}{b} = \frac{c}{d}$, then $\frac{a}{c} = \frac{b}{d}$ and $\frac{n}{1} = \frac{3}{2}$. Therefore, 2n = 3 and

n = $\frac{3}{2}$.

Example 2: if $\frac{x + 3}{x - 4} = \frac{3}{5}$, then

$\quad\quad\quad\quad$ 5(x + 3) = 3(x − 4)$\quad$multiply each side by 5(x − 4) or cross multiply
$\quad\quad\quad\quad$ 5x + 15 = 3x − 12$\quad$distributive property of multiplication with
$\quad\quad\quad\quad\quad\quad\quad\quad\quad\quad\quad\quad\quad\quad$respect to addition
$\quad\quad\quad\quad$ 2x = 27$\quad\quad\quad\quad\quad\quad$subtract 3x and 15 from each side
$\quad\quad\quad\quad$ x = $-\frac{27}{2}$ or $-13\frac{1}{2}$$\quad$divide each side by 2

After a clear concept of the use of the axioms of equality is obtained, it is much easier to think of the first step as cross multiplying. If a person asks you for the justification of cross multiplying, you should be able to respond correctly and with understanding.

Note that x was used as the variable. Any letter may be used as the variable.
It is a good idea to check the solution of an equation by substituting the value of the variable in the original equation. For example, if $3n + 7 = 28$, the solution is $n = 7$. Substituting 7 for the variable, the original equation becomes $3(7) + 7 = 28$ or $21 + 7 = 28$.

Solving Equations in which Variables are Used in Fractions

Sometimes it will be necessary to use cross multiplication to solve equations in which one or more variables are used.

Example 1: Solve $\frac{x+2}{4} = \frac{x-2}{3}$

$$\rightarrow \quad 4(x - 2) = 3(x + 2)$$
$$\rightarrow \quad 4x - 8 = 3x + 6$$
$$\rightarrow \quad x = 14$$

Example 2: Solve $\frac{x+3}{x-1} = \frac{x-2}{x-3}$

$$(x + 3)(x - 3) = (x - 1)(x - 2)$$

$$
\begin{array}{r}
x + 3 \\
\underline{x - 3} \\
x^2 + 3x \\
\underline{-3x - 9} \\
= x^2 \quad\quad -9
\end{array}
$$

Note that the distributive property was used in the above multiplication. It will also be used in the multiplication that follows.

$$(x - 1)(x - 2) =
\begin{array}{r}
x - 1 \\
\underline{= x - 2} \\
x^2 - x \\
\underline{-2x +2} \\
= x^2 - 3x +2
\end{array}
$$

Therefore, $x^2 - 9 = x^2 - 3x + 2$.
$$\rightarrow 3x = 11 \text{ or } x = \frac{11}{3} \text{ or } 3\frac{2}{3}$$

Using the cancellation property, x^2 was subtracted from each side. Then 3x was added to each side. Then 9 was added to each side to produce $3x = 11$. Divide each side by 3 to determine that $x = \frac{11}{3}$ or $3\frac{2}{3}$.

179

Exercise 55

1. Solve each of the following:

a) $n + 2 = 14$

b) $n - 5 = 11$

c) $n - 3 = 15$

d) $3n + 5 = 20$

e) $6n - 7 = 11$

f) $4n + 5 = 2n + 9$

g) $\frac{2}{3}p + 5 = 17$

h) $\frac{4}{5}p - 2 = 10$

i) $\frac{3}{4}p + \frac{1}{2} = \frac{5}{8}$

j) $\frac{n}{3} = \frac{1}{3}$

k) $\frac{5}{p} = \frac{2}{5}$

l) $\frac{2}{3} = \frac{x}{6}$

m) $\frac{n + 2}{4} = \frac{5}{6}$

n) $\frac{1}{n + 3} = 5$

o) $\frac{2}{3} = \frac{4}{n + 2}$

2. A number minus $7\frac{1}{4} = 10\frac{3}{4}$. What is the number?

3. 52 less than 8 times a number is 12. What is the number?

4. Solve each of the following:

a) $\frac{x + 4}{x + 3} = \frac{x - 2}{x - 4}$

b) $\frac{x - 5}{x + 3} = \frac{x - 1}{x + 4}$

c) $\dfrac{x+6}{x-2} = \dfrac{x+4}{x+2}$

d) $\dfrac{x+4}{x-5} = \dfrac{x+4}{x+5}$

Unit 13 – Ratios

OBJECTIVES

- solve problems using proportions
- solve problems using ratios

A ratio is a fraction. A proportion is the statement of equality between two ratios. $\frac{1}{2}$ is a ratio, $\frac{1}{2} = \frac{2}{4}$ is a proportion.

Ratios may be understood by an examination of the following problems.

Example 1: If 6 scoops of coffee make a pot of 10 cups of coffee, how many scoops are required to make 25 cups of coffee?

This may be written as 6 scoops is to 10 cups as n scoops is to 25 cups which is sometimes written as 6 : 10 = n : 25.

Or, it may be written as $\frac{6 \text{ scoops}}{10 \text{ cups}} = \frac{n \text{ scoops}}{25 \text{ cups}}$ or $\frac{6}{10} = \frac{n}{25}$

To solve this equation, we write it as 6 x 25 = 10n or 150 = 10n $\rightarrow$ n = 15.

Note that if $\frac{6}{10} = \frac{n}{25}$ then it is also true that $\frac{6}{n} = \frac{10}{25}$. 10n = 150 and n = 15.

Example 2: If 5 kg of grapes can be bought for $4.60, what is the cost of 7 kg?

Method 1: we are saying that the number of kg is to the cost as the number of kg is to the cost.
$\frac{5}{4.60} = \frac{7}{n}$ $\rightarrow$ 5n = 32.20 $\rightarrow$ n = 6.44

Therefore, the cost of 7 kg is $6.44.

In Method 2: we compare the number of kg to the number of kg and the cost to the cost.

$\frac{5}{7} = \frac{4.60}{n}$ $\rightarrow$ 5n = 32. 20 or n = 6. 44.

In Method 3: we find the cost of 1 kg. If 5 kg cost $4.60, then 1 kg costs $\frac{4.60}{5}$ = .92. Therefore, 7 kg costs 7 x .92 = $6.44.

Exercise 56

1. The ratio of one side of a shape is to its perimeter as 1 : 3. Could the shape be a triangle, a square, a rectangle? Give an example for each Yes answer. Explain if the answer is No.

Triangle   Explain

Square   Explain

Rectangle   Explain

2. It takes 2 kg of soybeans to make 5 kg of tofu. List three equivalent ratios of soybeans to tofu.   How many kilograms of soybeans does it take to make 35 kg of tofu?   How much tofu is made from 100 kg of soybeans?   Use two methods for the solution of each of the last two questions.

3. Is the ratio $\frac{3}{1}$ the same as the ratio $\frac{1}{3}$?   Explain

4. If a box can be filled in 20 seconds, how long will it take to fill 15 boxes? Solve this in two different ways.

5. If 1,000 watches cost $74,000, what is the cost of 10 watches? Solve this in two different ways.

6. Solve by using ratios. A man can cut a log in fourths in 12 minutes. How long will it take him to cut the same log into sixths?

7. A punch contains orange juice, mango juice, and ginger ale. The amount of orange juice to mango juice is 2 : 1, ginger ale to mango juice is 3 : 1. What is the ratio of orange juice to ginger ale?

8. Shirley used 3 tablespoons of baking soda to make 2 cakes. How many tablespoons of baking soda would she use to make 5 cakes? Solve this in two different ways.

9. Graham used 12 tiles to cover $\frac{2}{3}$ of his floor. How many tiles will he need to cover the entire floor? Solve this in two different ways.

10. John spent .25¢ on public transportation for every $2.00 earned. He earned $80 each day that he used public transportation. How much did he spend daily on transportation? Solve this in two different ways.

11. Observe the following colored cards.

W	G	B	Y	G	Y	W	B	Y	B
G	B	Y	G	Y	W	G	Y	Y	Y

a) What is the ratio of the white cards to the total number of cards?

What fraction of the cards is white?

What percent of the cards are white?

What decimal fraction of the cards is white?

b) What is the ratio of the blue cards to the yellow cards?

What fraction of the blue cards and the yellow cards are blue?

184

What decimal fraction of the blue cards and the yellow cards are blue?

What percent of the blue and yellow cards are blue?

c) What is the ratio of the green cards to the yellow cards?

What is the fraction of the green cards to the yellow cards?

What percent of the green and yellow cards are green?

d) What is the ratio of the blue cards to the white and green cards?

SELF-ASSESSMENT of the ATTAINMENT of the OBJECTIVES

5	4	3	2	1

- solve problems using proportions
- solve problems using ratios

Score   /10   Date _____

Section V – Decimal Fractions, Percent, The Solution of Equations, Ratios
Post–Test V

Answers can be found at the end of the book.

1. a) Increase 40 by 0.3   b) Increase 40 by $\frac{3}{10}$ c) Increase 40 by 30%

   d) Decrease 36 by 0.4   e) Decrease 100 by 20%   f) Decrease 30 by 80%

2.   Change each of the following to decimal fractions:

   a) $\frac{2}{3} =$ b) $\frac{7}{10} =$ c) $\frac{1}{2} =$ d) $\frac{1}{8} =$

3. Change each of the following to proper fractions.

   a) 0.35 =   b) 0.01 =   c) 0.63 =   d) 0.99 =

4. John earned $36,000 a year. The company offered each employee a bonus of 0.2 of his/her salary. How much money did John earn as a bonus?

5. Mary was offered a 3% increase on her salary of $27,000. What is her new salary?

6. Perform the following operations.
   a) 2. 6   b) 6. 8   c) 2. 4   d) $0.133\overline{)0.338}$
   $\underline{+\ 5.\ 7}$ $\underline{-\ 2.\ 5}$ $\underline{x\ 3.\ 2}$

186

7. Jack had a bucket of apples. He used 55% of the apples to make pies. What fraction of the apples was not used?

8. Shade the area according to the percent indicated.

a) 35%

b) 40%

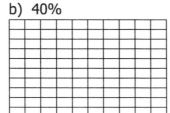

c) 60%

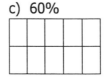

d) 10%

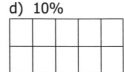

9. Change 24% to a decimal fraction and to a proper fraction.

decimal fraction   proper fraction

10. What is 10% of 15?

11. Harold spent 35% of $200. James spent 45% of $150. Who spent more money and by how much?

12. The selling price of a tool was $125. The salesman offered a discount of 20%. At what price was the tool sold?

13. a) Increase 75 by 20%   b) Decrease 250 by 24%

14. A house was listed at $230,000. The buyer received a 5% discount for paying immediately. The buyer then had to pay 12% taxes on the amount paid. What was the total amount paid?

15. What percent is 5 of 35?

16. If 250 ml of water are added to 400 ml of water, what is the percent of increase?

17. By what percent must you decrease 3,000 to get 2,000?

18. Solve each of the following:

a) $4n + 5 = 2n + 9$ b) $\dfrac{3}{4p} + \dfrac{1}{2} = \dfrac{5}{8}$ c) $\dfrac{2}{3} = \dfrac{x}{8}$

19. If it takes 2 kg of soybeans to make 5 kg of tofu, how much tofu is made from 100 kg of soybeans?

Score _____   Date _____

188

Section VI— Problem Solving Strategies
Pre–Test VI

Answers can be found at the back of the book.

1. What is the probability that two dice will have the same number on one throw of a pair of dice?

2. How many positive proper fractions in simplest form have denominators of 100?

3. If the area of a rectangle is 48 cm^2, what are the measures of the sides of the rectangles that can be formed?

4. If Peter had $7 more, he would have had three times as much as Donald. Donald had $5. How much money did Peter have?

5. Jack and Dan together weigh 118 kg. Dan is nine times heavier than Jack. How many kg does Dan weigh?

6. If in an army there is 1 officer for every 15 privates, how many officers are there in a corps consisting of 1,200 officers and privates?

7. The length of a square floor is 8 meters. Only square tiles of length of $\frac{1}{2}$ m are available. How many tiles are needed to cover the floor?

8. Write a number between 1 and 100. Add 5 to the number. Multiply this number by 2. Add 10 to this number. Multiply this number by 5. Repeat this three times using a different starting number. Compare the starting number to the result in each case and describe the pattern. (Use a separate piece of paper.)

9. List all four-digit numbers that can be made with the digits 3 and 5.

10. Using the 8 digit only, construct an addition problem such that the sum of the numbers is 1,000.

11. One number is multiplied by 100. Another number is divided by 100. The results are the same. What are the numbers?

12. List another pair of numbers that satisfy the conditions of number 11.

13. For every performer in a concert who frowned there were 6 who smiled. 66 performers smiled. How many performers were there?

14. Share 36 coins among four people so that two of them get two more coins than the other people. How many coins does each person get?

15. Steve was born in February 1958 and his daughter, Angela, was born in October 1981. In what year was Angela half the age of Steve?

16. Paul wanted to paint the walls of his living room. One wall measured 5 m by 7 m: the second had a surface of 4 m x 7 m: another wall had a surface of 6 m x 7 m; and the fourth wall had a measure of 5 m x 7 m. Paint was sold in liter cans. Paul was told that it will require 1 can of paint to cover 40 m^2. The cost of each can was $15.65. How much did Paul pay for the paint?

17. If a mango costs 35 cents, an apple 30 cents, a banana 15 cents, an orange 10 cents, and a pineapple 25 cents, list all of the sets of three fruits that Margaret could have bought for exactly 75 cents.

18. If the product of two numbers is 87, what is their sum? Give two answers.

19. If 10 horses can eat 10 sacks of oats in 10 days, how many days will it take 1 horse to eat one sack of oats?

Score _____   Date _____

Unit 14 — Problem Solving Strategies

OBJECTIVES

- solve problems that have one solution
- solve problems that have a finite number of solutions
- solve problems that have an infinite number of solutions
- solve problems that have no solution
  use the following strategies for solving problems
- dramatize it
- draw a diagram
- guess and test
- extend the thought beyond the problem
- look for a pattern
- create a simpler problem
- list all of the possibilities
- try special numbers or cases
- work backwards
- solve part of the problem and make a conjecture
- find a counter example
- use definitions
- use formulas
- use properties of the number system

Problem Solving

Problem solving is one of the most important components of a mathematics curriculum. Many problems have been solved in previous Units. However, a specific approach to the solutions was not necessary because the problems resulted from information that was provided in the text and as part of the examples. Most of the problems required one-step solutions and a few others required two-step solutions.

A problem with one solution: the score in a football game is 3 − 0 for the Red team. Then the Blue team scored 7 points. By how many points is the Blue team winning?

7 − 3 = 4. In this problem, the only answer is 4 and it is found using one operation only.

A problem with a finite number of solutions: find all rectangles that have an area of 24 cm².

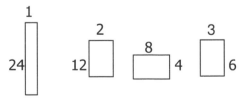

A problem with an infinite number of solutions is: n + 3 > 5. This problem is asking us to find a number which when added to 3 is greater than 5. Solution: any number greater than 2 will satisfy this statement. Therefore, the solutions are 3, 4, 5, 6, and so on if we are considering the Natural numbers. If we are considering the Real numbers, the solution will be "any number greater than two".

A problem with no solution: Find an even number and an odd number whose product is odd. Solution: It is not sufficient to say, "I can't". An explanation is necessary. It must be understood that if an even number is one of the factors, then that even number must be a factor of the product and therefore, the product must be even. Therefore, the solution is that there is no solution.

Strategies for Solving Problems

Dramatize It

One of the easiest ways to solve a problem is to devise a plan to act it out.

Example: John has 7 markers. He places 6 in one hand and 1 in the other hand. Which hand has 6 markers in it? Let John make the choice without your seeing it. Now ask John to multiply the number of markers in the right hand by 3 and the number of markers in the left hand by 2. If the 6 markers are in his right hand, his answer will be 20. If the six markers are in his left hand, his answer will be 15.

Draw a Diagram

Sometimes a problem may be difficult to solve because it is difficult to obtain a mental picture of the problem. When this occurs, draw a diagram.

Example: Ruth has a rectangular cake that is 24 cm^2. She wants to cut it into 36 equal pieces. How many cuts of the cake must be made?

By drawing a diagram, it becomes evident that it requires five cuts to make six pieces. Notice that it requires 5 cuts to make 6 pieces up and down (vertical cuts) and it takes 5 cuts horizontally to make 6 pieces.

Therefore, Ruth has to cut the cake 10 times in order to make 36 pieces.

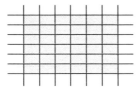

Guess and Test

Example: Use a calculator, any of the four basic operations (addition, subtraction, multiplication and division) and the numbers 17, 35, 7, and 60 to calculate as close as possible to the number 5,101. The solution of this problem requires a number of trials. There is no direct method for solving the problem. After a number of trials, it might be found that 17 x 35 = 595. 595 ÷ 7 = 85, 85 x 60 = 5,100 and this is the closest number to 5,101 that can result.

Extend the Thought Beyond the Problem

Example 1: The Magic Triangle was introduced in Unit I. The problem was to place the numbers 1, 2, 3, 4, 5 and 6 in the triangle such that the sum of the numbers on each side is equal to 9. The following is one solution.

Example 2. John and Jane solved this problem together and John asked what would happen if the numbers to be added were 7, 8, 9, 10, 11 and 12. They tried these numbers and found that the following resulted. In each case, the sum is 27.

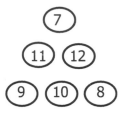

Example 3. Then Jane wondered what would happen if odd numbers only were used. It was decided to use the numbers 1, 3, 5, 7, 9 and 11. The following resulted. The sum in each case is 15.

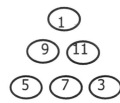

Example 4. John wondered if a generalization could be made. It was decided to use the numbers $n-3$, $n-2$, $n-1$, n, $n+1$ and $n+2$. The following resulted.

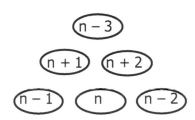

In this case, the sum of each side is $3n - 3$ where n is any number. This will be true as long as the numbers are consecutive.

The placement of the numbers in each figure is consistent, i.e. note the placement of the numbers with the greatest magnitude and the least magnitude and note the base of the triangle.

Each of the above Examples has alternate solutions that can be seen by alternating the positioning of the numbers.

Look for a Pattern

Example:

$1 = 1$
$1 + 3 = 4$
$1 + 3 + 5 = 9$

What do you notice about the numbers to the left of the equal sign? They are odd numbers and each new set of numbers consists of the addition of the next odd number. What do you notice about the numbers to the right of the equal sign? They are squared numbers and the number which is squared is equal to the number of addends to the left of the equal sign. $1 = 1$ and there is one term to the left of the equal sign. $4 = 1 + 3$ and this is the sum of the first 2 odd numbers, 1 and 3. $9 = 1 + 3 + 5$ and this is the sum of the first three odd numbers.

Two conjectures may be made from the above information. The next term in the series will contain the next odd number, 7 and the sum of these numbers will be 16-four being the number of addends. Therefore, the next line will be $1 + 3 + 5 + 7 = 16$. From this information we can determine the sum of the first n odd numbers. For example, the sum of the first 10 odd numbers is 100. The sum of the first n odd numbers is n^2.

We have made a conjecture based on three examples. You are sometimes right and sometimes wrong when you make a conjecture.

Let us make the conjecture that $n^2 - n + 41$ is a prime number. (A prime number is a number greater than 1 that has no factors other than 1 and itself.) We will begin by substituting numbers for n.

If $n = 1$, $n^2 - n + 41 =$ 41   which is prime
    $n = 2$, $n^2 - n + 41 =$ 43   which is prime
    $n = 3$, $n^2 - n + 41 =$ 47   which is prime
    $n = 4$, $n^2 - n + 41 =$ 53   which is prime
    $\vdots$
    $n = 11$, $n^2 - n + 41 =$ 151   which is prime
    $\vdots$
    $n = 17$, $n^2 - n + 41 =$ 313   which is prime
    $\vdots$
    $n = 20$, $n^2 - n + 41 =$ 421   which is prime
    $\vdots$
    $n = 40$, $n^2 - n + 41 =$ 1601   which is prime

We can see that the first 40 numbers are prime numbers. (Check them if you wish.) However, if we substitute n by 41 we have $(41)^2 - 41 + 41$ which equals $(41)^2$ and this is not a prime number because it has two factors of 41. This is called a counter-example and only one of these is needed to show that the conjecture is not true in all cases. When we discover a counter-example, it can be determined when a condition can be satisfied and when it cannot be satisfied.

Do the Problem

Example: Toss a pair of dice a number of times and record the positive difference of the number of dots showing upwards. Most people will jump to the conclusion that since there is an equal likelihood (probability) of each of the six dotted sides of a die landing upwards, there will be an equal number of positive differences. Try all possible results of tossing a pair of dice and list the difference for each. The possible differences are:

$6 - 1 = 5$	$5 - 1 = 4$	$4 - 1 = 3$	$3 - 1 = 2$	$2 - 1 = 1$	$1 - 1 = 0$
$6 - 2 = 4$	$5 - 2 = 3$	$4 - 2 = 2$	$3 - 2 = 1$	$2 - 2 = 0$	$1 - 2 = 1$
$6 - 3 = 3$	$5 - 3 = 2$	$4 - 3 = 1$	$3 - 3 = 0$	$2 - 3 = 1$	$1 - 3 = 2$
$6 - 4 = 2$	$5 - 4 = 1$	$4 - 4 = 0$	$3 - 4 = 1$	$2 - 4 = 2$	$1 - 4 = 3$
$6 - 5 = 1$	$5 - 5 = 0$	$4 - 5 = 1$	$3 - 5 = 2$	$2 - 5 = 3$	$1 - 5 = 4$
$6 - 6 = 0$	$5 - 6 = 1$	$4 - 6 = 2$	$3 - 6 = 3$	$2 - 6 = 4$	$1 - 6 = 5$

The range of results is 0 to 5. Why? The range is the difference between the highest and the lowest number.

Count the number of times each difference occurs. This is called the frequency of events and the results are called the theoretical probability.

Zero results 6 times, one 10 times, two 8 times, three 6 times, four 4 times, five 2 times. We can say that the probability of the difference being 0 is $\frac{6}{36}$. But, for example, the probability of the difference being 1 is $\frac{10}{36}$.

If you are in a classroom setting, each person should toss a pair of dice 10 times and record the positive differences. Examine how close they are to the theoretical probability. The teacher should have each participant in the class provide his/her results that will be charted for everyone to see. There is a strong likelihood that the average of the results tabulated will be closer to the theoretical probability than most of the results of the participants. This is due to the fact that the greater the sample provided, the closer the results will tend towards the theoretical probability. Repeat the tossing of dice a number of times to ensure that you have a sufficient sample.

Exercise 57

1. What is the probability of getting a positive difference of 5 with 1 throw of a pair of dice?   List these

2. What is the probability that the 2 dice will have the same number on 1 toss of a pair of dice?   List the possibilities

3. If a mango costs 35 cents, an apple 30 cents, a banana 15 cents, an orange 10 cents, and a pineapple 25 cents, what 3 fruits could Margaret have bought for exactly 75 cents.

4. If the product of 2 positive prime numbers (a prime number is a number greater than 1 that is divisible by 1 and itself only) is 87, what is their sum? List two results.
    and   .

5. A pie in the form of a circle is cut into 12 equal pieces. What is the measure of the angle of each piece?

Explain

6. Use each of the numbers 5, 32, 46, and 63 once in any combination. Find a series of operations that will result in a number close to 3. Use a calculator. Guess and test.

7) You have a wooden cube. You want to color the cube so that no two faces bordering on one another will have the same color. Is this possible?

Explain

8. If the perimeter of a rectangle is 48 square units, what are the measures of the sides of the rectangles that are possible? How many rectangles are possible?

List them

9. List all of the rectangles that you can make using 36 tiles (1 cm^2 each).

10. Write a method for finding the sum of the first n positive whole numbers where n is an even number.

11. The number 9238 has this property: the thousands digit is odd, the hundreds digit is even, and all four digits are different. How many four-digit numbers have this property?

12. Margaret, Denise, Maureen, and Stacey exchanged Valentine's cards. How many cards were sent?

13. If 10 horses eat 10 sacks of oats in 10 days, how many days will it take 1 horse to eat 1 sack of oats?

14. If Peter had $7 more, he would have 3 times as much as Donald. Donald had $5. How much money did Peter have?

15. a) How many $10 bills are there in 1 million dollars?

   b) How many $100 bills are there in 6 million dollars?

16. A businessman was traveling in a foreign country. The exchange rate on the dollar was 190. At breakfast the traveler noted that the bill was 2850 in the local currency or $15.83 in dollars. The businessman paid in local currency. Did he save or lose money?
Explain

17. Jack and Don together weigh 118 kg. Don is 9 kg heavier than Jack. How many kg does Don weigh?

18. Peter is half as old again as his brother who is ten years younger than Peter. How old is Peter?

9. The sum of Helen's marks in Mathematics and English was 124. She was lower than Betty in Mathematics by 3 marks although she got 4 more marks in Mathematics than in English. What was Betty's mark in Mathematics?

20. Elizabeth had set aside an amount for charitable donations. She gave half of her money and an additional $150 to her favorite charity. She has $400 left. What amount did Elizabeth set aside for charitable donations?

21. A roll of 10 dollar bills was divided among a group of men in such a manner that Ken got exactly 3 times as much as each of the others. If his share is $\frac{1}{4}$ of all the money, how many men were in the group?

22. A work crew ordered the following: 1 pizza for every 2 workers: 1 bag of chips for every 3 workers: 1 large cola for every 4 workers. 26 items were delivered. How many people ate?

23. 52 less than 8 times a number is 12. What is the number?

24. Sheila has $4.40 in quarters, dimes, and nickels. She has the same number of each coin. How many of each type does she have?

25. Place a number in each of the triangles so that the sum of any two triangles is equal to the number in the circle between them.

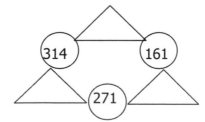

26. If 1 blue equals 3 greens, 6 reds equal 3 blues, and 3 yellows equal 9 reds, then 10 yellows will equal how many greens?

27. If in the army there is 1 officer for every 15 privates, how many officers are there in a corps consisting of 1,200 officers and privates?

28. Dr. Brown prescribed 4 pills to be taken, one every half hour. How long will it take to finish this medication?

29. How many positive proper fractions in simplest form have a denominator of 100?

30. The numbers from 1 to 600 are placed in a box. What is the probability that a number chosen at random will be divisible by 7 and 13?

31. Elizabeth baked a cake for the whole family. Dad ate $\frac{1}{6}$ of the cake. Bill ate $\frac{1}{5}$ of the remaining cake; Delores ate $\frac{1}{4}$ of the cake that remained after Bill took his piece; Shirley ate $\frac{1}{3}$ of what now remained; and Bobby ate $\frac{1}{2}$ of what remained after Shirley took her piece. How much of the original cake was left for Elizabeth to eat? Who ate the most cake?

Elizabeth ate   of the cake.   ate the most cake.

32. Use the magic triangle and the numbers 1, 2, 3, 5, 6, 7 so that the sum of the numbers on the three sides of the triangle will be the same. Do this in more than 1 way.

More Strategies for Problem Solving

Create A Simpler Problem

We have seen an example of this in the previous exercises.

Example: Find the sum of the numbers from 1 to 100. Develop a simpler problem.

Find the sum of the numbers from 1 to 10.

| 1 | 2 | 3 | 4 | 5 | 6 | 7 | 8 | 9 | 10 |

We note that $1 + 10 = 11$, $2 + 9 = 11$, $3 + 8 = 11$, $4 + 7 = 11$, $5 + 6 = 11$. There are 5 pairs of numbers each equal to 11. Therefore, the sum of the numbers is 5 x 11 or 55.

We can now add $1 + 2 + 3 + \ldots + 98 + 99 + 100$ by recognizing that there are 50 pairs of numbers each equal to 101. Therefore, the sum of the numbers from 1 to 100 is 50 x 101 which equals $50(100 + 1) = 5,000 + 50$ or 5,050.

If the number of terms to be added is odd, add all but the last number by the method shown above and then add the last number. For example, we would add
$1 + 2 + 3 + \ldots + 65 + 66 + 67$ by adding the first 66 numbers and then add 67.
$1 + 2 + 3 + \ldots + 65 + 66 = 33 \times 67$ which is 2,211 and to this we must add 67 to give us the sum 2,278.

Or, we could add the numbers $2 + 3 + 4 + \ldots + 65 + 66 + 67$ and then add 1 to this sum. $2 + 3 + 4 + \ldots + 65 + 66 + 67 = 33 \times 69$ which is 2,277 and to this we must add 1 to give us the sum 2,278.

List All of the Possibilities

Example: Under what conditions will the product of two positive whole numbers be an odd number?
even x even = even (There are two even numbers in the product.)
even x odd = even (There is one even number in the product.)
odd x even = even (There is one even number in the product.)
odd x odd = odd   (No even number is contained in the product.)

If no even number is contained in the factors, then no factor of 2 will be contained in the product.

Therefore, all factors must be odd for the product to be odd.

Try Special Numbers or Cases

Example: Which of the following shapes has exactly 4 lines of symmetry – a square, a rectangle, a circle? (A line of symmetry means that if the shape is folded on that line, the two parts of the shape will match exactly, i.e. one part will cover the other part exactly.) Construct a square and then draw lines of symmetry:

Note that a square has four lines of symmetry. However, a rectangle has only two lines of symmetry. At first glance, it may appear that the diagonals will be lines of symmetry. When we try to fold a rectangular piece of paper along the diagonal, it will be noted that the one part will not cover the other part. Try it.

Note that there are more than four lines of symmetry in a circle. In fact, there are an infinite number of such lines. Any line connecting two points on the circumference and passing through the center will form a line of symmetry. Therefore, among the three shapes, only a square has exactly four lines of symmetry.

Work Backwards

Example: The problem is, John started with the number 5 and performed three operations and the result of his computations was 327. Instead of starting at five and work upwards, you can also start at 327 to get to 5. The digits of the number 327 have a sum that is divisible by 3. Therefore, divide 327 by 3 to obtain 109. Since you know that 5 is a factor of 100, subtract 9 from 109 to obtain 100. Divide 100 by 20 to obtain 5.

If for some reason you were required to start at 5, you know what to do. Multiply by 20: add 9: multiply by 3. (Do this on a separate piece of paper.)

Solve Part of the Problem and Make a Conjecture

Example: Using the digits 4, 2, 7, 5, determine how many four-digit numbers can be written using each digit only once. If we write the first four-digit number as 4,275, then the numbers in which 4 is in the thousands position are: 4,257, 4,275, 4,572, 4,527, 4,725 and 4,752.

Note that if one digit – in this case 4 – is in the thousands position, 6 four-digit numbers may be written. The writing of 6 numbers of 4 digits will result regardless of the number placed in the thousands position. There are 4 choices for a number in the thousands position and for each of these placements, 6 four-digit numbers may be written. Therefore, the total number of four-digit numbers that may be written is 4 x 6 or 24. It should be noted that this will occur only when there is no 0 in the numbers and there are no repetitions of digits in the numbers. Think about this for a moment.

Find a Counter-example

This strategy is usually used to disprove a statement. Having a large number of examples in which a statement is true does not prove that the statement is true. On the other hand, one example of the statement being false is all that is required to render the statement false. Such a statement is called a counter-example.

Example: Robert said that one fraction is greater than another if the numerator and the denominator of the fraction are greater than the numerator and the denominator of the other fraction. He listed many examples such as $\frac{3}{5} > \frac{1}{2}$, $\frac{3}{4} > \frac{2}{3}$, $\frac{2}{7} > \frac{1}{5}$.

Then Helen interrupted Robert by giving the example of $\frac{3}{5}$ and $\frac{2}{3}$. 3 is greater than 2 and 5 is greater than 3, but $\frac{3}{5}$ is not greater than $\frac{2}{3}$. This example is called a counter-example.

Use Definitions

Many problems may be solved by the use of definitions. For example, when finding the area of a square shape, we note that the four sides are equal and the four angles are right angles by definition. Therefore, if we want to lay tiles on a square floor, we can determine the area of the floor and we know that each corner is a right angle.

Example: The length of a square floor is 8 meters. Therefore, the area of the floor is 64 m². Square tiles are available only in length of $\frac{1}{2}$ m. We know that 4 tiles of $\frac{1}{2}$ m² are required to cover 1 m². Therefore, 64 x 4 or 256 tiles are required to cover the floor.

Use Formulas

We can use formulas that were learned earlier in our study of mathematics.

Example 1: We have seen earlier that the sum of the interior angles of a regular polygon is (the number of sides − 2) x 180° or (n − 2) x 180°. If a regular polygon has 8 sides, then the sum of the interior angles is 6 x 180° or 1,080°.

Example 2: Find the measure of each angle in a regular hexagon. By definition, a regular hexagon has 6 sides. From the formula above, the sum of the interior angles is 720°. By definition, the interior angles of a regular polygon are equal. Therefore, the measure of each interior angle is 720 ÷ 6 or 120°.

Read The Problem Aloud

Reading the problem aloud will sometimes lead to the solution(s). For example, if we wish to change 0.75 to a common fraction, we will read 0.75 as seventy–five one hundredths. Therefore, we can write this as $\frac{75}{100}$ or $\frac{3}{4}$.

Exercise 58

1. If the numbers on a die were changed to 4, 5, 6, 7, 8, 9, and the die is cast, what is the probability that a 7 will show up?

Explain

2. Without using addition, add the numbers from 1 – 66. Show how you did this.

3. When is the product of two numbers even?

4. List all four-digit numbers that can be made using 1 and 2 only.

5. List all four-digit numbers that can be made with the digits 3 and 5.

6. Continue the pattern for the next three terms of:

   1.2 x 3, 2.3 x 4, 3.4 x 5,

7. Write the numbers as equivalent number sentences so that you can add the following mentally:

55 =
29 =
16 =   55 + 29 + 16 =

8. Use the digit 8 only and construct an addition problem such that the sum of the numbers is 1,000.

9. Use the digit 7 only and construct an addition problem such that the sum is 7,000.

10. Bob said that the answer to his problem is 31. He used three operations. Make a problem using three operations so that the answer will be 31.

11. One number is multiplied by 100. Another number is divided by 100. The results are the same.
What are the numbers?   and

List another pair of such numbers.   and

How many solutions do you think there are?   Explain

12. When the school choir was presenting a concert, for every performer who frowned there were 6 who smiled. There were 66 performers who smiled. How many people were in the choir?

13. Share 36 coins among 4 people o that 2 of them get 2 more coins than the other people. How many coins did each person get?

14. I have twice as many nickels as I have dimes. I have $4.40 in dimes.

How many nickels do I have?

How much money do I have?

15. In the diagram below, use R for red, B for blue, and G for green. Use a different color for each region. Color each region so that no two colors will border on one another.

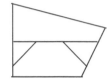

What is your conclusion?

16. Steve was born in February, 1958 and his daughter, Angela, was born in October 1981. In what year was Angela half of the age of Steve?

17. Paul wanted to paint the walls of his living room. One wall measured 5 m x 7 m: the second wall had a surface of 4 m x 7 m: another wall had a surface of 6 m x 7 m; and the fourth wall had a surface of 5 m x 7 m. Paint was sold in liters cans. He was told that 1 can of paint will be required to cover a surface of 40 m^2. The cost of each can was $19.65. How much did Paul pay for the paint?

18. A number of bicycles were bought for $40 each. Three fourths of them sold for $70 each and the remaining bicycles were sold for $30 each. The total profit was $1,200. How many bicycles were bought?

SELF-ASSESSMENT of the ATTAINMENT of the OBJECTIVES

	5	4	3	2	1

- solve problems that have one solution
- solve problems that have a finite number of solutions
- solve problems that have an infinite number of solutions
- solve problems that have no solution
  employ the following strategies for solving problems:
- dramatize it
- draw a diagram
- guess and test
- extend the thought beyond the problem
- look for a pattern
- do the problem
- create a simpler problem
- list all of the possibilities
- try special numbers or cases
- work backwards
- solve part of the problem and make a conjecture
- find a counter-example
- use definitions
- use formulas
- use properties of the number system

Score   /95   Date _____

Section VI—Problem Solving Strategies
Post – Test VI

Answers can be found at the end of the book.

1. What is the probability that two dice will have the same number on one throw of a pair of dice?

2. How many positive proper fractions in simplest form have denominators of 100?

3. If the area of a rectangle is 48 cm^2, what are the measures of the sides of the rectangles that can be formed?

4. If Peter had $7 more, he would have had three times as much as Donald. Donald had $5. How much money did Peter have?

5. Jack and Dan together weigh 118 kg. Dan is nine times heavier than Jack. How many kg does Dan weigh?

6. If in an army there is 1 officer for every 15 privates, how many officers are there in a corps consisting of 1,200 officers and privates?

7. The length of a square floor is 8 meters. Only square tiles of length of $\frac{1}{2}$ m are available. How many tiles are needed to cover the floor?

8. Write a number between 1 and 100. Add 5 to the number. Multiply this number by 2. Add 10 to this number. Multiply this number by 5. Repeat this three times using a different starting number. Compare the starting number to the result in each case and describe the pattern. (Use a separate piece of paper.)

9. List all four-digit numbers that can be made with the digits 3 and 5.

10. Using the 8 digit only, construct an addition problem such that the sum of the numbers is 1,000.

11. One number is multiplied by 100. Another number is divided by 100. The results are the same. What are the numbers?

12. List another pair of numbers that satisfy the conditions of number 11.

13. For every performer in a concert who frowned there were 6 who smiled. 66 performers smiled. How many performers were there?

14. Share 36 coins among four people so that two of them get two more coins than the other people. How many coins does each person get?

15. Steve was born in February 1958 and his daughter, Angela, was born in October 1981. In what year was Angela half the age of Steve?

16. Paul wanted to paint the walls of his living room. One wall measured 5 m by 7 m: the second had a surface of 4 m x 7 m: another wall had a surface of 6 m x 7 m; and the fourth wall had a measure of 5 m x 7 m. Paint was sold in liter cans. Paul was told that it will require 1 can of paint to cover 40 m². The cost of each can was $15.65. How much did Paul pay for the paint?

17. If a mango costs 35 cents, an apple 30 cents, a banana 15 cents, an orange 10 cents, and a pineapple 25 cents, list all of the sets of three fruits that Margaret could have bought for exactly 75 cents.

18. If the product of two numbers is 87, what is their sum? Give two answers.

19. If 10 horses can eat 10 sacks of oats in 10 days, how many days will it take 1 horse to eat one sack of oats?

Score _____   Date _____

Section VII – Simple Interest and Compound Interest, Break-Even Analysis, Frequency Distributions and Measures of Central Tendency, Probability, Practical Applications Of Mathematics
Pre–Test VII

Solutions can be found at the back of the book. Use a calculator if necessary.

1. Andre invested $2,400 at 6%, simple interest, annually for 3 years. How much will the investment be worth at the time of its termination?

2. At what percent must Sally invest $8,000 for 5 years to earn $3,000 in simple interest?

3. Bill was offered a loan of $4,000 at 6% annually and Harry was offered a loan of the same amount at 6% semi-annually. What was the difference in the amounts of interest over the year?

4. What is the effective rate of 8% quarterly? (Use a calculator that has the power key.)

5. Celia invested $3,000 compounded annually for 3 years at the rate of 4%. What was the value of her investment at the termination date?

6. Mary wants to organize a dinner at her club. Determine reasonable costs (both fixed and variable) and determine, by using the break even formula, the cost and the number of people who must attend in order to ensure a profit of $300 for the club.

_____

_____

_____

_____

_____

_____

_____

_____

_____

_____

_____

_____

_____

_____

_____

_____

_____

Cost   Number of people

7. In the year 2000, there were 2,300 births in a city in which the population was 148,500. In the year 1990, there were 1,850 births when the population was 42,000. Determine which year had the higher birth rate.

8. Construct a frequency distribution chart with percents for the following numbers:

32   36   28   27   29   32   29   28   35   36   29   27   28   32   29   27
   36   36   27   32   29   29   32   35   27   32   29   35

9. Paula bought tins of soup with the following capacities: 284 ml, 324 ml, 335 ml, and 265 ml. What was the average capacity of the tins?

212

10. Determine the median of the following weights:

   37 kg, 41 kg, 33 kg, 31 kg, 34 kg, 38 kg, 39 kg, 40 kg, 36 kg.

11. Identify the mode of the following distribution: 27, 30, 28, 30, 27, 28, 32, 30

12. Six white cards and 4 yellow cards were placed in a bag. John was chosen to randomly select 2 cards. What was the probability that both of the cards were white?

13. Two coins were tossed simultaneously. What was the probability that 2 heads faced up?

14. A basketball player scored 77 out of 120 foul shots. What was the player's scoring percent? Express this percent as a 3 decimal number.

percent   decimal number

Score _____   Date _____

Unit 15 — Simple Interest and Compound Interest

Note: The reader should have a calculator that has a power key (y^x).

OBJECTIVES

- demonstrate the use of simple interest
- knowing that I = P x R x T, find P, R, and T
- illustrate the difference between simple and compound interest
- illustrate the difference between the nominal rate and the effective rate

- calculate the effective rate using the formula $E = \left(1 + \frac{r}{n}\right)^n - 1$

- calculate the amount of an investment knowing the Principal and using the formula for the amount $P\left(1 + \frac{r}{n}\right)^{nt}$

Simple Interest

Interest is the amount of money earned (or owed) based on an amount invested (or borrowed) at a given rate.

Simple interest means that the rate remains the same throughout the transaction and no conversions (adding interest at determined intervals) are made. This is different from compound interest in which the interest is added to the principal at specific intervals. We will examine compound interest later in this Unit.

I is the symbol for interest, P stands for principal (amount invested or borrowed), R stands for rate in percent, T stands for time of investment or loan.

The basic formula for simple interest is: I = P x R x T, that is, the interest is equal to the principal multiplied by the rate, multiplied by the time.

Example 1: Patricia invested $500 for 1 year at the rate of 5%. How much was her money worth after 1 year?

I = P x R x T or I = 500 x .05 x 1 = 25.

This tells us that $25 interest was earned.
Therefore, the principal is now $100 + 25 or $125 and the transaction is finished.

Example 2: Heather borrowed $500 for 1 year at the rate of 6%. How much money will she have paid back at the end of the year?

I = P x R x T or I = 500 x .06 x 1 = 30. (In many instances, the interest charges are collected at the beginning of the transaction or throughout the transaction.)

This tells us that Heather will have to pay interest charges of $30. After one year, Heather will have paid $530.

Since I = P x R x T, it follows that $R = \frac{I}{P \times T}$ and $T = \frac{I}{P \times R}$.

Example 3:   Donald invested $600 for 2 years. His interest was $96. At what rate did he invest his money?

$R = \frac{I}{P \times T}$ or $R = \frac{96}{600 \times 2}$ → R = .08 or 8%.

Example 4: For how long will Brenda have to invest $400 at 7% to earn 140?

$T = \frac{I}{P \times R}$ or $T = \frac{140}{400 \times .07}$ → T = 5.

Brenda would have to invest $400 at 7% for 5 years to earn $140 of simple interest.

Example 5: John invested $8,000 for 3 years at 4.5% simple interest. What will be the value of his investment at its termination date?

I = P x R x T   I = 8000 x .045 x 3 or 1080. John will earn $1,080 interest and his investment will be worth 8,000 + 1,080 or $9,080.

If a time period for the transaction is less than one year, the interest is calculated by using 365 days for a year except during a leap year when it is 366 days.

Example 6: Bill borrowed $720 at 6% for 90 days. How much money did he pay at the termination of the loan?

a) Using the accurate interest method, $I = \frac{720 \times .06 \times 90}{365}$ or 10.65.

Therefore, Bill paid $720 + $10.65 or $730.65.

b) Another method for calculating interest is by using the exact time method. For example, if interest was to be accumulated from December 31 until April 15, the number of days would be calculated and this number would be used for the number of days. In this case, the number of days is 105 (106 if it is a Leap Year).

Exercise 59

1.   Andre invested $2,400 at 6% simple interest for 3 years. How much will his investment be worth at the time of its termination?

2. Jean borrowed $3,600 at 5% simple interest for two years. How much will Jean have paid back at the termination of the loan?

3. How many years will it require for Gerry to make at least $30,000 simple interest on an investment of $100,000 at 7%?

4. At what percent must Sally invest $8,000 for 5 years to earn $2,000 simple interest?

5. How much money must Henry invest at 6% for 8 years to earn simple interest of $1,200?

6. Use the exact time method to calculate the simple interest on $10,000 at 5% from January 15 until May 15, 2009.

7. Determine the simple interest on $750 at $7\frac{1}{2}$% for 58 days.

8. Find the simple interest on $825 at 4% for 80 days.

9. Janice borrowed $1,200. The bank charged 5% at the time the loan was made. How much money did Janice receive?

10. Peter bought a tool for $125 cash or $150 in 90 days. What percent of discount was allowed for the cash sale?

11. Find the principal necessary to yield $810 in 90 days at 6% simple interest.

12. Gordon invested $5,500 for 4 months. He received $4\frac{1}{2}$% simple interest on his money. How much interest did he earn?

13. Peter invested $8,000. Part of his money was invested at 7% simple interest and on the other part he lost 5% simple interest. If his net gain was $260, how much money was invested at 7%?

14. If $3,000 more is invested at $2\frac{1}{2}$% than at 3 %, the annual income is $350. How much is invested at each rate?

Compound Interest

It is necessary to distinguish between nominal rates and effective rates in order to understand the meaning of compound interest.

The nominal rate is the stated annual rate. The nominal rate means the yearly rate if no further information is provided. That is, if the rate is quoted at 6%, it is understood that this is an annual rate.

The effective rate is the actual rate for one year and it may differ from the nominal rate. The effective rate is the nominal rate compounded by the number of conversions each year. For example, if the rate is quoted at 6% semi-annually, then this means that after 6 months, the interest is added to the principal, and this new amount becomes the principal for the next 6 months.

The interest on $100 at 6% is 100 x .06 or $6.

The interest on $100 at 6% semi-annually is calculated as follows: $100 \times .06 \times \frac{1}{2} = 3$.

$3 is the interest earned in 6 months. This amount is added to the original principal, $100, and the new principal is $103.

$103 \times .03 \times \frac{1}{2} = 3.09$ This amount is added to the new principal:

$103 + 3.09 = 106.09$.

The interest is $6.09. Therefore, the effective rate of 6% semi-annually is 6.09%. This may seem to be relatively small, but with many more conversions, or the investment of large sums of money, the difference becomes significant.

The computation used to obtain the effective rate of 6.09% (as above) is:
$1.609 = (1.03)^2$. Therefore, r = 1.0609 – 1 = 0.0609 or 6.09%.

The above calculation may be facilitated by using a calculator with a power button (key – usually y^x). Practice by inserting 5 and then press the power button and then insert 3. The answer should be 125. Then clear and insert (1.03). Then press the power button and then press 3. The answer should be 1.0927.

In general, the effective rate can be found by using the formula where:

$$E = \left(1 + \frac{r}{n}\right)^n - 1$$

> E is the effective rate
> r is the stated (nominal) rate
> n is the number of conversions per year

If the transaction is to take place over a number of years, let n represent the number of conversion periods each year and t is the number of years of the transaction. Then the formula becomes $E = \left(1 + \frac{r}{n}\right)^{nt} - 1$ where t equals the number of years. Multiply n x t and use the power key.

Example 1: Find the effective rate of 4% converted semi-annually.

Using the formula $E = \left(1 + \dfrac{r}{n}\right)^{nt} - 1$ the effective rate is $\left(1 + \dfrac{.04}{2}\right)^{2} - 1 = .0404 =$ 4.04%.

Example 2: Find the effective rate of interest equivalent to 6% converted semi-annually.

$$r = \left(1 + \dfrac{.06}{2}\right)^{2} - 1 = .0609 = 6.09\,\%$$

Care should be taken when interest rates are quoted as monthly. 6% monthly means that the interest is added to the principal at the end of each month or 12 times a year.

For example, the effective rate is 6% monthly then the monthly rate is 0.5%. After one year, the principal is increased by a factor of $(1 + 0.005)^{12}$ and this is equal to 1.0617. Using the formula we have $E = \left(1 + \dfrac{.06}{12}\right)^{12}$ or $(1 + 0.005)^{12}$ and this is approximately equal to 1.0617%.

Compound interest is calculated by adding the interest to the principal after each conversion period. Many investments are compounded monthly, weekly, or daily. Therefore, it is important to determine the effective annual rate.

Finding the Amount

We use the formula $P\left(1 + \dfrac{r}{n}\right)^{nt}$ to find the amount of an investment. Note that $P\left(1 + \dfrac{r}{n}\right)^{nt}$ is the Principal (amount invested) and $\left(1 + \dfrac{r}{n}\right)^{nt}$ is the effective interest rate. t is the number of years.

Example 1: Find the amount of $1,000 invested at 6% quarterly for 3 years. We will use the formula $1,000(1.015)^{12}$ that is, $1,000 \times 1.09344$ which is $1093.44.

Example 2: Russell invested $2,000 at 8% compounded daily. Determine the amount of money in the account after 2 years. The formula will be $A = 2000\left(1 + \dfrac{.08}{365}\right)^{365 \times 2}$ or 2346.68

Exercise 60

1. Determine the effective rate of 8% quarterly.

2. Steve borrowed money at 4% quarterly. What was the effective rate?

3. Celia invested $3,000 at 5% compounded annually for 3 years. What was the value of the investment at the termination date?

4. Rita negotiated a loan for $1,500 for 2 years at 5% semi-annually. How much did she have to pay back by the end of the transaction?

5. Find the interest on $5,000 for 2 years at 4% compounded quarterly.

6. Charles bought a second-hand car for $4,500. He paid $1,200 cash and borrowed the remainder at 6% semi-annually. If the car was paid for in 1 year, what was the total amount that Charles paid?

7. Find the amount of interest on an investment of $843 at 6% compounded semi-annually for 7 years.

8. What is the difference between the simple interest and the interest compounded quarterly on $600 at 8% for 2 years?

9. A couple wished to buy a house in a certain area. They offered to purchase the house directly from the owner by paying immediately. They said that this would save the agent's commission of 7% or $10,000. How much was the house worth?

10. John invested $500 at 8% converted monthly and Ann invested $500 at 9% compounded semi-annually. Who earned more interest in one year and by how much?

SELF-ASSESSMENT of the ATTAINMENT of the OBJECTIVES

	5	4	3	2	1
- demonstrate the use of simple interest					
- knowing that I = P x R x T, find P, R, and T					
- illustrate the difference between simple and compound interest					
- illustrate the difference between the nominal rate and the effective rate					
- calculate the effective rate using the formula $E = \left(1 + \frac{r}{n}\right)^n - 1$					
- calculate the amount of an investment knowing the Principal and using the formula for the amount $P\left(1 + \frac{r}{n}\right)^{nt}$					

Score   /30   Date_____

Unit 16-Break — Even Analysis

OBJECTIVES

- illustrate the difference between fixed costs and variable costs by using examples
- demonstrate a break-even point by using examples
- develop a break even analysis for a small party or meal
- demonstrate the ability to determine costs
- demonstrate the ability to determine the number of persons or things in this analysis
- determine both cost price and selling price in an analysis

Break-even analysis is a method of calculating the amount of business that must be conducted or the costs and sales required so that no money is lost and no money is earned. Once the break-even analysis has been determined, decisions may be made regarding profit revenues. If the business cannot break even, then the business should be abandoned or more realistic expenses and revenues must be made to ensure that the business does provide a forecast of a break-even financial plan and an appropriate amount that is the profit. There are two types of expenses: fixed costs and variable costs.

Fixed Costs

Fixed costs will not vary according to the amount of business conducted.
James wishes to open a clothing store in which he will sell men's suits that are purchased from a supplier.

Some examples of fixed costs are: rental or purchase of space, charges for electricity, heating, telephone, taxes, marketing, salaries and fringe benefits, licenses, permits, insurance, security, costs of registering or incorporating, breakage or theft, office furnishings including electronic machines, office supplies, etc. all of which are independent of the number of goods or services sold.

Variable Costs

For the clothing store, variable costs may include the number of suits and other saleable goods bought, materials for packaging, etc. Variable costs fluctuate according to the amount of goods or services sold.

Break—Even Point

A break-even point is reached when the total revenues are equal to the fixed costs plus the variable costs or $TR = F + Vx$ where TR is the total revenue, F is the fixed costs, V is the variable costs, and x is the number of articles or services provided.

The following conditions must be understood when developing a break-even analysis:

1. Some of the variable costs such as furnishings and office equipment may be less in future years.

2. A break-even analysis must be revised on a regular basis. It would require much experience to develop a break-even analysis that would last a full year. Seasonal sales fluctuations will require periodic alterations to the analysis, but if the analysis requires major alterations, the owner(s) may wish to re-think their costs or their sales figures.

James wishes to open a clothing store and he will calculate the fixed cost and the variable cost. His fixed costs for one year will amount to $125,600.

The variable costs are determined by considering the number of suits that may be sold and the price paid for these suits. In addition, markdown costs and any discounts must be factored into the calculation. James may proceed by using any of the following methods:

Method 1. Determine how many articles must be sold. James estimates (after a market review) that he can buy suits for $125 each and sell them for $240 each. How many suits must he sell to break even without using markdowns or discounts?

By applying the formula TR = F + Vx, James determines that his fixed costs are $125,600 and his variable costs are $125x. (x is the number of suits bought.) Therefore, his total cost is $125,600 + $125x. The total revenues are $240x, that is, the selling price of each suit multiplied by the number of suits that must be sold.

240x = 125,600 + 125x
115x = 125,600
x = 1092.17

This tells us that he must sell at least 1,093 suits each year to break even. Now James has to make a decision. Can he sell more than 1,093 suits in one year?

Method 2. Determine the selling price of each article to ensure that the price is competitive. James estimates that he can sell 1,100 suits that he can purchase at $125 for each. He wishes to determine a selling price.
TR = F + Vx
TR = 1100x

F + Vx = 125,600 + 1100 x 125   →   1100x = 125,600 + 137,500
                                →   1100x = 263,100
                                →   x = 239.18

This tells us that James will have to sell the suits at $239.18 (round off to $240) in order to break even. James has to make a decision. Is he able to sell the suits at a price greater than $240 and remain competitive? How many suits must he sell in order to realize a reasonable profit?

Method 3. Determine the cost price for each article.

$$TR = F + Vx$$
$$1,100 \text{ x } 240 \quad = 125,600 + 1,100x$$
$$264,000 \quad = 125,600 + 1,100x$$
$$1,100x \quad = 138,400$$
$$x \quad = 125.82$$

That is, James must purchase the suits for $125.82 to break even. James must decide on the cost of each suit. Can he obtain these for that cost? After calculations such as the above, an owner must factor in discounts and markdowns, goods returned goods that cannot be sold, theft, etc. When this has been completed, sufficient profit must be considered. Profit may result from one or a combination of the following: decrease costs, increase sales, and increase the selling price of goods or services.

Profit Included in the Break–Even Analysis

Business people sometimes want to ensure that there is a profit for the company or the sponsors of an event. In this case, the profit will be added to the formula as follows:

$$TR = P + F + Vx. \text{ (where P is the profit)}$$

Using the example of James opening a clothing store, we will add the fact that he wishes to realize a profit of $60,000 a year. The formula now becomes:

$$TR = P + F + Vx.$$

To find the break-even point, we will now use $240x = 60,000 + 125,600 + 125x$. Therefore, $115x = 185,600$ or $x = 1613.91$ suits which when rounded is 1,614 suits. When James sees this number, he will immediately determine that he must have average sales of 31 suits each week.

Exercise 61

Mary wants to organize a dinner at her club. Determine the costs, the revenues, and the number of people who must attend by using the break-even formula so that the club will realize a profit of at least $300.

_____
_____
_____
_____
_____
_____
_____
_____

_____
_____
_____
_____
_____
_____
_____
_____
_____
_____
_____
_____
_____
_____
_____

2. A caterer wished to make a profit equal to 3 times the cost of the food. The caterer wishes to supply a supper for 35 people. By using a break-even analysis, determine the cost per person. Develop a reasonable menu and include the cost of any help required to cater this meal.

_____
_____
_____
_____
_____
_____
_____
_____
_____
_____
_____
_____
_____
_____
_____
_____
_____
_____
_____
_____

3. John and Mary Hanson want to start a manufacturing company that produces copper pipes. Develop a break-even analysis such that the Hanson family will make an annual profit of $100,000.

_____
_____
_____
_____
_____
_____
_____
_____
_____
_____
_____
_____
_____
_____
_____
_____
_____
_____
_____
_____
_____
_____

SELF-ASSESSMENT of the ATTAINMENT of the OBJECTIVES

	5	4	3	2	1
- illustrate the difference between fixed costs and variable costs by using examples					
- demonstrate a break–even point by using examples					
- develop a break–even analysis for a small party or meal					
- demonstrate the ability to determine costs					
- demonstrate the ability to determine the number of persons or things in this analysis					
- determine both cost price and selling price in the analysis					

Score   /30   Date _____

226

Unit 17—Frequency Distributions and Measures of Central Tendency

OBJECTIVES
- use percentages to display data
- use ratios to display data
- develop a frequency distribution chart
- use graphs (or charts) to display data
- demonstrate the ability to compute the mean of a set of numbers
- explain, in writing, the meaning of the word mean
- explain, in writing, the meaning of the word median
- explain, in writing, the meaning of the word mode
- demonstrate how you would find the median of a set of numbers
- demonstrate how you would find the mode of a set of numbers
- solve problems using frequency distributions
- solve problems involving the use of the mean or the median or the mode

We saw that the use of graphs was a method for presenting large amounts of data. The use of measures of central tendency is another method for organizing, displaying, and interpreting data.

Using Percentages or Ratios to Display Information

Information may be displayed by changing the data into a percentage or into a ratio.

Example 1: A court dealt with 50 cases during a given month. 38 of the defendants were accused of wrongdoing and 12 were acquitted.

The frequency of events is the number of cases in each category.

The number of accused was 38. The frequency of events, 38, is the ratio of the number accused to the total number of cases, 50. Therefore $\frac{38}{50}$ or 0.76 or 76% were accused. In the same way, it can be determined that $\frac{12}{50}$ or 24% of the defendants were acquitted. Of the 76% accused, percentages can be found for the various lengths of sentences.

sentenced	frequency	ratio	percentage
5 or more years	15	$\frac{15}{38}$	39.5%
more than 3 and less than 5 years	10	$\frac{10}{38}$	26.3%
3 years or less	13	$\frac{13}{38}$	34.2%
acquitted	12	$\frac{12}{50}$	24%

Example 2: Using the data of the above example, 15 persons received sentences of 5 years or more. 10 persons received sentences of more than 3 and less than 5 years. 13 persons received sentences of 3 years or less. Although this example is somewhat

trivial, the point to be made is that seeing the data in its ratio form or in its percentage form provides a better understanding of the data.

However, if 20 or fewer cases are involved, the data should be listed in frequencies and not percents. For example, if the sample consists of 10 males and 10 females, the percents are 50% male and 50% female. An increase of 1 female will alter the percentages to 52.38 female and 47.62% male. On the other hand, if the sample consists of 500 males and 500 females, an increase of 1 female will change the percentage of females by 0.05. Instead of 50% females, there will be 50.05%. The greater the number of cases there are, the less effect a small change will have on the percentage. It is for this reason that the frequency (number) of cases should always be listed.

Example 3: A supervisor complained to the Executive Director of an agency that, of 155 full-time employees, only 50 were in his department. Yet, the supervisor's division handled 2,820 of the 6,410 cases handled by the agency. This communication of information is not very useful to the Executive Director. Instead of bombarding the Executive Director with large numbers that are difficult to comprehend, the supervisor should have stated that the percentage of workers in his department is 32.26%.

The cases handled by his department were 43.99%. This type of presentation facilitates understanding by the Executive Director.

Number of workers $\frac{50 \times 100}{155}$ = 32.26% number of workers

$\frac{2820 \times 100}{6410}$ = 43.99% amount of work done

Using Percentages Based on Hundreds or Thousands

Sometimes rates are calculated on bases other than percent. For example, if a city has a population of 1,200 people and 130 of the people died last year, the percent of deaths was $\frac{130 \times 100}{1200}$ or 10.83%.

Or, we could base the rate per 1,000 people in the community and calculate as follows:

$\frac{130 \times 1000}{1200}$ or 108.3 or 10.83%.

The statistic listed above would be more meaningful if the death rate per thousand people during the previous years was known. By knowing the previous death rates, a comparison may be made regarding an increase, a decrease, or an unchanged death rate.

228

Exercise 62

1. A school made a study of the ancestries of the families of its students. The data indicated that there were 124 Irish families, 98 Scottish families, 156 Italian families, 87 Oriental families, 56 Arabic families, and 102 families from Eastern European countries.   Determine the ratios and the percentages of each group.   (Use a calculator.)

Irish

Scottish

Italian

Oriental

Eastern European

2. A University having a population of 1,250 students reported that there were 175 students studying Business courses, 83 Engineering courses, 137 Natural Science courses, and 212 studying Humanities courses.   Determine the ratio and the percentage of each group of students. (Use a calculator to find the percents.)

Business

Engineering

Natural Sciences

Humanities

3. In the year 2000, there were 2,300 births in a city in which the population was 148,500. In the year 1990, there were 1,850 births when the population was 42,000. Determine which year had the higher birth rate.

4. A school district consisted of 10,500 students. 8,800 of these students studied mathematics. How many students per thousand studied mathematics? What percent of the students studied mathematics?

Number per thousand   Percent

Using Frequency Distributions

If we wish to determine the frequency of ages of persons in a class, we may proceed as follows:

1. Use a tally sheet to find the frequency:

Age	Frequency			%
< 21	///	3		6.8
21–25	̸T̸H̸L̸ //	7		15.9
26–30	̸T̸H̸L̸ ̸T̸H̸L̸ /	11		25.0
31–35	̸T̸H̸L̸ ////	9		20.5
36–40	̸T̸H̸L̸ ///	8		18.2
41–45	////	4		9.1
> 45	//	2		4.5
	Total	44		100

2. Determine the total – in this case 44 participants.
We may not wish to have so many categories of ages. We may wish to use only the following: < 21, 21 – 30, 31 – 40, and > 40.

Age	Frequency			%
< 21	///	3		6.8
21–30	̸T̸H̸L̸ ̸T̸H̸L̸ ̸T̸H̸L̸ ///	18		40.9
31–40	̸T̸H̸L̸ ̸T̸H̸L̸ ̸T̸H̸L̸ //	17		38.6
> 40	̸T̸H̸L̸ /	6		13.6
	Total	44		99.9

It should be noted that the total percent is not always equal to 100%. The difference from 100% results from the fact that some numbers in the calculation may be recurring decimal fractions or some numbers may be "rounded off". Notice that the difference is in the age group 31-40.

Exercise 63

1. Display a frequency distribution chart for age categories:
   < 21, 21 – 5, 36 – 50, 51 – 65, and > 65.

2. Construct a frequency distribution chart with percents for the following numbers:

| 27 | 32 | 27 | 28 | 35 | 27 | 32 | 28 | 36 | 35 | 29 | 27 | 29 | 32 |
| 27 | 32 | 28 | 36 | 29 | 36 | 35 | 29 | 32 | 32 | 29 | 29 | 36 | 29 |

Charts Used for Displaying Data

Graphs (or charts) may be used for displaying data obtained through frequency distributions.

Example: A Marriage Counseling Clinic provided the following data regarding the visitors to the Clinic. This data may be displayed using a Pie Chart, a Bar Graph, or a Line Graph.

Status	Frequency	Percentage
Single	20	50%
Married	14	35%
Divorced	6	15%
Total	40	100%

If we had wanted to compare one year's events with those of other years, we may proceed as follows:

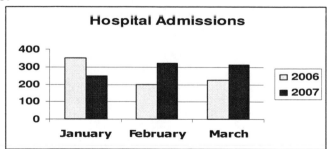

If we are comparing automobile accidents of males and females over the past 3 years, the chart below is one method that may be used.

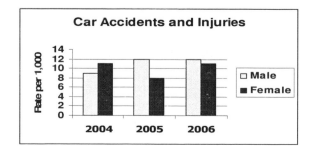

Exercise 64

1. Use a frequency distribution graph to find the percent of each of the following sets of data: sales at a clothing store were recorded as: first week $2,300, second week $4,200, third week $3,600, fourth week $3,100. Then construct a bar graph and a line graph to display the information.

2. Interpret the graph below regarding automobile accidents. Write everything that you can determine from the chart.

Car accidents and injuries

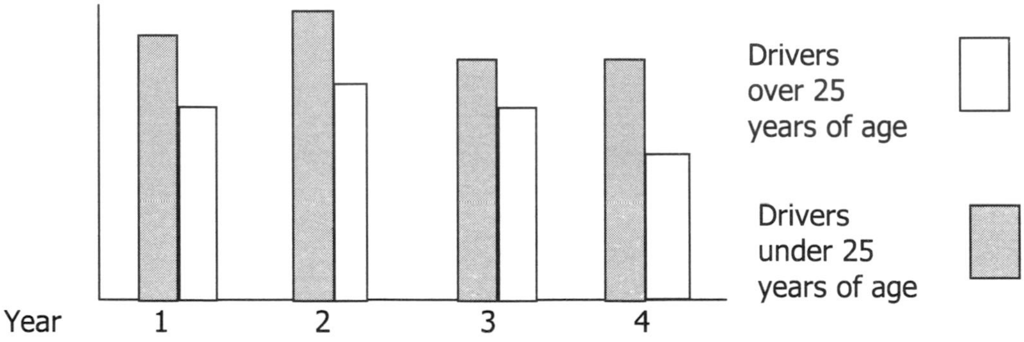

Note that sometimes numbers are not necessary but trends are.

Measures of Central Tendencies

The three most commonly used measures of central tendency are the mean, the median, and the mode. These three measures provide a number (or numbers) that tell us much about the sample under consideration.

The Mean

The mean is the average score of a distribution.
The mean is obtained by dividing the total sum of the items in the sample by the number of items.

Example 1: The weight of individuals in the class was recorded. The results in kilograms were as follows: 86.3, 87.5, 80.7, 83.2, 85.7, 63.4, 65.7, 72.4, 63.4, 77.1 and 63.4. The mean is equal to the sum of the numbers divided by the number of weights or $\frac{828.8}{10}$ = 76.54 kg.

Example 2: Ten people wrote a special examination. The scores were: 86, 82, 91, 79, 84, 31, 85, 82, 93 and 90. The mean equals $\frac{803}{10}$ = 80.3.

The question to be asked is, "Is this mean indicative of the group?" The answer is "no" because nobody else within the group had a score close to 31. The score of 31 skewed the results. This score of 31 made a large difference because the number of cases in the sample was relatively small. As we have seen earlier, when the number of samples increases, the results are less and less affected by a small increase or decrease.

We can avoid this situation if we examine the numbers before we begin. In this case, 31 should have been discarded before finding the mean. Then the mean would have been $\frac{772}{9}$ = 85.8 which is more indicative of the scores.

The mathematical formula for the mean is $M = \dfrac{\sum\limits_{i=1}^{n} Xi}{n}$ where M = "the mean", Σ is the symbol for "the sum of", $\Sigma(X_1)$ is "the sum of the scores $x_1, x_2, x_3 \ldots x_i$ and n is "the number of items in the sample".

Exercise 65

1. Paula bought tins of soup with the following capacities: 284 ml, 324 ml, 280 ml, 335 ml, and 265 ml. What was the average (mean) capacity of the tins?

2. Allan bought 11 bags of 5 lbs (2.27 kg) of potatoes, 7 bags of 10 lbs (4.54 kg), and 2 bags of 20 lbs (9.08 kg). What was the mean weight of the bags of potatoes? Determine this in pounds and in kilograms. (1 kg = 2.2 lb and 1 lb = 0.454 kg.)

lbs   kg

3. Find the mean of the following numbers: (use a calculator if you wish)
2146, 3479, 6263, 1296, 1816.

4. List three instances in your daily life where you may want to find the mean.

5. Why would you want to find a mean?

6. Comment on the following: an engineer was commissioned to build a bridge. He measured the height of the masts of 100 ships, determined the average, and built the bridge to that height.

7. Agnes is 104 years old. Her son suggested that she should see a doctor. Agnes replied that she checked the number of deaths last year in the municipality and found that there were very few people who died at the age of 104. Comment on Agnes' reasoning.

8. A country reported that the birth rate dropped from last year to 10.5 live births for every 1,000 population. Mary argued that you cannot have 10.5 for the number of births because you can't have a half of a baby. Is Mary correct or is the statistic a valid one? Comment.

9. Tom kicked a football 3 times and had an average distance of 44 yards. He kicked it again and his average dropped to 43 yards. How far did the fourth kick travel?

The Median

The median is the number (or numbers) that divide a set of numbers into two groups: those that are less than and those that are greater than the median. Therefore, the numbers in the sample space (those being considered) must be placed in order of magnitude (ascending or descending).

Example 1: If we have ages listed as 28, 32, 25, 33, 39, 27, 31, 33, 29, 25, 26, we would list these in ascending or descending order. In ascending order, the ages are: 25, 25, 26, 27, 28, 29, 31, 32, 33, 33, and 39. Since there is an odd number of ages listed (11), the median will be the 6th age which is 29. Therefore, we call 29 the median of this frequency. Note that there are 5 ages below 29 and there are 5 ages above 29. We can think of a median as the number that cuts the distribution in two just as the median strip of a highway cuts a highway in two. If there is an odd number of numbers in the sample space, the median is the number in the middle of a sample that is in ascending or descending order. If there is an even number of numbers in the sample space, the median is the average of the two numbers in the middle.

Example 2: Let the data be 11, 12, 13, 16, 17, 20, 25, 26. The median will be between 16 and 17 because there is an even number of items in the sample. The average is $\frac{16 + 17}{2}$ or 16.5 (even though 16.5 is not in the sample).

Notice that there are 4 numbers less than 16.5 and there are 4 numbers greater than 16.5.

Exercise 66

1. Find the median of the following weights: 37 kg, 41 kg, 33 kg, 31 kg, 34 kg, 38 kg 39 kg, 40 kg, 36 kg.

2. Find the median of the following test scores: 74, 68, 81, 77, 65, 79, 80, 66, 82, 81.

3. List an instance in which you may want to find the median of a set of data.

4. Explain the meaning of a median to someone who does not know its meaning.

The Mode

The mode is the most frequently used item in a distribution and it can be found by inspection.

Example 1: Determine the mode of the following frequency distribution:
(1), 3, 6, (1), 5, 6, 7, 5, (1), 5, (1). By inspection, we note that 1 appears four times, 5 three times, 6 twice, 3 once and 7 once. Therefore, the mode is 1.

Some frequency distributions contain two or more modes.

Example 2: Determine the mode of the frequency distribution:
1, 3, 6, 1, 5, 6, 7, 5, 1, 6. By inspection, we note that 1 appears three times, 6 three times, 5 twice, 3 once, and 7 once. Therefore, there are two modes: 1 and 6.

Exercise 67

1. Identify the mode(s) of the following distribution:

27, 30, 28, 30, 27, 28, 32, and 30.

2. Identify the mode(s) of the following distribution:

27, 28, 30, 27, 31, 32, 30, 27, 30.

3. List an instance in which you would want to identify the mode.

SELF-ASSESSMENT of the ATTAINMENT of the OBJECTIVES

	5	4	3	2	1
- use percentages to display data					
- use ratios to display data					
- develop a frequency distribution chart					
- use graphs (or charts) to display data					
- demonstrate the ability to compute the mean of a set of numbers					
- explain, in writing, the meaning of the word mean					
- explain, in writing , the meaning of the word median					
- explain, in writing, the meaning of the word mode					
- demonstrate how you would find the median of a set of numbers					
- demonstrate how you would find the mode of a set of numbers					
- solve problems using frequency distributions					
- solve problems involving the use of the mean or the median or the mode					

Score   /40   Date _____

Unit 18 – Probability

OBJECTIVES

- explain, in writing, the meaning of the word probability
- explain, in writing, the meaning of the words favorable events
- explain, in writing, the meaning of unfavorable events
- illustrate what is meant by a sample space
- explain what is meant by P(A) and P(B) = P(A) x P(B)
- illustrate what is meant by P(A) + P(B) – P(A and B)
- solve problems involving probability

Probability

A probability is a number between 0 and 1 that measures the likelihood of an event happening. An event is the outcome of a trial. An event can be simple or compound. An example of a simple event is tossing a die and having the face with 5 dots facing upwards. An example of a compound event is tossing a a red die and a blue die and having conditions attached. (See sample space for tossing a red die and a blue die on the next page.)

If a coin is unbiased, there are only two possibilities of outcomes, "heads" or "tails". It is presumed that the coin will not land on an edge. If we want a "head" to show, those tosses that result in "heads" showing are called favorable outcomes. Those that show tails are unfavorable outcomes. The total number of favorable and unfavorable outcomes is called the number of possible outcomes.

The mathematical probability of an event is the number of favorable outcomes divided by the number of possible outcomes. $P = \frac{f}{n}$ where P is the probability of something happening, f is the number of favorable outcomes, and n is the number of possible outcomes. The probability of not getting a favorable result when something happens is $Q = \frac{u}{n}$ where Q is the probability of something not happening, u is the number of unfavorable outcomes and n is the number of possible outcomes.

Note that $P + Q = 1$. For example, if we are tossing a die and we wish to have the number 5 showing, the probability of this happening is $P = \frac{1}{6}$. The probability that 5 will not show is $Q = \frac{5}{6}$. $P + Q = \frac{1}{6} + \frac{5}{6} = 1$.

The mathematical probability is the number to which a series of outcomes tend.

Example 1: If we tossed a coin 5 times, the mathematical probability is $\frac{1}{2}$ that on each toss of the coin the "head" will face up. The probability of "heads" facing up after 5 tosses is $\frac{0}{5}, \frac{1}{5}, \frac{2}{5}, \frac{3}{5}, \frac{4}{5}$ or $\frac{5}{5}$. There could be a huge discrepancy between these results and realistic expectations.

Probability expectations should not be made on the results of a few events. The expected outcomes will approach the theoretical probability as the number of events increases. For example, there is usually no tendency towards the expected probability when tossing a coin 5 times. However, if 100 tosses were made and the results tabulated, the tendency towards the probability being $\frac{1}{2}$ may become apparent. If 1,000 tosses were made and tabulated, the tendency would become even more apparent. If more tosses were made, the expected probability would be more apparent. If the purpose of the trials is to determine the probability, it is necessary to have as many trials as possible.

Example 2: If we tossed a fair coin 5 times, it is quite possible that a "heads" will show 4 or 5 times. If we tossed the same coin 1,000 times, the positive outcomes may be 491, 508, 511, 493, 487, or any number that is close to or equal to 500. The point to be made is that the probability will tend towards the mathematical probability as the number of tosses increases.

Care must be taken when a probability is chosen. For example, if a die is colored red on four faces and blue on two faces, there are only two types of outcomes. However, we would not say that the probability of blue showing is $\frac{1}{2}$. The probability of blue showing is $\frac{2}{6}$ or $\frac{1}{3}$ since there are six faces to a die and only two of them are blue.

A sample space is a listing of all possible outcomes. The sample space for tossing a coin is H and T and for tossing a die is 1, 2, 3, 4, 5, 6, since a die has six sides.

We will call the probability of an event happening in a favorable manner as P(A). For more than one event, we will use P(B), P(C), etc.

The following is a sample space for throwing 2 dice, one of which is red and the other die is blue. We will use an ordered pair in which the first number is the one showing on the red die and the second number is the one showing on the blue die. (r, b) will be the ordered pair. We could have used (b, r) but we must remain consistent after the choice has been made. For example after one toss, if the red die shows 4 and the blue die shows 1, the ordered pair will be (4, 1).

Notice that there are 36 ordered pairs in the sample space. The range for each die is from 1 to 6. In this case, these are the only outcomes possible.

Sample space for tossing a red die and a blue die.

		outcome of blue die						
		1	2	3	4	5	6	
	1	(1 , 1)	(1 , 2)	(1 , 3)	(1 , 4)	(1 , 5)	(1 , 6)	
outcome of	2	(2 , 1)	(2 , 2)	(2 , 3)	(2 , 4)	(2 , 5)	(2 , 6)	
red die	3	(3 , 1)	(3 , 2)	(3 , 3)	(3 , 4)	(3 , 5)	(3 , 6)	
	4	(4 , 1)	(4 , 2)	(4 . 3)	(4 , 4)	(4 , 5)	(4 , 6)	
	5	(5 , 1)	(5 , 2)	(5 , 3)	(5 , 4)	(5 , 5)	(5 , 6)	
	6	(6 , 1)	(6 , 2)	(6 , 3)	(6 , 4)	(6 , 5)	(6 , 6)	

If two or more probabilities are to be obtained and you wish to know the probability of them all happening at once, the probabilities must be multiplied.

That is, P(A) and P(B) = P(A) x P(B).

Example 3: When tossing two colored dice, what is the probability that the red die will show a 3 and the blue die will be less than 4?

(1) The probability that the red die will show a 3 is $\frac{6}{36}$ or $\frac{1}{6}$.

(2) The probability that the blue die is less than 4 is $\frac{18}{36}$ or $\frac{1}{2}$.

(3) Therefore, the probability that the red die will show 3 and the blue die will show less than 4 is $\frac{1}{6}$ x $\frac{1}{2}$ or $\frac{1}{12}$ which is $\frac{3}{36}$. (Check with the outcome chart.) The ordered pairs are those that are common to the two sets: (3, 1) (3, 2) (3, 3).
We could have written this as P (A) x P(B) = $\frac{1}{6}$ x $\frac{1}{2}$ = $\frac{1}{12}$ or $\frac{3}{36}$.

Example 4: When tossing two colored dice, what is the probability that the red die will show a 4 [P(A)] or the blue die will be greater than 3 [P(B)] ?

The word "or" has two meanings in mathematics. It can mean "one or the other", or "both". In this case, the probability that red is showing 4 is $\frac{6}{36}$.

The probability that the blue is greater than 3 is $\frac{18}{36}$ or $\frac{1}{2}$.
However, 3 ordered pairs, (4, 4) (4, 5) (4, 6) were counted in each probability.

Therefore, we have $(\frac{6}{36} + \frac{18}{36}) - \frac{3}{36}$ or $\frac{21}{36}$. Observe the sample space on the previous page to see a graphic illustration of this result.

In general, using "or" in the inclusive meaning will be:
$$P(A) \text{ or } P(B) = P(A) + P(B) - P(A \text{ and } B).$$

Example 5: In a garment cleaning company, the probability of an item being torn is $\frac{21}{36}$ and the probability of it being lost is $\frac{1}{6}$. Note that some garments may be both torn and lost. In this case, "or" means "one or the other, or both".

If we let P(A) = $\frac{21}{36}$, the probability that it was torn and P(B) = $\frac{1}{6}$, the probability that it was lost, then P(A or B) = P(A) + P(B) − P(A and B).
That is, P(A or B) = $\frac{2}{5}$ + $\frac{1}{6}$ − ($\frac{2}{5}$ x $\frac{1}{6}$) or P(A or B) = $\frac{17}{30}$ − $\frac{2}{30}$ = $\frac{15}{30}$ or $\frac{1}{2}$.

Exercise 68

1. What is the probability of drawing an ace from a deck of shuffled cards?

2. What is the probability of drawing a spade from a deck of shuffled cards?

3. When tossing two colored dice, what is the probability that the red die will show a number ≥ 4 and the blue die will be ≤ 3? (Check with the sample space after solving the problem.)

4. Make a sample space using the tossing of two dice and taking the positive difference of the numbers showing.

a) What is the range of differences that is possible?

b) What is the probability that the difference will be 0?

c) What is the probability that the difference will be 1?

d) What is the probability that the difference will be 2?

e) What is the probability that the difference will be 3?

f) What is the probability that the difference will be 4?

g) What is the probability that the difference will be 5?

h) What is the probability that the difference will be 6?

5. Three white cards and 2 yellow cards are placed in a bag. We wish to take 2 cards from the bag without looking. What is the sample space?

6. Using the information from problem 5, what is the probability of selecting:

a) 2 white cards

b) 2 yellow cards

c) 1 yellow card or 1 white card?

240

7. Two coins are tossed simultaneously: what is the sample space?

a) What is the probability of two heads showing?

b) What is the probability of at least one tail showing?

8. In a toy factory, $\frac{1}{4}$ of the toys are damaged and $\frac{2}{5}$ of the toys are packaged improperly. What is the probability that a toy that starts in the production line will be placed in a box correctly?

SELF-ASSESSMENT of the ATTAINMENT of the OBJECTIVES

	5	4	3	2	1
- explain, in writing, the meaning of the word probability					
- explain, in writing, the meaning of the words favorable events					
- explain, in writing, the meaning of unfavorable events					
- illustrate what is meant by a sample space					
- explain what is meant by P(A) and P(B) = P(A) x P(B)					
- illustrate what is meant by P(A) + P(B) – P(A and B)					
- solve problems involving probability					

Score   /35   Date _____

Unit 19 – Practical Applications of Mathematics

OBJECTIVES
- develop a problem involving a perpetuity
- solve problems involving perpetuities
- solve problems involving house maintenance
- solve problems involving liquids
- solve problems regarding sports statistics

Perpetuities

Perpetuities are amounts of money that will provide a sum of money (interest) without affecting the capital investment and therefore, will continue indefinitely (or for a limited amount of time).

Many scholarship funds and endowment funds are established as perpetuities. Some people set aside (invest) an amount of money so that it will produce an annual supplement to their retirement income. The major difficulty is that the amount of money invested must be fairly large, and the investment must be secure and consistent over a long period of time. Depending upon the conditions of investment, the principal may be transferred and changed according to the financial market fluctuations.

Some people make annual contributions and their investment becomes an annuity which is beyond the scope of this book.

Example 1: John wants to provide a university scholarship of $3,000 and he wants this scholarship to be offered on a perpetual basis. How much money must he invest? Let us assume that a rate of 5% is considered as a safe rate over many years. We will calculate this as we did with simple interest. We know that $I = P \times R \times T$.

John wants the interest to be $3,000. He is investing at the rate of 5% and he wants the $3,000 to be realized in one year. Therefore, $3,000 = P \times .05 \times 1$ or $300,000$ which is $5P$. Therefore, $P = \$60,000$. John must invest $60,000 to yield $3,000 at 5% so that the principal for the next year will remain $60,000. It can be seen that the formula is $A\infty = \dfrac{R}{I}$ where $A\infty$ is the amount of dollars to be invested, R is the return (interest) in dollars, and I is the interest rate.

Some people establish a perpetuity well in advance of their retirement by investing a certain amount that will accrue interest to bring the original investment to the amount that will start the perpetuity. Many organizations accept endowments with the condition that they not be used until after a number of years so that the initial endowment will be more valuable.

242

Example 2: Karen wants to retire when she reaches her 60th birthday. She estimates that she will require $4,000 a year to supplement her retirement income. How much money must she have to invest in order to yield $4,000 if the expected rate is 4.8%?

$A\infty = \frac{R}{I}$ where R = $4,000 and I = 4.8% or 0.048.

Therefore, Karen must invest $\frac{4000}{0.048}$ or $83,333.33.

Exercise 69

1. Maurice wishes to establish an annual scholarship of $2,000 annually. How much money must he invest if the interest is 4.2%?

2. Helen wants to upgrade her computer by spending $500 each year with the proceeds from her perpetuity. Her expected rate of return is 5% annually. How much money must she invest?

3. Stan wanted to tile the ceiling of his playroom that is 6.8 m long and 5.2 m wide. He can buy tiles measuring 40 x 40 cm. How many tiles must he buy in order to cover the ceiling?

4. Steve was planning to put pine boards on the walls of his room. Each board required 8 nails. He estimated that he would use 80 boards. He decided to buy nails that were packaged and contained 125 nails. Each package of nails cost $1.65. How much money did Steve pay for the nails?

5. Lisa was making a punch. She started with 215 milliliters of water and then added the following: 355 ml of orange juice, 710 ml of grape juice, 120 ml of mango juice, and 1 liter of ginger ale. Her punch glasses contain 150 ml of liquid. How many glasses of punch can Lisa serve?

6. A basketball player scored 77 out of 120 foul shots. What is the player's scoring percent? Express this number as a three-digit decimal number.

Scoring percent _____ As a decimal _____

7. A goaltender made 350 stops on 405 shots. What is his save average?

(3-digit decimal) _____ . What is his save percentage?

8. A baseball pitcher threw 120 times during a game. He threw 80 strikes and the other 40 were balls.

What is his strike/ball ratio? _____ What percent of the pitches were strikes?

What decimal fraction of the pitches were strikes?

Write the ratio of strikes to balls as a common fraction.

SELF-ASSESSMET of the ATTAINMENT of the OBJECTIVES

- develop a problem involving a perpetuity
- solve problems involving perpetuities
- solve problems involving house maintenance
- solve problems involving liquids
- solve problems regarding sports statistics

5	4	3	2	1

Score ___ /25 Date _____

Section VII – Simple Interest and Compound Interest, Break- Even Analysis, Frequency Distributions and Measures of Central Tendency, Probability, Practical Applications of Mathematics
Post–Test VII

Answers can be found at the end of the book.

1. Andre invested $2,400 at 6%, simple interest, annually for 3 years. How much will the investment be worth at the time of its termination?

2. At what percent must Sally invest $8,000 for 5 years to earn $3,000 in simple interest?

3. Bill was offered a loan of $4,000 at 6% annually and Harry was offered a loan of the same amount at 6% semi-annually. What was the difference in the amounts of interest over the year?

4. What is the effective rate of 8% quarterly? (Use a calculator that has the power key. y^x)

5. Celia invested $3,000 compounded annually for 3 years at the rate of 4%. What was the value of her investment at the termination date?

6. Mary wants to organize a dinner at her club. Determine reasonable costs (both fixed and variable) and determine, by using the break even formula, the cost and the number of people who must attend in order to ensure a profit of $300 for the club.

_____
_____
_____
_____
_____
_____
_____
_____
_____
_____
_____
_____
_____
_____
_____
_____
_____
_____

Cost   Number of people

7. In the year 2000, there were 2,300 births in a city in which the population was 148,500. In the year 1990, there were 1,850 births when the population was 42,000. Determine which year had the higher birth rate.

8. Construct a frequency distribution chart with percents for the following numbers:

   32   36   28   27   29   32   29   28   35   36   29   27   28   32   29   27
      36   36   27   32   29   29   32   35   27   32   29   35

9. Paula bought tins of soup with the following capacities: 284 ml, 324 ml, 335 ml, and 265 ml. What was the average capacity of the tins?

10. Determine the median of the following weights:

      37 kg, 41 kg, 33 kg, 31 kg, 34 kg, 38 kg, 39 kg, 40 kg, 36 kg.

11. Identify the mode of the following distribution: 27, 30, 28, 30, 27, 28, 32, 30

12. Six white cards and 4 yellow cards were placed in a bag. John was chosen to randomly select 2 cards. What was the probability that both of the cards were white?

13. Two coins were tossed simultaneously. What was the probability that 2 heads faced up?

14. A basketball player scored 77 out of 120 foul shots. What was the player's scoring percent? Express this percent as a 3 decimal number.

percent   decimal number

Score _____   Date _____

Section VIII – Operations Using Sets
Pre–Test VIII

Answers can be found at the end of the book.

1. Construct a Venn diagram in which U = {1, 2, 3, 4, 5} and B = {3, 4}.

2. Using the information in number 1 write the complement of B.

3. If A = {6, 8, 10, 12} and B = {10, 12, 14}, then A ∩ B =
and A U B =

4. If A = {1, 2, 3, 4} and B = {5, 6, 7}, then A ∩ B =

5. What is the intersection of the set of Natural numbers and the set of Integers?

6. If A is a set of numbers between 80 and 110 and B = 90 < x < 100, where x is an odd number, then A ∩ B =

7. If A = {5, 10, 15, 20} and B = all odd Natural numbers less than 20, then A U B =

8. What is Ra U Re?   What is Ra ∩ Re?

Solve the following problems by using Venn Diagrams:

9. In a class, 36 students study Mathematics, 24 study English and 30 study French. There are 18 students who study Mathematics and French; 9 who study Mathematics and English. 3 study all three subjects. How many students are in the class? How many study Mathematics but not English? How many study exactly two subjects? How many study exactly one subject?
Number of students in the class   How many study Mathematics but not English?

How many students study exactly two subjects ?   How many study exactly one

subject ?

10. In a league consisting of 8 teams, three sportswriters chose the following teams to win on a particular day. The first sportswriter chose Montreal, Toronto, Detroit, and New York to win: the second chose Chicago, Toronto, Montreal, and Atlanta to win; and the third chose Montreal, Detroit, Boston, and Chicago to win. Washington was not chosen to win by any of the three sportswriters. What teams were scheduled to play against each other on this particular day?

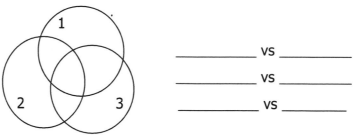

_____ vs _____

_____ vs _____

_____ vs _____

Score_____   Date _____

Unit 20—Operations Using Sets

OBJECTIVES

- write an example of a Universal set
- write a set that is a subset of a Universal set
- write the complement of this set
- write two sets and show their intersection by using a Venn diagram
- use the same two sets and show their union by using a Venn diagram
- write two sets that are disjoint
- write the meaning of an empty set
- list three sets and show them on a diagram using three circles
- write an example using the identity element for intersection
- write the meaning of the union of two sets
- solve problems using the intersection of sets
- solve problems using the union of sets
- solve problems using Venn diagrams

Operations Using Sets

The operations of addition, subtraction, multiplication, and division were studied in Unit 1. These operations were performed on elements of sets, for example, elements of the set of Natural numbers and the set of Real numbers. Now we will examine other operations performed on sets. The set that contains all of the elements to be considered is called the Universal set, or U. The three operations will be called complement, union, and intersection.

Number Lines and Venn Diagrams

In Unit 9, we discussed the Real number line – a continuous straight line, the points of which can be placed in a one-to-one correspondence with the elements of the set of Real numbers.

Venn Diagrams

It is convenient to picture sets by enclosed areas. Therefore, the set 1, 2, 3, 4, may be pictured as:

   or   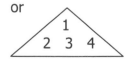   or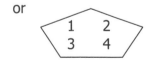

Although it is conventional to use circles to picture sets and rectangular shapes to picture the Universe, other shapes may be used without sacrificing mathematical understanding.

Example: If U = {1, 2, 3, 4, 5} and A = {3, 4}, the Venn Diagram will look like:

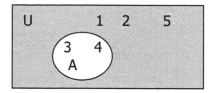

Complement of a Set

Those elements of the Universe that do not satisfy the conditions (in this case, being an element of the set A) also form a subset of the Universe. In the diagram above, the complement of the set A is the set {1, 2, 5}. That is, 1, 2, 5 are elements of the Universe but are not elements of the set A. We write the complement of the set A as A'.

The empty set denoted by {   } has no members (elements).

The complement of a set A has the following properties that are determined by definition:

U' = the empty set, { }.   The complement of the empty set = U, and (A')' = A.

The Intersection of Sets

The intersection of the set A and the set B is denoted by A ∩ B. ·
The intersection of sets A and B is a set that contains all of the elements that are contained In both of the sets A and D.

Example: If x is a Natural number and if A = the set 3 < x < 7 and B = the set −1 ≤ x ≤ 5, then the set A = {4, 5, 6} and the set B = {−1, 0, 1, 2, 3, 4, 5}. Therefore, A ∩ B = {4, 5} because 4 and 5 are members of the set A and of the set B.

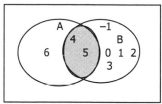

In the above diagram, 4 and 5 are contained in both the set A and the set B and are placed in the area that is common to both sets. 6 is an element of the set A only.
− 1, 0, 1, 2, 3 are elements of the set B only.

Disjoint Sets

Sets are said to be disjoint if and only if they have no common elements.

Example: If A = {1, 2, 3, 4} and B = {7, 8, 9}, then A and B are said to be disjoint because there are no elements that are contained in both A and in B.

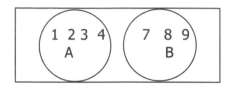

A and B are disjoint sets.
The intersection of disjoint sets is the empty set.

Exercise 70

1. If U = 1, 2, 3, 4. . . 14, 15, write the complement of each of the following sets:

a) A = 2, 4, 6, 8, 10

   A' =

b) B = 1, 2, 3, 13, 14, 15

   B' =

c) C = 1, 2, 3 . . . 12

   C' =

d) D = 10, 11, 12, 13, 14, 15

   D' =

2. Which of the points in the diagram belong to A and which belong to A'?
   U = {a, b, c, d}

A = _____ A' = _____

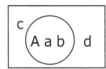

The Operation of Intersection

The intersection of the set A and the set B (written A ∩ B) is the set of all elements that are contained in the set A and in the set B.

In the diagram below, the shaded area represents A ∩ B, that is, the intersection of the set A and the set B.

Example 1: If the Universe is the set of Natural numbers and A = {1, 2, 3} and B = {1, 3, 4} then A ∩ B = {1, 3}.

Note how the elements of each set are placed. We see that 1 and 3 are in the set A and in the set B and are placed in the intersection.

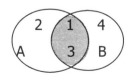

2 is an element of the set A but not of the set B, and 4 is an element of the set B but not of the set A. 1 and 3 are elements of the set A and of the set B.

252

Example 2: Let C = {1, 2, 3, 4} and D = {5, 6, 7, 8, 9}. Find C ∩ D.
The two sets, C and D are disjoint if and only if C ∩ D = { }.

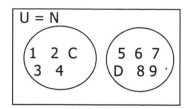

Example 3: If E = {1, 2, 3, 4, 5, 6} and F = {3, 4, 5}, then E ∩ F = {3, 4, 5} and this is the set F. In this case, F is said to be a proper subset of E because all of the elements of F are also elements of E.

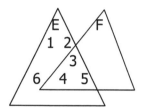

Exercise 71

1. Find the intersection of each of the following where the Universe is equal to the set of integers. Draw a diagram for each operation.

a) A = {– 2, – 1, 0, 1, 2} and B = {– 5, – 4, – 3, – 2, – 1, 0}. Determine A ∩ B.

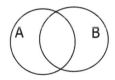

b) A = 3 < x < 7 and B = –1 ≤ x ≤ 5. Determine A ∩ B

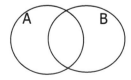

2. List the set that results from each of the following operations:

a) If A = {1, 2, 3, 4, 5, 6} and B = {– 5, – 4, – 3, – 2, – 1, 0, 1, 2, 3, 4}, find A ∩ B.

b) If A = {3, 7, 11, 15, 19, 23} and B = {5, 7, 9, 11, 13} find A ∩ B.

c) If A is the set of odd numbers and B = 90 < x < 100, find A ∩ B.

3. If A = 1, 2, 3 and B = an empty set, what is A ∩ B?

4. Given the diagram, list each of the following:

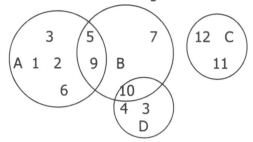

a) A ∩ B =   b) A ∩ D
c) B ∩ C =   d) B ∩ D =
e) A' =   f) B' =
g) D' =   h) C' =
i) (A ∩ B)' =   j) A' ∩ B' =

Properties of Sets Using Intersection

We have seen that the number systems exhibit properties under the operation of addition, subtraction, multiplication and division. Now let us examine the properties of the Universe of sets with respect to intersection.

Closure: by definition of the intersection of two sets, A and B, the intersection, A ∩ B is a set. A set results even if the sets A and B are disjoint. The result of the intersection of two disjoint sets is the empty set.

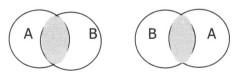

A ∩ B = the empty set, { }.

The commutative property: a Venn diagram will be used to picture A ∩ B and B ∩ A.

Note that A ∩ B and B ∩ A are represented by the same area.
Therefore, A ∩ B = B ∩ A.

254

Example 1: If A = {1, 2, 3, 4} and B = {3, 4, 5, 6} then A ∩ B = {3, 4}. It is also true that B ∩ A = {3, 4}.

The associative property: Intersection is a binary operation; that is, it operates on exactly two sets at a time (we have seen this in the operations of addition, subtraction multiplication and division).

We will use Venn Diagrams to show that A ∩ B ∩ C = A ∩ (B ∩ C) = (A ∩ B) ∩ C. Note the following:

Diagrams for three intersecting sets.

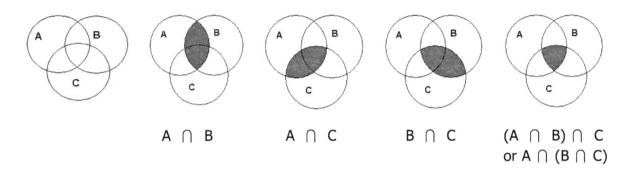

A ∩ B   A ∩ C   B ∩ C   (A ∩ B) ∩ C
                                              or A ∩ (B ∩ C)

A ∩ (B ∩ C) = (A ∩ B) ∩C

Example 2: Use Venn diagrams to show A ∩ (B ∩ C) where A = {1, 2, 3, 5}, and

B = {2, 3, 5} and C = (1, 2}.

Upon examining the three sets, it should be noted that 2 is contained in each set. Therefore, 2 is placed in the space common to each set.

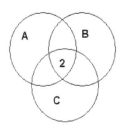

1 is contained in the sets A and C.   Therefore, 1 will be placed in the intersection of A and C but not in the part of the intersection of all three sets.

255

3 is contained in the sets A and B and is placed in that part of the intersection of A and B that does not contain 2.

4 is contained in the set A but in no other set. Note where 4 is placed.

5 is contained in the sets A and B.

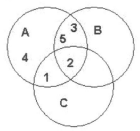

Therefore, A ∩ (B ∩ C) and (A ∩ B) ∩C are the same.
A ∩ (B ∩ C) is {1, 2, 3, 5} ∩ [{2, 3, 5} ∩ {1, 2}]
           = { 2, 3, 5} ∩ {1, 2}
           = {2}

And (A ∩ B) ∩C = [{1, 2, 3, 5} ∩ { 2, 3, 5}] ∩ {1, 2}
           = {2, 3, 5} ∩ {1, 2} = {2}

There exists an identity element: if A is a proper subset of B, then A ∩ B = A. A is a proper subset of B if and only if all of the elements of the set A are also contained in the set B.

Example 3: Let A = {1, 2, 3} and let B = {1, 2, 3, 4, 5}. It should be noted that all of the elements contained in the set A are also contained in the set B.

Therefore, A ∩ B = A. In this case, the set A is the identity element just as 1 is the identity element when we multiply 8 x 1 = 8. The empty set, { }, can also be used as the identity element. In general, for any subset of U, the Universe of all sets, U is the identity element. (A is a proper subset of B if all of the elements of A are also contained in B.)

The operation of intersection also has the property of transitivity and the cancellation properties.

If A ∩ B = A ∩ C and A ∩ C = A ∩ D, then A ∩ B = A ∩ D. Property of transitivity.
If A ∩ B ∩ C = D ∩ E ∩ C, then A ∩ B = D ∩ E. Cancellation property.

Exercise 72

1. Which of the two sets in each of the following will be the Universe for the two sets?

a) A = 1, 2, 3, 4, 5 and B = 1, 2, 3, 4, 5, 6, 7, 8

b) C = 10, 12, 14, 16, 18 and D = 1 ≤ n ≤ 25

c) P = 4, 5, 6, 7 and Q = 6, 5, 7, 4

2. Complete each of the following:

a) A ∩ U =   b) A ∩ empty set =   c) A ∩ A =

3. Complete each of the following:

a) What is the complement of an empty set?

b) What is the complement of U?

c) What is the complement of A'?

The Operation of Union

The Union of sets A and B (written A U B) is a set whose elements are contained in the set A or in the set B or in both. The "or" is used in the inclusive sense meaning in one or the other or both.

In the diagram below, the shaded area represents the union of the set A and the set B.

Example 1: If A = {1, 2, 3} and B = {1, 3, 4} then A U B = {1, 2, 3, 4}. The diagram above illustrates the union by the shaded area. Note the placement of the elements.

Example 2: If E = {1, 2, 3} and F = {1, $-$ 2, $-$ 3} then E U F = {$-$ 3, $-$ 2, $-$1, 1, 2, 3}.

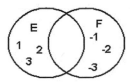

Example 3: If M = {1, 2, 3, 4, 5, 6} and N = {3, 4, 5} then M U N = {1, 2, 3, 4, 5, 6} where U = M.

Since all of the elements of the set N are also elements of the set M, N is said to be a proper subset of M.

Exercise 73

1. List the set that results from each of the following:

a) If A = {1, 2, 3, 4, 5, 6,} and B = {4, 5, 6, 7, 8} then A U B =

b) If {C =10, 11, 12, 13, 14, 15, 16} and D = {12, 14, 15, 16} then C U D =

2. Name the Union of the following sets of numbers:
a) N U I =   b) Ra U Re =
c) Ra U I =   d) N U Re =

3. If the Universe is {2, 4, 6, 8, 10, 12, 14, 16, 18, 20} and A = {4, 8, 12, 16, 20} and B = {6, 8, 10, 12} find:

a) A' =   b) B' =
c) A U B =   d) A' U B =
e) A U B' =   f) A' U B ' =
g) A U A' =   h) B U B' =

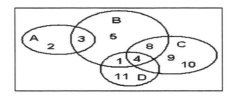

4. Complete each sentence using the diagram above.
a) A U B =   b) A U D =
c) B U C =   d) B U D =
e) A' =   f) B' =
g) C' =   h) (A U B)' =
i) (D U B)' =   j) A' U B' =

Properties of Sets Using Union
The properties that were considered using intersection, the property of closure, the commutative property, the associative property, and the existence of an identity element, can be demonstrated using the operation of Union. However, the identity element for the operation Union is as follows.

If A = {1, 2, 3, 4, 5} and B = {3, 4} it should be noted that B is a proper subset of A. Therefore, A U B = {1, 2, 3, 4, 5} or A. The identity element for Union is the set that contains all of the elements of the other set when the operation of Union is used.

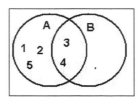

The Distributive Property Using Union

Under the Universe of Real numbers, a(b + c) = ab + ac. This is the distributive property of multiplication with respect to addition.

However, under the Universe of all sets, there exist two distributive properties.

1. The distributive property of intersection with respect to Union,
$$A \cap (B \cup C) = (A \cap B) \cup (A \cap C).$$

Note that A ∩ (B U C) and (A ∩ B) U (A ∩ C) are represented by the same shaded area.

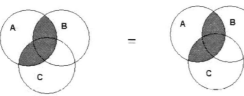

2. The distributive property of Union with respect to intersection:
$$A \cup (B \cap C) = (A \cup B) \cap (A \cup C).$$

Note that A U (B ∩ C) and (A U B) ∩ (A U C) are represented by the same shaded area.

The operation of Union also has the property of transitivity and the cancellation properties.

Exercise 74

1. Use a diagram and two sets to show that A U B is closed.

2. Show that A U B is commutative by drawing diagrams using sets.

3. Write T for true and F for false for each of the following:

259

If A is a subset of B, then A U B = A   ; A U B = B   ; A U A' = Universe   ;

A is a subset of A U B   ; B is a subset of A U B   ; A U { } = { }   ;

A U { } = { }   ; { } U Universe = { }   ; { } U { } = Universe   .

Problems Solved by Venn Diagrams

The number of elements in a finite set A is indicated by the symbol n(A).

Example 1: If A = {2, 3, 6, 8}, then n(A) = 4. If B = {− 1, 0, 1}, then n(B) = 3.
If C = the empty set, then n(C) = 0.

If A ∩ B = an empty set, then n(A U B) = n(A) + n(B). That is, if two sets are disjoint, then the number of elements in their Union is equal to the sum of the numbers in each set.

Example 2: Let A = {1, 2, 3, 4} and B = {8, 9, 10, 11, 12}. Since A ∩ B = an empty set, n(A) = 4 and n(B) = 5, then n(A U B) = 4 + 5 or 9.

Example 3: Let U = all the children living in a two family dwelling. Let J = all of the children in the Jones family (Ann, Betty, Cathy) and let S = all of the children in the Smith family (Don, Ella, Frank, Geraldine). The total number of children in the dwelling is 7. Note that J ∩ S equals an empty set. n(J ∩ S) = 0.

The Venn Diagram will illustrate the above statement.
n(J U S) = n(J) + n(S) = 3 + 4 = 7.

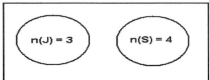

A different situation arises when the two sets have elements in common. If we wish to determine the number of marbles in the possession of the children living in the dwelling in the above example, and we know that the Smith children have 103 marbles and all of the girls in the dwelling have 147 marbles, it does not necessarily follow that the total number of marbles is 103 + 147. Because there are two sets that are not disjoint, that is, there are girls common to both sets.

Let S = {Don, Ella, Frank, Geraldine} and the set of girls in the dwelling G = {Ann, Betty, Cathy, Ella, Geraldine}. Therefore, S ∩ G = {Ella, Geraldine}. If we count 103 + 147 marbles, we will have counted Ella's and Geraldine's marbles twice. Therefore, to obtain an accurate total, we must now subtract the number of marbles owned by Ella and Geraldine. This example leads to the following definition.

If A ∩ B ≠ an empty set, then n(A U B) = n(A) + n(B) − n(A ∩ B).

260

Example 4: Let C = {2, 4, 6, 8} and D = {1, 2, 3, 4, 5}, then C ∩ D = {2, 4}. Now n(C) = 4, n(D) = 5, and n(C ∩ D) = 2. Therefore, n(C U D) = 4 + 5 – 2 = 7.
List C U D and count the number of elements.

Note that this is the same type of thinking that was used in probability.

Exercise 75

1. Indicate the number of elements in each of the following sets:

a) Universe = N and – 5 ≤ x ≤ 2
b) Universe = I and   – 2 ≤ x ≤ 0
c) Universe = I and   – 4 < x ≤ 4
d) Universe = N and – 4 ≤ x < 5

2. Determine the number of elements in each of the following:

a) A U B where A = {1, 2, 3, 4, 5} and B = {– 1, – 2, – 3, – 4}

b) A U B where A = {1, 2, 3, 4, 5, 6, 7} and B = {2, 4, 6}

c) A U B where x is an Integer and – 3 ≤ x < 1 and B = – 5 < x < 0

d) A U B where x is an Integer.   A = – 5 ≤ x < 0 and B = 0 < x < 4

3. If A = {1, 2, 3, 4}, B = {2, 3, 4, 5} and C = {4, 5, 6, 7} find the number of elements in each of the following:

a) (B ∩ C)   b) (A ∩ B) U C   c) A ∩ (B U C)

Example: In a class, 46 students study Mathematics, 36 study English and 38 study French. There are 18 students who study Mathematics and French only; 9 who study Mathematics and English only: and 15 who study English and French only. 3 study all three subjects. How many students are in the class? How many study exactly two subjects? How many study exactly one subject?

We know that 3 students study all three subjects. Therefore, we place 3 in the intersection of the three sets. Now, 15 students study Mathematics and English only. We place these students in the intersection of M and E.

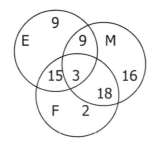

Since 15 pupils study English and French there are 15 pupils who are in the intersection of E and F. Since 18 students study Mathematics and French only, they are placed in the intersection of M and F. 46 students study Mathematics. We have 9 + 3 + 18 accounted for. Therefore, there are 16 students placed in the set M. 36 study English. We have accounted for 9 + 3 + 15. Therefore, 9 students are placed in the set E. 38 students study French. We have accounted for 15 + 3 +18. Therefore, we place 2 in the set F.

The total number in the class is 72. 27 students study exactly one subject and 3 students study the three subjects. 42 students study exactly two subjects.

Exercise 76

1. In a league consisting of 8 teams, 3 sportswriters chose the following teams to win on a particular day. The first sportswriter chose Montreal, Toronto, Detroit, and New York: the second chose Chicago, Toronto, Montreal, and Atlanta to win; and the third chose Montreal, Detroit, Boston, and Chicago to win. Washington was not chosen to win by any of the 3 sportswriters. Which teams were scheduled to play against one another on this particular day?

_____   _____

_____   _____

_____   _____

2. A doctor prescribed vitamins A, B, C to a group of 100 people. He prescribed vitamin A to 28 people; vitamin B to 30; vitamin C to 42; vitamin A and B only to 8; vitamin A and C only to 10; vitamin B and C only to 5; vitamin A, B and C to 3.
How many people did not have to take vitamins?
How many people took vitamin C only?   How many people took exactly two vitamins?

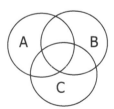

3. A used car dealer advertised 40 cars with the following "extras": 27 cars had radios; 34 had heaters; 11 had white-wall tires; 2 had radios only; 1 had white-wall tires only; 8 had radios and white-wall tires; 5 were equipped with all three "extras".

How many of the cars had heaters and white-wall tires?

How many had heaters and radios only?

How many had exactly two "extras"?

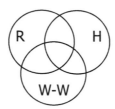

SELF-ASSESSMENT of the ATTAINMENT of the OBJECTIVES

	5	4	3	2	1
- write an example of a Universal set					
- write a set that is a subset of a Universal set					
- write the complement of this set					
- write two sets and show their Intersection by using a Venn diagram					
- use the same two sets and show their Union by using a Venn					
- write two sets that are disjoint					
- write the meaning of an empty set					
- list three sets and show them on a diagram using three circles					
- write an example using the identity element for Intersection					
- write the meaning of the Union of two sets					
- solve problems using the Intersection of sets					
- solve problems using the Union of sets					
- solve problems using Venn diagrams					

Score /65   Date _____

Section VIII – Operations Using Sets
Post–Test VIII

Answers can be found at the back of the book.

1. Construct a Venn diagram in which U = {1, 2, 3, 4, 5} and B = {3, 4}.

2. Using the information in number 1 write the complement of B.

3. If A = {6, 8, 10, 12} and B = {10, 12, 14}, then A ∩ B =
and A U B =

4. If A = {1, 2, 3, 4} and B = {5, 6, 7}, then A ∩ B =

5. What is the intersection of the set of Natural numbers and the set of Integers?

6. If A is a set of numbers between 80 and 110 and B = 90 < x < 100, where x is an odd number, then A ∩ B =

7. If A = {5, 10, 15, 20} and B = all odd Natural numbers less than 20, then A U B =

8. What is Ra U Re?   What is Ra ∩ Re?

Solve the following problems by using Venn Diagrams:

9. In a class, 36 students study Mathematics, 24 study English and 30 study French. There are 18 students who study Mathematics and French; 9 who study Mathematics and English. 3 study all three subjects. How many students are in the class? How many study Mathematics but not English? How many study exactly two subjects? How many study exactly one subject?

Number of students in the class   How many study Mathematics but not English? How many students study exactly two subjects?   How many study exactly one subject?

10. In a league consisting of 8 teams, three sportswriters chose the following teams to win on a particular day. The first sportswriter chose Montreal, Toronto, Detroit, and New York to win: the second chose Chicago, Toronto, Montreal, and Atlanta to win; and the third chose Montreal, Detroit, Boston, and Chicago to win. Washington was not chosen to win by any of the three sportswriters. What teams were scheduled to play against each other on this particular day?

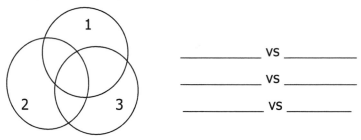

_____ vs _____

_____ vs _____

_____ vs _____

Score_____   Date _____

Section IX — Relations and Graphs
Pre–Test IX

Answers to these problems can be found at the end of the book.

Plot each of the following:

1. n is an Integer and $-4 \leq n \leq 3$

- 6 -5 -4 -3 -2 -1 0 1 2 3 4 5 6

2. n is a Real number and $-2 < n < 4$

-6 -5 -4 -3 -2 -1 0 1 2 3 4 5 6

3. n is a Real number and $-3 < n$ and $4 > n$

- 6 -5 -4 -3 -2 -1 0 1 2 3 4 5 6

4. If the Universe is {1, 2, 3, 4, 5} list all of the ordered pairs in which the second component is equal to the first component squared.

5. Plot the following points: $(3, -5), (-3, 5), (-3, -5), (3, 5)$

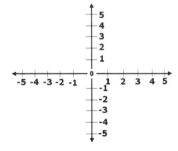

6. Plot the points (4, 3) and (3, 4). Are they at the same position?

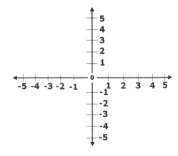

7. Using the Natural numbers as the Universe, plot the points that will satisfy the condition y = x.

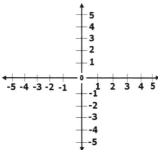

8. Using the Real numbers as the Universe, construct the graph of y = 2x + 1.

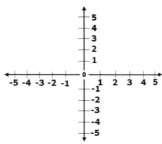

9. Using the Real numbers as the Universe, construct the graph of $0 \leq x \cap 0 \leq y \leq 2$.

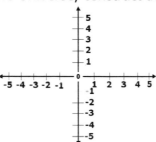

10. Determine the slope of the lines on which the points A (2, 3) and B (4, 6) are on the given line.

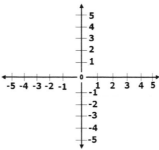

11. Find the midpoint of a line segment whose endpoints have the coordinates (3, 1) and (8, 5).

Score _____   Date _____

267

Unit 21—Relations and Graphs

OBJECTIVES

- write an example of a relation
- tell which component is listed first in an ordered pair
- draw a Cartesian plane
- name the quadrants in this plane
- place an ordered pair in each quadrant
- demonstrate the ability to write the coordinates of a number of points on the plane
- demonstrate the ability to plot points on a plane having been given a linear equation
- after having drawn the graph of a linear equation, determine the area that satisfies the condition, is greater than
- determine the intersection of the graphs of two linear equations
- find the intersection of two conditions that contain inequalities
- find the union of two conditions containing inequalities
- determine the slope of a line segment
- write the slope of a line in mathematical symbolism
- explain when the slope of a line is positive
- explain when the slope of a line is negative
- explain when the slope of a line is 0
- determine the length of a line segment
- separate a line segment in a given ratio
- find the condition of a linear relation

A Review of the Number System

The following is a review of the number system as outlined in Unit 9.

The set of Natural numbers is the set of positive Whole numbers and the number line is as follows:

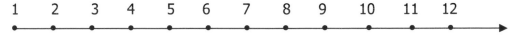

The set of Integers consists of the positive Whole numbers, the negative Whole numbers, and zero. The number line is as follows:

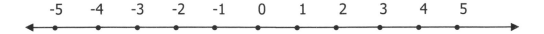

The set of Rational numbers consists of the positive Whole numbers, the negative Whole numbers, zero, and all numbers that can be written in the form of $\frac{a}{b}$ where a and b are Integers and $b \neq 0$. The number line is dense and is as follows:

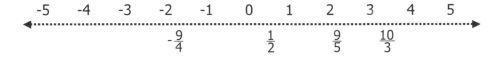

268

Note that between any two Whole numbers there are an infinite number of numbers. The set of Real numbers consists of the Rational numbers plus the Irrational numbers (non-terminating, non-recurring decimal fractions) such as $\sqrt{2}$, etc. On the Real number line, every point on the line is coordinated to a number and every Real number has a point on the number line. The Real number line is continuous.

Plotting Points on a Line

It is important to know the set of numbers (called the Universe) when plotting points. Examine the following examples:

Example 1: If n is a Natural number, plot the following:

n = 8   1   2   3   4   5   6   7   8   9   10   11   12

n > 7   1   2   3   4   5   6   7   8   9   10   11   12

n ≥ 4   1   2   3   4   5   6   7   8   9   10   11   12

n < 5   1   2   3   4   5   6   7   8   9   10   11   12

n ≤ 3   1   2   3   4   5   6   7   8   9   10   11   12

n > 4 and n < 8   1   2   3   4   5   6   7   8   9   10   11   12

n < 3 or n > 7   1   2   3   4   5   6   7   8   9   10   11   12

Notice that the words "and" and "or" were used in the last two examples. "and" means that both of the conditions must be fulfilled. "or" means that one, or the other, or both of the conditions must be fulfilled. The word "or" is used in the inclusive sense – meaning one or the other or both.

Compare this with Union that means "or" and Intersection that means "and".

Example 2: If n is an Integer, plot the following:

n < − 5   -9   -8   -7   -6   -5   -4   -3   -2   -1   0   1

n ≥ − 3 and n ≤ 2   -6   -5   -4   -3   -2   -1   0   1   2   3   4

If n is a Rational number it is best to use a dotted line ---------- that indicates that although there are many fractions between the Whole numbers, there is still room for more numbers.

Example 3: If n is a Rational number, plot the following:

n > − 2 and n < 4

$$-6 \quad -5 \quad -4 \quad -3 \quad -2 \quad -1 \quad 0 \quad 1 \quad 2 \quad 3 \quad 4 \quad 5$$

○- -○

The open circle ○ means that the number is not included.

If n is a Real number, then the number line is continuous. That is, every point on the number line is coordinated to a Real number and every Real number has a point on the line. Therefore, we will use a solid line to plot the points.

Example 4: If n is a Real number, plot the following: n ≥ − 3 and n ≤ 4

$$-6 \quad -5 \quad -4 \quad -3 \quad -2 \quad -1 \quad 0 \quad 1 \quad 2 \quad 3 \quad 4 \quad 5$$

The closed circle ◉ means that the number is included.

Exercise 77

1. If n is a Natural number, plot the following.

a) n > 4 and n < 6

$$1 \quad 2 \quad 3 \quad 4 \quad 5 \quad 6 \quad 7 \quad 8 \quad 9 \quad 10 \quad 11$$

b) n ≥ 3 or n ≤ 5

$$1 \quad 2 \quad 3 \quad 4 \quad 5 \quad 6 \quad 7 \quad 8 \quad 9 \quad 10 \quad 11$$

2. If n is a variable, plot the following on the Integer number line.

a) n > 0 or n < − 4

$$-6 \quad -5 \quad -4 \quad -3 \quad -2 \quad -1 \quad 0 \quad 1 \quad 2 \quad 3$$

b) n > − 3 and n < − 1

$$-6 \quad -5 \quad -4 \quad -3 \quad -2 \quad -1 \quad 0 \quad 1 \quad 2 \quad 3$$

3. If n is a Rational number, plot the following:

a) n < 6 and n > − 4

$$-5 \quad -4 \quad -3 \quad -2 \quad -1 \quad 0 \quad 1 \quad 2 \quad 3 \quad 4 \quad 5 \quad 6 \quad 7$$

b) n < 5 or n ≥ − 3

$$-5 \quad -4 \quad -3 \quad -2 \quad -1 \quad 0 \quad 1 \quad 2 \quad 3 \quad 4 \quad 5 \quad 6 \quad 7$$

4. If n is a Real number, plot the following:

a) n ≤ 5 and n > − 2

$$-4 \quad -3 \quad -2 \quad -1 \quad 0 \quad 1 \quad 2 \quad 3 \quad 4 \quad 5 \quad 6$$

b) n > − 4 or n < 2

$$-6 \quad -5 \quad -4 \quad -3 \quad -2 \quad -1 \quad 0 \quad 1 \quad 2 \quad 3 \quad 4$$

270

5. If n is a Real number, plot each of the following:

a) n + 3 = 7   -6 -5 -4 -3 -2 -1   0   1   2   3   4   5

b) 2n + 4 = 6   -6 -5 -4 -3 -2 -1   0   1   2   3   4   5

c) 5 + n = 9   -6 -5 -4 -3 -2 -1   0   1   2   3   4   5

d) 3n > 12   -6 -5 -4 -3 -2 -1   0   1   2   3   4   5

e) 4n + 1 < 17   -6 -5 -4 -3 -2 -1   0   1   2   3   4   5

f) 2n + 7 ≤ 19 -6 -5 -4 -3 -2 -1   0   1   2   3   4   5

g) 3n + 2 ≥ 14   -6 -5 -4 -3 -2 -1   0   1   2   3   4   5

Ordered Pairs

We have seen equations and inequalities that contained one variable. For example, in $2n + 1 = 6$, there is one variable n and we have found a value or values that satisfy the condition(s). This type of open sentence is called a relation.

Now we shall examine relations that contain two variables. For instance, "x > y" is a condition that selects numbers from the given Universe. (Unless otherwise stated, we will use the set of Real numbers as the Universe.) x > y is a relation containing two variables, x and y and it has no truth value until replacements are made for both x and y. If we say that x = 1 and y = 3, then the open sentence is false because 1 is not greater than 3. If we say that x = 4 and y = 2, then the open sentence is true because 4 > 2. Note that a pair of replacements is made for x and y in x > y.

If x = 1 and y = 2 then 1 > 2 is false, but if x = 2 and y = 1 then 2 > 1 is true.
If x = 1 and y = 3 then 1 > 3 is false, but if x = 3 and y = 2 then 3 > 1 is true.
If x = 1 and y = 4 then 1 > 4 is false, but if x = 4 and y = 3 then 4 > 3 is true.
If x = 1 and y = 5 then 1 > 5 is false, but if x = 5 and y = 1 then 5 > 1 is true.

We see that a pair of replacements is made in each case: one for the variable x, and one for the variable y. Further, we see that the order in which the replacements are made makes a difference in the result. 1 > 2 is false but 2 > 1 is true.

We symbolize an ordered pair of numbers by enclosing them in parentheses where the first number refers to the replacement for x and the second number refers to the replacement for y. The ordered pair x and y is written (x, y).

We call x the first component and y the second component of the ordered pair.

For the open sentence x > y, some of the ordered pairs that satisfy the relation are: (2, 1), (3, 1), (3, 2), (4, 1), (4, 2), (4, 3) and so on.

271

Example: If the Universe is 1, 2, 3, 4, 5, 6, 7, 8, 9, 10, list the ordered pairs that satisfy the condition that the second component is twice the first component. That is, y = 2x. The ordered pairs are: (1, 2), (2, 4), (3, 6), (4, 8), (5, 10). We would not use (6, 12) because 12 is not in the Universe.

Exercise 78

1. Fill in the missing component in each of the following ordered pairs so that the first component will be three times the second component:

a) (, 3a) b) (, – 2) c) (– 6,)   d) (0,), e) (, $\frac{1}{2}$)

2. If the Universe = {1, 2}, list the ordered pairs that are possible.

3. If the Universe is {1, 2, 3, 4, 5, 6, 7, 8, 9}, list all of the ordered pairs in which the second component is the first component squared.

4. If two people were standing at the same intersection, and one walked 3 blocks east and five blocks north, and the other person walked five blocks east and 3 blocks north, would the 2 people arrive at the same place if all of the streets were straight and all of the intersections were right angles?

Explain:

The Cartesian Plane

We have seen how to construct the Real number line.

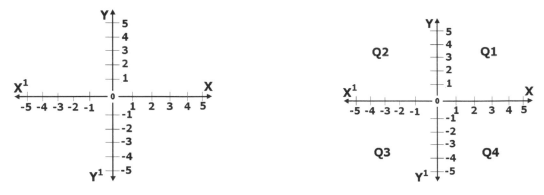

Instead of constructing the Real number line horizontally, we could have constructed it vertically. We will construct the vertical number line so that the zero coincides with the zero on the horizontal number line. The horizontal axis is named X'X and the vertical axis will be named Y'Y. We have now separated the plane into 4 regions

272

each of which is called a quadrant. Notice that the quadrants (represented by Q) are numbered in a counterclockwise direction. (See diagram above.)
It should be noted that if the coordinate of x is positive and the coordinate of y is positive, then the point is in Q1.
If the coordinate of x is negative and the coordinate of y is positive, the point is in Q2.

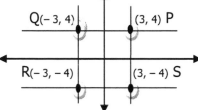

```
        (−, +) │ (+, +)
    ───────────┼───────────→
        (−,−)  │ (+, −)
               │
```

If the coordinate of x is negative and the coordinate of y is negative, the point is in Q3.

If the coordinate of x is positive and the coordinate of y is negative, the point is in Q4.

Choose a point P in Q1 and draw a perpendicular line to X'X. If this line meets X'X at 3, draw a perpendicular line to YY' and if this line meets YY' at 4 the coordinates of P are (3, 4).

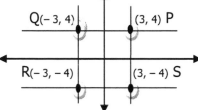

Choose a point P in Q2 and draw similar lines. Note that if the lines meet X'X at − 3 and YY' at 4, the coordinates of the point Q are (− 3, 4).

If a point is chosen in Q3 such that the vertical line meets XX at − 3 and meets YY at − 4, the coordinates of that point are (− 3, − 4).

If a point is chosen in Q4 such that the vertical line meets XX at 3 and the horizontal line meets YY at − 4, the coordinates of the point are (3, − 4).

It should be noted that in all cases, we count on the x-axis first, and then on the y axis. When we refer to the point (2, − 3), we mean that we have counted 2 spaces to the right on the XX axis and 3 spaces down on the YY axis. This is why (2, − 3) is called an ordered pair. The order is that the number on the x axis is the first component and the number on the y axis is the second component of the ordered pair. Therefore, the point (3, − 2) is not the same as the point (− 2, 3).

Note the position of each of the following points.

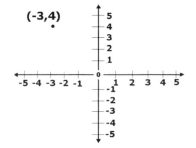

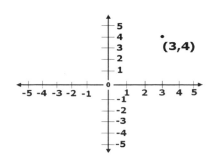

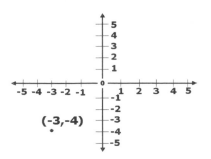 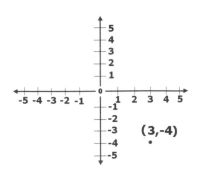

Example: Plot the points on the following plane. Indicate the ordered pairs that are coordinated to each point. (− 2, 3), (4, 4), (2, − 5), (− 5, 2), (3, − 2), (− 3, − 2). Write the coordinates for each point on the plane.

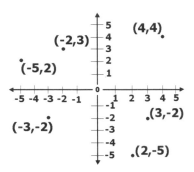

Exercise 79

1. Write the coordinates of each point in the following plane:

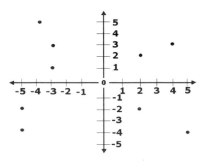

2. Plot the following points on the graph:
   (3, − 4), (0, 5), (0, − 2), (3, 0), (5, − 3), (− 4, − 3), (− 2, − 3)

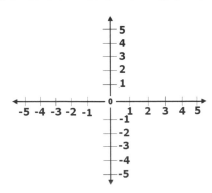

274

3a) (3, 3), (– 3, 3),
   (–3, – 3), (3, – 3)

b) (0, 4), (– 4, 0),
   (4, 0)

c) (3, 2), (– 3, 2),
   (– 3, – 2), (3, – 2)

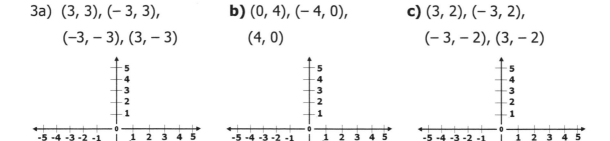

Plotting Linear Equations and Inequalities

A linear equation is an equation in which the highest power of the variable is 1. For example, $x + y = 7$. Notice that there are two variables in this equation and when no exponent is listed, it is meant to be 1. Other equations have variables to a higher exponent. $x^2 + 5x + 6 = y$ contains the variable x to the second degree (or we say that x is squared). $x^3 = y$ has a variable in which the exponent is 3. We read this as x cubed. The highest exponent of the variables indicates the type of graph that will result. We will confine ourselves to relations whose variables have an exponent of 1. As you will see, the graphs of such relations will be dots in a straight line or a straight line if the Universe is the set of Real numbers. It is for this reason that they are called linear relations.

Example 1:   Using the Natural numbers as the Universe, plot the points that will satisfy the condition that $x = y$. Although we cannot write all of the ordered pairs, let us consider the following. If $x = 1$, then $y = 1$; if $x = 2$, then $y = 2$; if $x = 3$, then $y = 3$; if $x = 4$, then $y = 4$ and so on.

An easy way to determine the ordered pairs is to make a chart.
Note that as we assign a value to x, we get a corresponding value for y. We say that y is a function of x. We wish to draw the graph of $y = x$ where the Universe is the Natural numbers.

x	1	2
y	1	2

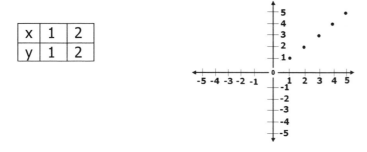

Example 2: If the Universe is the set of Integers, the graph of x = y will be the following:

x	1	− 2
y	1	− 2

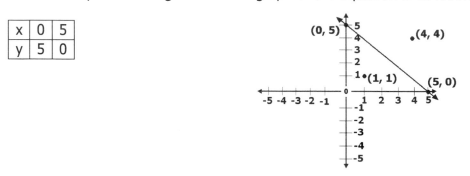

Example 3: With the Universe being the Real numbers, construct the graph of x + y = 5.

We will write this equation as y = 5 − x. (Note that we have subtracted x from each side of the equation.) Then we will assign a number to x and get the corresponding value of y. It is fairly simple when we let x = 0 and find the value of y, and then let y = 0 and find the value of x − when this can be done.

At this stage, you should note that because we are dealing with linear equations, only two sets of ordered pairs are necessary because two points will determine the position and the slope of a straight line. The graph of the equation is as follows.

x	0	5
y	5	0

It should be noted that the graph of the linear equation separates the plane into three regions. All points on the line satisfy the condition "is equal to". All points on one side of the line satisfy the condition "is greater than", and all points on the other side of the line satisfy the condition "is less than". Select any point to the right of (or above) the graph (as observed by the reader), say (4, 4). In y = 5 − x. If y = 4 and x = 4, the relation becomes 4 > 5 − 4 or 4 > 1 and this is a correct statement.

Choose any other point to the right of the graph and you will find that the relation "is greater than" and this is a correct statement.

Now choose a point below the graph, say (1, 1). Substituting in y = 5 − x we obtain 1 < 5 − 1. That is, 1 < 4. By choosing any other point in the same region (to the left of the graph), the relation will be "is less than." For instance, if the point is (1, 1), then y = 5 − x becomes 1 R 5 − 1. The R means "has some relationship to". But 1 < 5 − 1. Every point in this region will have the relationship "is less than".

276

In the previous diagram (but not in all graphs) the three regions are: the graph of the equation that satisfies the relation "is equal to"; the region to the right of the graph (as looked at by the reader) whose coordinates satisfy the condition "is greater than"; and the region to the left of the graph is the region whose coordinates satisfy the condition is "is less than".

Example 4: x – 2y = 4

x	0	4
y	– 2	0

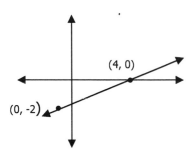

Choose the point (5, 0). x – 2y = 4 becomes 5 – 0 R 4. But 5 > 4. Therefore, all points below (or to the right of the graph) have the relationship "is greater than".

Example 5: Consider the equation y = x. If x is 0, y is 0: if x is 1, y is 1, if x is 2, y is 2, if x = – 3, y = – 3 and so on. Therefore, the graph of y = x is:

x	2	3
y	2	3

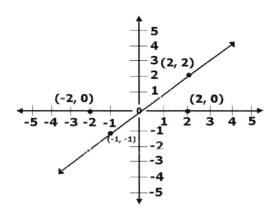

Notice that we are dealing with the set of Real numbers.
Now choose the point (2, 0) to the right of the line. If we replaced x and y by these coordinates, we would have "0 has some relationship to 2". What is this relationship? It is that "2 is greater than 0".

Choose another point above the line (as you look at the page) say (– 2, 0). This tells us that – 2 has some relationship to 0. This relationship is "is less than". That is – 2 < 0. The coordinates of any points in this region will satisfy the relationship "is less than". Now choose a point on the line. Let us select (2, 2). In y = x, where y = 2 and x = 2, we see that the relationship is "is equal to".

Example 6: Construct the graph of y ≤ 2x + 4.
We will construct the graph of y = 2x + 4.
The graph is:

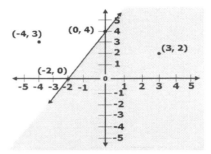

x	0	− 2
y	4	0

In the region above and to the left of the graph (as you look at the diagram) choose any point, say (− 4, 3). Substitute these values in the relation and obtain y R 2x + 4. We obtain 3 R − 4. We know that 3 is greater than − 4 and the point (− 4, 3) was chosen at random. Therefore, all points in this region have the relationship "is greater than".

If we now choose a point on the other side of the line say (3, 2) we have 2 R 6 + 4 or 2 R 10. We know that 2 is less than 10, and therefore, all points in this region have the relationship "is less than".

Exercise 80

1. Draw the graph of each of the following. The Universe is the set of Real numbers

a) x = − y

b) y = 2x

c) y = 2x + 1

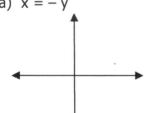 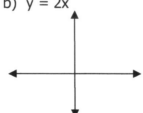 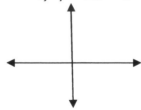

2. Determine the graph that satisfies each of the following and shade the region that satisfies the condition.   Use the Real numbers as the Universe and shade the relationship determined by the condition,

a) x ≥ 3

b) y ≥ 4

c) y > 2x − 3

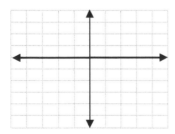 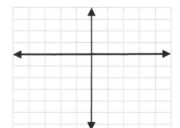 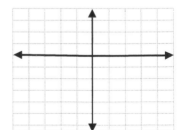

278

$y \geq 3x - 2$ e) $y \leq 2x + 3$ f) $y \geq x - 4$

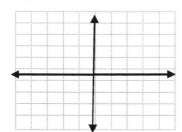 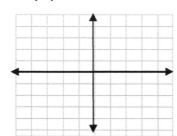 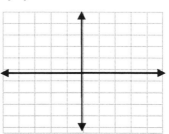

The Union or Intersection of Relations

Example: Using the set of Real numbers, determine x + y = 5 and 2x − y = 1.

Draw the graph of each relation.

$x + y = 5$ and $2x - y = 1$

x	0	5
y	5	0

x	0	1
y	− 1	1

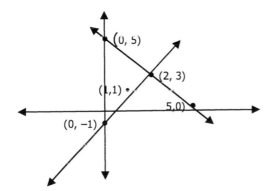

This is a graphical representation of the solution of a simultaneous equation.

$x + y = 5$
$\underline{2x - y = 1}$
$3x \quad\quad = 6$ (addition)
$\quad x \quad = 2$

Substitute in either equation.

$x + y = 5$
$2 + y = 5$
$\quad\quad y = 3$

Notice that all points on the line satisfy the condition x + y = 5 and all of the points on the other line satisfy the condition 2x − y = 1. Therefore, the point at which the graphs intersect is common to the two graph lines. That is, x + y = 5 ∩ 2x − y = 1 is the point (2, 3). This is the intersection of the lines.

All points on the line x + y = 5 satisfy this condition and all points on the line 2x − y = 1 satisfy its condition. Therefore, the union of x + y = 5 and 2x − y = 1 consists of all of the points on both lines.

The Solution of Simultaneous Equations

If two or more linear equations in two variables have a common solution, they are called a system of simultaneous equations.

Example 1: Solve the following: $x + y = 7$ and $2x + y = 9$.
We wish to eliminate one of the variables, in this case, y.

$x + y = 7$
$\underline{2x + y = 9}$ Subtract the second equation from the first equation.
$-x \quad\ = -2$ or $x = 2$.   Substitute this value of x in one of the original
                    equations.

$x + y = 7 \rightarrow 2 + y = 7 \rightarrow y = 5$ Subtract 2 from each side of the equation.
Therefore, the solution is (2, 5).

Example 2: Solve the following: $3p + 2q = 10$, and $p - q = -5$
We cannot eliminate one variable by addition or subtraction unless we multiply the second relation by 2 to eliminate the q's.

$3p + 2q = \quad 10$
$\underline{2p - 2q = -10}$ Add
$5p \quad\quad = \quad 0$ $p = 0$ Substitute for p in one of the original equations.
$3p + 2q = 10 \rightarrow 0 + 2q = 10 \rightarrow 2q = 10 \rightarrow q = 5$. Therefore, the solution is (0, 5).

The following are steps to be taken to find the union and/or intersection of relations involving conditions of inequality.

Example 3: Find the intersection of $2x + 3y \geq 12$ and $x - 2y \leq 4$.

x	0	6
y	4	0

x	0	4
y	−2	0

Step1. Draw the line that satisfies the condition $2x + 3y = 12$.

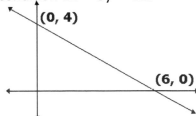

Step 2. Draw the line that satisfies the condition $x - 2y = 4$.

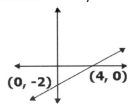

3: Determine the region in which all of the points satisfy the condition $2x + 3y \geq 12$ and shade that area.

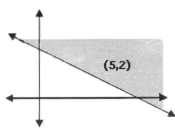

Step 4: Determine the region in which all of the points satisfy the condition $x - 2y \leq 4$ and shade that area.

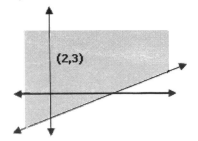

Step 5. Combine the two shaded areas.

Step 6. Indicate the area that satisfies both conditions.

Step 7: The area that satisfies the two conditions is to the right of the line passing and above the line through (0, 4) and (6, 0) and above the line passing through (0, − 2) and (4, 0).

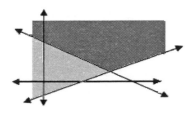

Exercise 81

1. Using the set of Real numbers, determine the intersection of each of the following:

a) x + y = 6 and 2x − 3y = 2

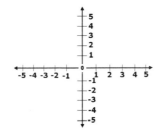

b) 2x − y = 5 and 2x + y = 7

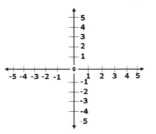

c) 3x ı y = 10 and 4x   5y = −12

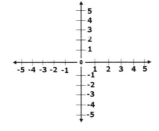

d) 4x + 5y − 9and 3x − y − 2

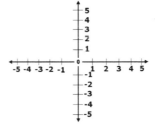

e) 2x + y = 6 and 6x − y = 2

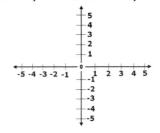

f) x + 2y = 5 and 2x − 3y = − 4

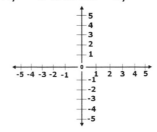

1. Solve each of the above as simultaneous equations and check your answers with the graphical results in number 1.

a) x + y = 6 and 2x − 3y = 2

b) 2x − y = 5 and 2x + y = 7

c) 3x + y = 10 and 4x − 5y =-12

d) 4x + 5y = 9 and 3x − y = 2

1. Using the set of Real numbers as the Universe, find the intersection of each of the following:

a)   x ≥ 0, y ≥ 0

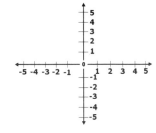

∩ =

b) x ≥ y, y ≤ 4

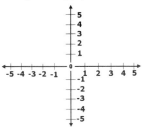

∩ =

c)   x ≤ 4 and x − y ≥ 0

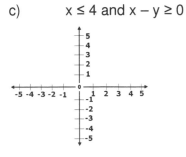

∩ =

d) 0 ≤ x ≤ 3 and 0 ≥ y ≥ 2

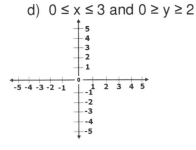

∩ =

e) $2 \leq x \leq 5$ and $-5 \leq y \leq -2$

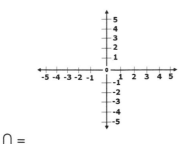

∩ =

f) $2 \leq x \leq 5$ and $1 \leq y \leq 4$

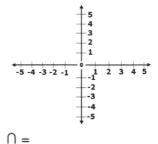

∩ =

The Slope of a Line Segment

We are familiar with the slope of a roof, the slope of a ski hill, and the slope of a road. Consider the line segment in the following diagram. It is neither horizontal nor vertical. We may wish to know the slope of this line segment. We can do this by placing it on the Cartesian plane.

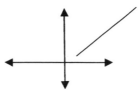

When the line is on the Cartesian plane, and the Universe is the set of Real numbers, every point on the plane has a set of coordinates – that is, a specific value for x and a specific value for y.

We will choose any point P_1 on the line segment and let its coordinates be (x_1, y_1). We will choose another point P_2 on the line segment and let its coordinates be (x_2, y_2). A perpendicular line will be drawn from P_1 to the x-axis and a line horizontal with the x-axis will be drawn to meet the perpendicular line at Q. Therefore, the coordinates of the point Q will be (x_1, y_2).

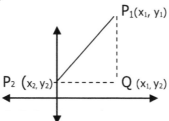

The slope of the line is the ratio $\dfrac{P_1Q}{P_2Q}$ or $\dfrac{\text{rise}}{\text{run}}$ or $\dfrac{y_1 - y_2}{x_1 - x_2}$ or $\dfrac{\Delta y}{\Delta x}$.

It should be noted that $x_2 \neq x_1$ because if they were equal, the denominator would equal 0 and division by 0 is undefined.

The run is often referred to as Δx. This is read "delta x". It should be noted that this is the usual symbol used for the rate of change of x or the "difference between" usually found by subtraction. It does not mean that x is multiplied by Δ. In a similar fashion, Δy is used for the rate of change of y and is often referred to as the rise.

Example 1: Determine the slope of the line on which the points A (2, 3) and B (4, 6) are on the given line.

The following is the graph of the line:

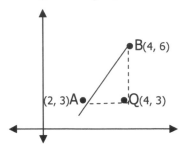

Plot the points A and B and draw a line segment to pass through them.
Draw BQ parallel to the Y-axis. Note that the x coordinates of all points on BQ are 4.
Draw AQ parallel to the X-axis. Note that the y coordinates of all points on AQ are 3.
Therefore, the point Q at which these lines intersect has coordinates (4, 3).

The length of BQ is $y_1 - y_2$ or $6 - 3$ or 3. Therefore, the rise (or Δy) is 3.

The length of AQ is $x_1 - x_2$ or $4 - 2$ or 2. Therefore, the run (or Δx) is 2.

The slope is equal to the $\frac{\text{rise}}{\text{run}}$ or $\frac{y_1 - y_2}{x_1 - x_2}$ or $\frac{3}{2}$.

The above example was done using Quadrant 1. The same method will apply when using other quadrants. With a little bit of practice, the determination of the slope of a line can be shortened. The following example will demonstrate this fact.

Example 2: Find the slope of the line in which A (5, − 1) and B (− 4, 3) are points on the line.

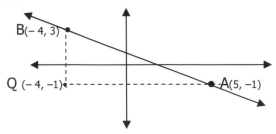

The rise is $3 - (-1)$ or 4. The run is $(-4) - 5$ or -9. Therefore, the slope is $-\frac{4}{9}$.

284

The slope of a line that goes from left to right is negative. The slope of a line that goes from right to left is positive.

Example 3: Determining the slope of a line may be made easier by letting the slope of the line be represented by "m" and defining the slope of a line to be: $m = \frac{y_1 - y_2}{x_1 - x_2}$.

Example 4: Find the slope of a line passing through (– 2, 6) and (7, 3).

$m = \frac{6 - 3}{-2 - 7} = \frac{3}{-9}$ or $\frac{-1}{3}$

I should be noted that the slope of a horizontal line is 0 because the rise is 0. The slope of a horizontal line is undefined because the run is 0 and when 0 is the denominator, the fraction is undefined.

For example,

a) y = 3   b) x = 4

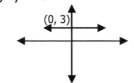   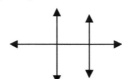

The rise is 0.   The run is 0.
Therefore, the slope is 0.   Therefore, the denominator is 0.
                                      Division by 0 is undefined.

Exercise 82

1. Find the slope of the line passing through the given points by using the formula.

a) (2, 6), (3, 4) m =   b) (3, 7), (– 4, – 10) m =

b) (5, – 2), (5, 5) m =   d) (3, 4), (– 6, 4) m =

d) (– 2, 5), (8, – 3) m =

2. Find the slope of the line y = – 3
3. Find the slope of the line x = – 4

Determining the Length of a Line Segment

You may have observed that a right angled triangle results at the point at which the drawn lines intersect. In any right angled triangle, $h^2 = a^2 + b^2$. That is, the square on the hypotenuse is equal to the sum of the squares on the other two sides. A proof of this fact will be found in the next Unit.

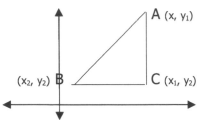

The measure of AC is $y_1 - y_2$ and the measure of BC is $x_1 - x_2$.

Therefore, $AB^2 = (y_1 - y_2)^2 + (x_1 - x_2)^2$.

In the diagram above, let A have coordinates (5, 4); B have coordinates (1, 1); and then C will have the coordinates (5, 1).

$Y_1 - Y_2 = 4 - 1$ or 3
$X_1 - X_2 = 5 - 1$ or 4

Therefore, $h^2 = (y_1 - y_2)^2 + (x_1 - x_2)^2$ or $h^2 = 9 + 16$ or $25 \rightarrow h = 5$

If $P(x_1, y_1)$ and $Q(x_2, y_2)$ are two points, then the length of PQ is $\sqrt{\Delta x^2 + \Delta y^2}$ or $\sqrt{(x_1 - x_2)^2 + (y_1 - y_2)^2}$.

Note from the above, $\sqrt{(x_1 - x_2)^2 + (y_1 - y_2)^2} = \sqrt{4^2 + 3^2} = \sqrt{15 + 9} = \sqrt{25} = 5$
Therefore, the sides are 3, 4 and 5.

Separating a Line Segment in a Given Ratio

Example: Find the midpoint of a line segment whose endpoints have the coordinates (3, 1) and (8, 5).

In the diagram below, let A be the point with coordinates (3, 1) and let B be the point with coordinates (8, 5). Complete the figure as shown.

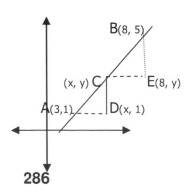

The triangles ADC and CEB are similar, ADC and CEB are right angles, AC = CB, and $\angle CAD = \angle BCE$. Therefore, AD = CE.
$x - 3 = 8 - x \rightarrow 2x = 11$
$x = 5.5$
Also DC = EB
$y - 1 = 5 - y \rightarrow 2y = 6 \rightarrow y = 3$
Therefore, the coordinates of the point C are (5.5, 3).

286

The midpoint of a line segment is $\left(\dfrac{x_1 + x_2}{2}, \dfrac{y_1 + y_2}{2}\right)$. Check with the above diagram.

In general, a formula for finding the coordinates of a point that separate a given line in any ratio is as follows:

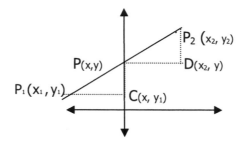

The triangle $P_1C\,P$ is similar to the triangle PDP_2.

Therefore, $\dfrac{P_1C}{PD} = \dfrac{P_1P}{P\,P_2}$.

That is, $\dfrac{x - x_1}{x_2 - x} = \dfrac{a}{b}$ (any ratio)

Solving for x, $bx - bx_1 = ax_2 - ax$

$\quad bx + ax = ax_2 + bx_1$

$\quad x(b + a) = ax_2 + bx_1$

$\quad x = \dfrac{ax_2 + bx_1}{a + b}$

In the same way, let $\dfrac{P_1P}{P\,P_2} = \dfrac{a}{b}$ (any ratio).

That is, $\dfrac{y - y_1}{y_2 - y} = \dfrac{a}{b}$

$ay_2 - ay = by - by_1$

$ay_2 + by_1 = ay + by$

$ay_2 + by_1 = y(a + b)$

Therefore, $y = \dfrac{ay_2 + by_1}{a + b}$.

Therefore, the coordinates of the point P that separates the line in the ratio of $\dfrac{a}{b}$ are

$\dfrac{ax_2 + bx_1}{a + b}, \dfrac{ay_2 + by_1}{a + b}$

Exercise 83

1. Determine the coordinates of the midpoint of the line that joins.

a) (3, 2), (1, 4)

b) (0, 0), (12, 4)

c) $(9, 3), (5, -2)$

d) $(-2, 8), (-4, -2)$

2. Find the coordinates of the point that divides the line joining $(4, -5), (-1, 2)$ in the ratio $3 : 2$.

3. If the points $(4, -1), (6, 0), (7, -2)$ are vertices of a square, determine the coordinates of the fourth vertex.

4. Show that $(5, -1), (3, 4), (7, 2)$ are on a straight line.

5. A line segment is drawn from the point $(25, 30)$ to the X-axis. How long is the segment?

6. The point A is on the positive Y-axis and its distance to the origin is 18 units. Find its coordinates.

7. A rectangle has coordinates $(8, 0), (0, 0)$ and $(0, 6)$. Write the coordinates of the fourth vertex.

Finding the Condition of a Linear Relation

A linear relation can be written in the form, $ax + by + c = 0$

288

We have seen earlier that one and only one straight line can pass through two points. We defined the slope of a line in terms of two given points. The requirements necessary to define a unique line are: a point on the line and the slope of the line; or any two points on the line.

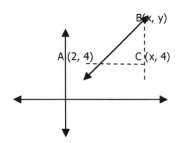

Example 1: Find the equation of the line that passes through the point A (2, 4) with a slope of $\frac{2}{3}$.

Choose any point, B, on the line. Let B have the coordinates (x, y).

$m = \dfrac{\Delta y}{\Delta x} = \dfrac{y-4}{x-2}$

But $m = \frac{2}{3}$

Therefore, $\dfrac{y-4}{x-2} = \dfrac{2}{3} \rightarrow 3y-12 = 2x-4 \rightarrow 2x-3y = 8$ or $2x-3y+8 = 0$.

Example 2: Find the condition of the linear relation whose graph passes through $(-7, 3)$ and whose slope is $-\frac{7}{5}$.

Condition: $m = \dfrac{y-y_1}{x-x_1}$ [where $x - x_1 \neq 0$], where $m = -\frac{7}{5}$ and $(x_1, y_1) = (-7, 3)$

Therefore, $-\dfrac{7}{5} = \dfrac{y-3}{x-(-7)}$

$-7(x+7) = 5(y-3)$

$\rightarrow -7x - 49 = 5y - 15 \rightarrow 7x + 5y + 34 = 0$.

Example 3: Find the condition that determines the line passing through the points $P(-8, -5)$ and $(4, 1)$

$\dfrac{\Delta y}{\Delta x} = \dfrac{1-(-5)}{4-(-8)} = \dfrac{6}{12} = \dfrac{1}{2}$

Condition: $m =$ [where $x - x_1 \neq 0$].

Therefore, $\dfrac{1}{2} = \dfrac{y-1}{x-4} \rightarrow x-4 = 2(y-1) \rightarrow x-4 = 2y-2 \rightarrow x - 2y - 2 = 0$ is the condition.

Exercise 84

1. Write the condition in the form of ax + by + c = 0 for each of the following:

a) the slope is 4 and one point on the line is (3, 2)

b) the slope is 5 and one point on the line is (– 2, 3)

c) m = – 3 and one point on the line is (4, – 3)

d) m = $-\frac{2}{3}$ and one point on the line is (3, – 7)

e) The slope is 0 and one point on the line is (5, – 8)

2. When is the slope

a) equal to 0

b) undefined

c) negative

d) positive

3. Determine the condition in the form of ax + by + c = 0 for each of the following:

a)

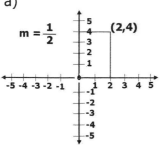

$m = \dfrac{1}{2}$ (2,4)

b)

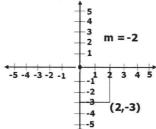

m = -2

(2,-3)

c)

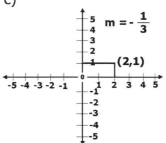

$m = -\dfrac{1}{3}$

(2,1)

4. Find the condition that determines the straight line through each of the following pairs of points:

a) (2, – 5), (6, 3)

b) (1, 1), (4, 2)

c) (8, 8), (0, 7)

d) (0, 0), (– 4, 20)

e) (5, 0), (0, – 5)

SELF-ASSESSMENT of the ATTAINMENT of the OBJECTIVES

	5	4	3	2	1
- write an example of a relation					
- tell which component is listed first in an ordered pair					
- draw a Cartesian plane					
- name the quadrants in this plane					
- place an ordered pair in each quadrant					
- demonstrate the ability to write the coordinates of a number of points on the plane					
- demonstrate the ability to plot points on a plane having been given a linear equation					
- after having drawn the graph of a linear equation, determine the area that satisfies the condition, is greater than					
- determine the intersection of the graphs of two linear equations					
- find the intersection of two conditions that contain inequalities					
- find the union of two conditions containing inequalities					
- determine the slope of a line segment					
- write the slope of a line in mathematical symbolism					
- explain when the slope of a line is positive					
- explain when the slope of a line is negative					
- explain when the slope of a line is 0					
- determine the length of a line segment					
- separate a line segment in a given ratio					
- find the condition of a linear relation					

Score   /95   Date _____

292

Section IX – Relations and Graphs
Post–Test IX

The answers can be found at the back of the book.

Plot each of the following:

1. n is an Integer and $-4 \leq n \leq 3$

$$\begin{array}{ccccccccccccc} -6 & -5 & -4 & -3 & -2 & -1 & 0 & 1 & 2 & 3 & 4 & 5 & 6 \end{array}$$

2. n is a Real number and $-2 < n < 4$

$$\begin{array}{ccccccccccccc} -6 & -5 & -4 & -3 & -2 & -1 & 0 & 1 & 2 & 3 & 4 & 5 & 6 \end{array}$$

3. n is a Real number and $-3 < n$ and $4 > n$

$$\begin{array}{ccccccccccccc} -6 & -5 & -4 & -3 & -2 & -1 & 0 & 1 & 2 & 3 & 4 & 5 & 6 \end{array}$$

4. If the Universe is {1, 2, 3, 4, 5} list all of the ordered pairs in which the second component is equal to the first component squared.

5. Plot the following points: $(3, -5), (-3, 5), (-3, -5), (3, 5)$

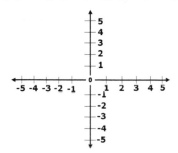

6. Plot the points (4, 3) and (3, 4). Are they at the same position?

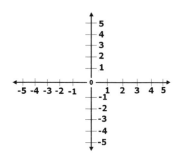

293

7. Using the Natural numbers as the Universe, plot the points that will satisfy the condition y = x.

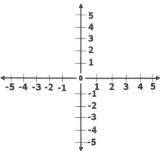

8. Using the Real numbers as the Universe, construct the graph of y = 2x + 1.

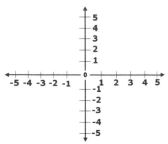

9. Using the Real numbers as the Universe, construct the graph of $0 \leq x \cap 0 \leq y \leq 2$.

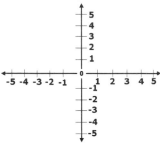

10. Determine the slope of the lines on which the points A (2, 3) and B (4, 6) are on the given line.

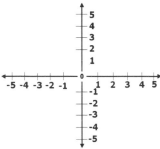

11. Find the midpoint of a line segment whose endpoints have the coordinates (3, 1) and (8, 5).

Score _____ Date _____

294

Section X — Mathematical Logic
Pre–Test

Answers can be found at the end of the book.

1. Complete the following:

    Isosceles triangles have two equal sides.
    ABC is an isosceles triangle.
    Therefore,

2. Complete the following truth table:

p	q	p ∧ q
T	T	
T	F	
F	T	
F	F	

3. Complete the following truth table:

p	q	p V q
T	T	
T	F	
F	T	
F	F	

4. Write the contrapositive of, "if two triangles are congruent, they are similar".

5. Use the truth table to determine if p V q has the same truth value as q V ~p.

p	q	~p	p V q	q V ~p
T	T			
T	F			
F	T			
F	F			

6. Complete the following:

p	q	(p∧q)	(p∧q)∧ q	(p ∧ q)∧ p
T	T			
T	F			
F	T			
F	F			

Score _____   Date _____

295

Unit 22 – Mathematical Logic

OBJECTIVES

- state an axiom
- write a postulate
- write a proposition
- explain inductive reasoning by using an example
- give an example of the use of deductive reasoning
- complete a truth table using conjunction
- complete a truth table using disjunction
- write an example of a syllogism
- negate a sentence
- explain when an implication is true
- write a truth table for equivalence
- write the contrapositive of "if two parallel lines are extended, they will never meet"
- define a tautology
- write the converse of "if ABC is a circle, its area is πr^2.

Mathematical Logic

Mathematical logic (at this level) deals with declarative sentences that have a truth value. That is, these sentences may be classified as either true or as false. For example, $3 + 7 > 9$ is a sentence that is true: whereas, the sentence $3 + 7 < 9$ is a statement that is false. Notice that each conveys a statement.

There must be no ambiguity regarding the classification of sentences due to grammatical errors, the possibility of an exception, the use of undefined terms or any other condition that renders the statement ambiguous. The statements should be based upon previous learning using axioms, postulates, propositions, definitions and proofs.

The Nature of Mathematics

Mathematics (at this level) consists of the use of axioms (self-evident truths), for example, "a number is equal to itself"; postulates (statements that are assumed), for example, "a point has position but no magnitude"; propositions (statements that require proof), for example, "in a right angled triangle, the square on the hypotenuse is equal to the sum of the squares on the other two sides" (the proof of this proposition is contained in this Unit); definitions, for example, "a square is a plane shape in which the four sides are equal and each interior angle is 90º"; and properties of the number system, for example, "the order in which numbers are added will not alter the sum" or on a specific type of concept such as sets and relations.

Inductive and Deductive Reasoning

You were asked to make conjectures in many instances in the previous Units. Some of the conjectures were true but there was no way of ensuring that the conjecture was always true. Some conjectures that were made were: "the sum of the angles of a triangle is equal to 180º". It can be proven that this conjecture is true and this will be done in this Unit. On the other hand, after testing a number of cases, some people may have made the conjecture that $n^2 - n + 41$ will always result in a prime number. But we saw earlier that when a number replaces n, it is a prime number when n is replaced by 1, 2, 3, . . .40. However, when n is replaced by 41 it is not a prime number. $41^2 - 41 + 41 = 41^2$ and this is not a prime number because it has two factors of 41. Mathematicians refer to this as a counter-example. Something may be true in many instances, but all it takes to disprove the statement is one example.

There are two types of reasoning: inductive and deductive reasoning.

Inductive Reasoning

In inductive reasoning, a general rule is developed after a number of individual cases have been considered. In other words, we go from individual cases to develop a general statement. In many (but not all) of the cases, the generalization is correct. For instance, we have made the conjecture that the sum of the angles of a triangle is 180º. From many triangles that have had the angles measured accurately, nobody has found a triangle (on a plane) in which the sum of the angles is not 180º. We will have an opportunity in this Unit to prove this statement deductively.

Deductive Reasoning

In deductive reasoning, the general statement is shown to be true and then this statement is applied to individual cases.

Deductive reasoning is based upon the proper use of a syllogism that is defined as an argument stated in logical form consisting of three parts: the first is called the major premise; the second is called the minor premise, and the third statement is called the conclusion. For example:

All squares are rectangles (by definition). This is the major premise.
ABCD is a square. This is the minor premise.
Therefore, ABCD is a rectangle. This is the conclusion.
In this syllogism, the major premise is true. The minor premise is true. Therefore, the conclusion is true.

Another example is. In a right angled triangle, the square on the hypotenuse is equal to the sum of the squares on the other two sides. Let ABC be a right angled triangle and we will name the sides a, b, and h. What we want to prove is that $h^2 = a^2 + b^2$. Notice that we have chosen any right angled triangle.

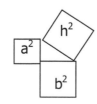
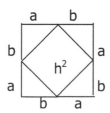

Proof: We extended the side b by the length of a and we extended the length of a by the length of b. We then drew a square in which the sides are a + b. We then constructed a square on the side h. We want to prove that $a^2 + b^2 = h^2$.

The area of the larger square is equal to h^2 + 4 times the area of the small triangles and these are all equal.

Therefore, $(a + b)^2 = h^2 + 4(\frac{1}{2} ab)$.

$(a + b)(a + b) = a^2 + ab + ab + b^2 = a^2 + 2ab + b^2$ (distributive property)

Therefore, $a^2 + 2ab + b^2 = h^2 + 2ab$. Subtract 2ab from each side.

Then $a^2 + b^2 = h^2$.

It should be noted that any right angled triangle was used. No specific measurements were used for the sides of the triangle. The measurement of a, b, and h could have any measurement (provided that the sum of any two sides is greater than the other side). When this has been proven deductively, we can apply this fact to any other right angled triangle without looking for a counter-example.

Putting the above in the form of a syllogism, we have: p = the square on the hypotenuse of a right angled triangle is equal to the sum of the squares on the other two sides. (This is the major premise and it is true). ABC is a right angled triangle. (This is the minor premise and it is true.)

Therefore, the square on the hypotenuse of the triangle ABC is equal to the sum of the squares on the other two sides. This is the conclusion and it is true because it has been proven. Now we can apply this information to all other right angled triangles.

A set of numbers that satisfies the condition $a^2 + b^2 = h^2$ is called Pythagorean triplets, so called because the theorem was developed by Pythagoras, an early Greek mathematician. For example, if a triangle has sides that measure 3, 4, and 5, they are Pythagorean triplets because $3^2 + 4^2 = 5^2$. (9 + 16) = 25. There are many other Pythagorean triplets. Can you list some?

Other Useful Conjectures

Example 1: Some of the conjectures that may be useful in deductive reasoning are:

Two lines were drawn parallel and a line (a transversal) was drawn.
Measure and insert the measure in the eight angles in the diagram at the right.

Examine your measurements and then check with the following:

$\angle1 + \angle2$, $\angle3 + \angle4$, $\angle5 + \angle6$, $\angle7 + \angle8$, $\angle1 + \angle3$, $\angle2 + \angle4$, $\angle5 + \angle7$, $\angle6 + \angle8$ are each equal to 180°. A straight line angle is formed.

$\angle1 = \angle4$, $\angle2 = \angle3$, $\angle5 = \angle8$, $\angle6 = \angle7$. These are called vertically opposite angles.

$\angle1 = \angle5$, $\angle3 = \angle7$, $\angle2 = \angle6$, $\angle4 = \angle8$.

$\angle1 + \angle7 = 180°$, $\angle3 + \angle5 = 180°$, $\angle2 + \angle8 = 180°$, $\angle4 + \angle6 = 180°$.

At this stage, we are only making conjectures (that are true). Time and space do not allow for the proofs of many propositions that lead to this. What we are saying is that if a transversal (a straight line) cuts two parallel lines, the above facts are true.

Example 2: The sum of the angles of a triangle is equal to 180°.

Let ABC be any triangle. We wish to prove that the sum of the angles of this triangle is 180°.

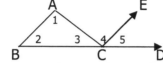

Proof: Extend BC to D and draw a line CE parallel to AB.
$\angle1 = \angle4$ alternate angles
$\angle2 = \angle5$
$\angle4 + \angle5 = \angle1 + \angle2$ equals added to equals
$\angle4 + \angle5 + \angle3 = \angle1 + \angle2 + \angle3$ Add $\angle3$ to each side.
But $\angle5 + \angle4 + \angle3 = 180°$.
Therefore, $\angle1 + \angle2 + \angle3 = 180°$. Property of transitivity.

The following conjectures can be proven and we will accept them as true.

1. If the measures of the angles of one triangle are equal to the measures of the angles of another triangle, then the triangles are similar and the corresponding sides are proportional. That is $\frac{a}{d} = \frac{b}{e} = \frac{c}{f}$.

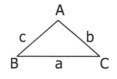

2. From the above, if ABC and DEF are two similar triangles, and if the measure of BC is twice the measure of EF, then AB is twice the measure of DE, and AC is twice the measure of DF.

Exercise 85

1. a) Write two sets of Pythagorean triplets.

b) How many sets of Pythagorean triplets do you think there are?

Explain

2. List two conjectures that have been made and that are true.

3. Tell whether each of the following syllogisms is True or False and then tell why.

a)   Good cars are expensive.
       The model A is a good car.
       Therefore, the model A is expensive.   Why ?

b)   Isosceles triangles have two equal sides.
       PQR is an isosceles triangle.
       Therefore, PQR has two equal sides   Why?

c)   Even numbers are divisible by 2.
       6 is an even number.
       Therefore, 6 is divisible by 2   Why?

d)   Natural numbers are greater than or equal to 1.
       − 4 is a Natural number.
       Therefore, − 4 is greater than or equal to 1   Why?

e)   Rectangles are squares.
       PQRS is a rectangle.
       Therefore, PQRS is a square   Why?

f)   Rhombuses are squares.
       ABCD is a rhombus.
       Therefore, ABCD is a square   Why?

4. In the diagram, ABC is an angle. At the points D, E, F perpendicular lines have been drawn to BC to meet BC at P, Q, R. Therefore, similar triangles have been formed. Write at least 5 proportions that exist in this diagram.

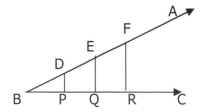

Negating a Statement

Let p be any statement. Let ~p be the negation of that statement.

It is possible to negate a statement. For example, 2 + 5 = 8 is a false statement. The negation of the statement is, "It is not true that 2 + 5 = 8" (or 2 + 5 ≠ 8). If we name the statement p, then p = 2 + 5 = 8 and its negation, ~P is 2 + 5 ≠ 8. The symbol, ~, is called a curl and ~p is read "not p". It should be noted that if p is true, then ~p is false and if p is false, then ~p is true.
We can set up a truth table using T for True and F for False.

p	~p
T	F
F	T

Conjunctions

We can combine statements by "and" to form a conjunction. For example, let p = the set of all positive Whole numbers and let q be x = 5. The joining together of these two statements by using the conjunction "and" will be the set of all positive Whole numbers and x = 5. This will be written as p ∧ q and the truth table is as follows.
Note the sequence in which the table was drawn. In the first column, write T T F F and in the second column, write T F T F to get all of the possibilities. From the table, it can be seen that the conjunction of two statements is true only when both statements are true. Otherwise, it is false.

p	Q	p ∧ q
T	T	T
T	F	F
F	T	F
F	F	F

Sometimes we may wish to consider a conjunction to be true if at least one of the statements is true. In this case, the Truth Table will be:

p	q	p ⊕ q
T	T	T
T	F	T
F	T	T
F	F	F

Therefore, the type of conjunction that you are dealing with must be made very clear.

Exercise 86

1. Write three mathematical sentences in which the truth value is True.

2. Write three mathematical sentences in which the truth value is False.

3. Can we start at 2n + 1 in order to write six consecutive odd numbers?

Explain

4. Write the negative of each of the following statements.

a) 4 x 5 = 30

b) John is smart

c) Natural numbers are Integers.

5. Complete the following Truth Table.
a)

p	q	p ∧ q	is the same as	q ∧ p
T	T			
T	F			
F	T			
F	F			

b) What property is illustrated by the above?

6. Construct a truth table for ~p ∧ ~q.

p	q	~p	~q	~p ∧ ~q
T	T			
T	F			
F	T			
F	F			

Disjunctions

Another connective can be used for "or". If the first sentence is x > 5 and the second sentence is x < 5, then the connective "or" (the symbol is V) and if p = x > 5 and if q = x < 5, then the connector "or" will be p V q. This leaves four possibilities.
x is greater than 5 or x is less than 5
x is greater than 5 or x is not greater than 5
x is not greater than 5 or x is less than 5
X is not greater than 5 or x is greater than 5

The Truth Table for disjunction is.

p	q	p ∨ q
T	T	T
T	F	T
F	T	T
F	F	F

Notice from the table that the disjunction is false only when the two statements are false. Otherwise, it is true.

Implications

p	q	p → q
T	T	T
T	F	F
F	T	T
F	F	T

"All squares are rectangles" is called the antecedent and "ABCD is a rectangle" is called the consequent. This can be written as "All squares are rectangles. ABCD is a square. Therefore, ABCD is a rectangle. Or, more simply, ABCD is a square → ABCD is a rectangle.

Notice that an implication is true except when the antecedent is true and the consequent is false.

Example: If a triangle is isosceles, then two sides of the triangle are equal. This can be written as if p, then q or p implies q, or as p → q. Since p and q are both true, then the implication is true. If we had said that if a triangle is isosceles, then all sides have a different measure. Then the implication is p → q if a triangle is isosceles, then the triangle has three sides that are different and this is false because the antecedent is true and the consequent is false.

Equivalences

Observe the truth table below which shows that ~q → ~p is the same as p → q. We will use the symbol ↔ for equivalence which means "the same as".

p	q	~q	~p	~q → ~p	↔	p → q
T	T	F	F	T		T
T	F	T	F	F		F
F	T	F	T	T		T
F	F	T	T	T		T
1	2	3	4	5		6

Note that columns 1 and 2 are the possibilities for p and q. Columns 3 and 4 are the negations of q and p. Column 5 is the implication "if not q, then not p". Column 6 is the table for the implication p → q and this is identical to column 5, ~q → ~p and this is what we wanted to show. Notice that columns 5 and 6 are identical. This may be written as (~p → ~q) ↔ (p → q). Note that the equivalence symbol points both ways.

If we say that x + 5 = 8 implies that x = 3, and if x = 3, then x + 5 = 8. Notice that we have an implication going one way and another implication going the other way. In other words, if we write p ↔ q, this means that if p then q, and if q then p. This is stated as "if and only if" and as p if q and p only if q. We say that these are equivalent statements and the symbol used is ↔.

Contrapositives

The contrapositive of p→q is ~q→~p. The contrapositive is a conditional statement derived from another by negating and interchanging the antecedent and the consequent.

Example: To prove that two parallel straight lines will not meet if they are extended in both directions, it can be assumed that they do meet and then shown that this assumption is false.

Let p be "two parallel lines are extended" and let q be "they will not meet".

This is p → q. ~q → ~p is the contrapositive of p → q.

We will set up the following truth table.

	q	~p	~q	~q → ~ p	↔	p → q
T	T	F	F	T		T
T	F	F	T	F		F
F	T	T	F	T		T
F	F	T	T	T		T

By examining the truth table, we can see that ~q → ~p is the same as p → q. That is, ~q → ~p is equivalent to p → q. Applying this to the example above, it is telling us that "if two parallel lines are extended, they will not meet" is the same as saying "if the lines do meet, they are not parallel".

Exercise 87

1. Construct a truth table for p V ~q.

2. When is a conjunction true?

304

3. Construct a truth table for ~p V q.

4. Complete the following truth table and compare ~(p V q) with ~p ∧ ~q:

p	q	~p	~q	p V q	~(p V q)	~p ∧ ~q
T	T					
T	F					
F	T					
F	F					

Conclusion

5. Write the contrapositive of the following:

If two triangles are congruent, they are similar.

6. Write in plain words what each of the following means and give an example of each:

a) p → q

b) q V p ↔ p V q

c) ~q → ~p

7. Determine if the following is logically equivalent by using the truth tables.
(p ∧ q) ↔ (~p V q).

p	q	~p	p ∧ q	q V (~p)

305

8. Use a truth table to determine if (p V q) has the same truth value as q V (~p).

p	q	~p	p V q	q V (~p)

Tautologies

A tautology is a statement in which the truth value is always true.
For example, 2 + 2 = 4 or 2 + 2 ≠ 4. In this instance, there are no other possibilities.

The following truth table will illustrate a use of the associative property in symbolic logic.

A Tautology

p	q	r	p ∧ q	(p ∧ q) → r	q → r	p → (q → r)	((p∧q)→ r)↔(p→(q ∧r))
T	T	T	T	T	T	T	T
T	T	F	T	F	F	F	T
T	F	T	F	T	T	T	T
T	F	F	F	T	T	T	T
F	T	T	F	T	T	T	T
F	T	F	F	T	F	T	T
F	F	T	F	T	T	T	T
F	F	F	F	T	T	T	T .

Note the arrangement of the T's and F's. Eight rows are required because there are 2 choices, T or F, and there are three premises ($2^3 = 8$).

Converse Statements

The converse of the statement, "if ABC is a triangle, then the sum of the angles is 180º" is "if the sum of the angles of ABC is 180º then ABC is a triangle".
If we let p be "if ABC is a triangle" and let q be "the sum of the angles is 180º", we want to show that (p → q) ↔ (q → p). We will set up a truth table.

p	q	p → q	q → p	(p → q) ↔ (q → p)
T	T	T	T	T
T	F	F	T	T
F	T	T	F	F
F	F	T	T	T
		implication	converse	equivalence

We have shown that an implication is equivalent to its converse.

Exercise 88

1. Determine whether the following is a tautology: $\sim(p \lor q) \rightarrow (\sim p \lor \sim q)$.

2. Write the contrapositive of each of the following.

a) If n is any Natural number, then n + 1 is odd.

b) 3x + 4 = 13 if and only if x = 3.

3. Write two statements and construct a truth table to show a proof by using the converse.

4. Write the converse of the following: If 8 = 2 + 6, then 2 + 6 = 8.

5. Write two statements to show that $(p \land q) \rightarrow (\sim q \land \sim p)$.

SELF-ASSESSMENT of the ATTAINMENT of the OBJECTIVES

Objective	5	4	3	2	1
- state an axiom					
- write a postulate					
- write a proposition					
- explain inductive reasoning by using an example					
- explain an example of the use of deductive reasoning					
- complete a truth table using conjunction					
- write an example of a syllogism					
- negate a sentence					
- write the truth table for disjunction					
- write the truth table for equivalence					
- write the contrapositive for "if two parallel lines are extended they will not meet"					
- define a tautology					
- write the converse of "if ABC is a circle, its area is πr^2"					

Score ____/65____   Date _____

308

Section X— Mathematical Logic
Post Test-X

Answers can be found at the end of the book.

1. Complete the following:

    Isosceles triangles have two equal sides.
    ABC is an isosceles triangle.
    Therefore,

2. Complete the following truth table:

p	q	p ∧ q
T	T	
T	F	
F	T	
F	F	

3. Complete the following truth table:

p	q	p V q
T	T	
T	F	
F	T	
F	F	

4. Write the contrapositive of, "if two triangles are congruent, they are similar".

5. Use the truth table to determine if p V q has the same truth value as q V ~p.

p	q	~p	p V q	q V ~p
T	T			
T	F			
F	T			
F	F			

6. Complete the following:

p	q	(p∧q)	(p∧q)∧ q	(p ∧ q)∧ p
T	T			
T	F			
F	T			
F	F			

Score _____   Date _____

Answers to Pre–Tests and Post–Tests

RC means reader's choice. The answer will vary according to the data that the reader inserts.

Pre–Test and Post–Test I

1) is less than; is equal to; is greater than   **2)** 7   **3)** (9 + 8) + (7 + 6) = 17 + 13 = 30 or (9 + 6) + (8 + 7) = 15 +15 = 30   **4)** 779   **5)** 98   **6)** 864   **7)** 15   **8)** 9312   **9)** 297   **10)** 5668   **11)** 37   **12)** 45 kg   **13)** 28   **14)** 23 (10 + 5) = 230 + 115 = 345   **15)** 33, 36, 39, 42, 45, 48   the sum of the digits is divisible by 3 or identify the first number that is divisible by three and select each third number thereafter.   **16)** 1, 2, 4, 8, 16, 32, 64   **17)** 351, 13(1 + 26) = 13 + 338 = 351

Pre–Test and Post–Test II

1) 121 132 143 154 165   **2)** 13   **3)** Division by zero is undefined (Any number multiplied by 0 is 0.)   **4)** 18.62   **5)** 102(100 − 1) = 10200 − 102 = 10,098   **6)** 23 x 4 Press M⁺, 37 x 26 Press M⁺ = 1,054 (To clear Memory, Press MC)   **7)** 17, 23   **8)** We are using the sequence 1, 2, 3, 4, 5, 6. or, increase the difference by 1. **9a)** 12   **b)** 44   **10)** CCLVII   **11)** 112   **12)** 15,256.08   **13)** 624   **14)** 77   **15)** 35

16)

		Total
walk	~~HHI~~ /	6
swim	~~HHI~~ ////	9
cycle	///	3

17)

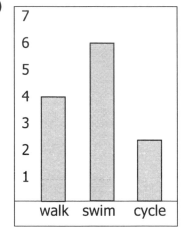

18) RC

19) RC

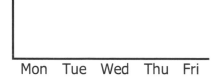

20)

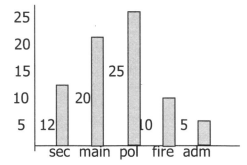

310

Pre–Test–and Post–Test III

1) obtuse, right, reflex, acute   **2)** equilateral, right, isosceles, scalene   **3)** 14; (1, 27 ,27), (3, 26, 26), (5, 25, 25). . . (25, 15, 15), (27, 14, 14)   **4)** parallelogram, rhombus, rectangle, square   **5)** 4: 1 x 24, 2 x 12, 3 x 8, 4 x 6   **6 a)** right-triangle with legs 6 and 4 or a scalene triangle with a base of 12 and a height of 2. There are many choices.   **7)** 540°   **8)** 24.62   **9a)** use any three points on the circumference. **b)** OQ   **c)** MP   **d)** NT   **e)** MN or PQ or PQM   **f)** POQ   **10)** 43.96   **11)** bisect a 90° angle twice   **12a)** 0   **b)** 3   **c)** 1   **d)** 0 (unless it is an isosceles right triangle)   **e)** 4   **f)** 2   **g)** 0   **h)** 4   **i)** 1   **j)** 4

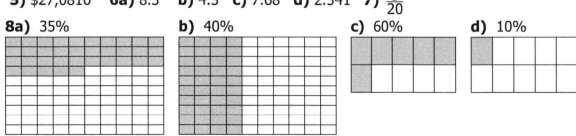

Pre–Test and Post–Test IV

1) 2 + 3 = 3 + 2   **2)** 1   **3)** 2(3 x 4) = (2 x 3)4   **4)** 2(3 + 4) = 2 x 3 + 2 x 4   **5)** If 3 x 5 x 4 = 15 x 4, then 3 x 5 = 15   **6)** subtraction   **7)** 0   **8)** Column a = 0, 8, −14, 11, 5. Row b = − 7, 5, 2, 7, 3. Sum of column a) is 10 and sum of row b) is 10.   **9a)** − 2   **b)** 12   **c)** − 12   **d)** 2   **10)** 56, 56, − 56, − 56,   **11)** 5   **12a)** − 9   **b)** 9,   **c)** 0,   **d)** 10   **13a)** − 4   **b)** − 4,   **c)** 4,   **d)** −1   **14a)** recurring, **b)** terminating   **15)** division by 0 is undefined   **16 a)** $\frac{6}{5}$ **b)** $\frac{1}{12}$ **c)** $\frac{10}{21}$ **d)** $\frac{1}{8}$ **e)** $\frac{73}{12}$ or $6\frac{1}{12}$ **f)** $\frac{17}{10}$ or $1\frac{7}{10}$ **g)** $1\frac{5}{8}$ **h)** $\frac{20}{21}$ **i)** $\frac{247}{20}$ or $12\frac{7}{20}$ **j)** $11\frac{14}{25}$ **k)** $\frac{5}{4}$ or $1\frac{1}{4}$ **l)** $\frac{15}{28}$ **m)** $\frac{36}{65}$ **17a)** 75   **b)** 35   **c)** 36   **d)** 12   **18)** division

Pre–Test and Post–Test V

1a) 52   **b)** 52   **c)** 52   **d)** 21.6   **e)** 80   **f)** 6   **2a)** 0.6   **b)** 0.7   **c)** 0.5   **d)** 0.125   **3a)** $\frac{35}{100}$ or $\frac{7}{20}$ **b)** $\frac{1}{100}$ **c)** $\frac{63}{100}$ **d)** $\frac{99}{100}$ **4)** $7,200

5) $27,0810   **6a)** 8.3   **b)** 4.3   **c)** 7.68   **d)** 2.541   **7)** $\frac{9}{20}$

8a) 35%   **b)** 40%   **c)** 60%   **d)** 10%

9) 0.24, $\frac{24}{100}$ or $\frac{6}{25}$ **10)** 1.5   **11)** Harold spent $70: James spent$67.50. Harold spent $2.50 more than James. by $2.50   **12)** $100   **13a)** 90 **b)** 190   **4)** $244,720   **15)** 14.286%   **16)** 62.5%   **17)** $33\frac{1}{3}$%   **18 a)** 2 **b)** 6 **c)** $\frac{16}{3}$ or $5\frac{1}{3}$ **19)** 250 kg

Pre–Test and Post–Test VI

1) $\frac{1}{6}$ **2)** 40 **3)** 1 x 48, 2 x 24, 3 x 16. 4 x 12, 6 x 8 **4)** $8 **5)** 106.2 kg **6)** 75

7) 256 **8)** Drop the 0 and subtract 10from the two digit number that you started with. **9)** 16 answers: 3333, 3335, 3353, 3355, 3533, 3535, 3553, 3555, 5333, 5335, 5353, 5355, 5533, 5535, 5553, 5555 **10)** 888 + 88 + 8 + 8 + 8 or (8 + 8 + 8 + 8 + 8) in the ones column, 8 + 8 in the tens column, and 8 in the hundreds column
11) 1 and 10,000; or 2 and 20,000, etc. **12)** 100 and 1,000,000: 1 and 10,000: 3 and 30,000, etc. **13)** 77 **14)** 8, 8, 10, 10 **15)** 2004 **16)** $62.60 **17)** M, A, O or M, B, P or A, A, B or P, P, P **18)** the numbers are: 1 and 87: 3 and 29) **19)** 1 day

Pre–Test and Post–Test VII

1) $2832 **2)** 7.5% **3)** $3.60 **4)** 8.243**%** **5)** $3374.59 **6)** RC
7) 1990 (4%) 2000 (15%) **8)**

27	ʜʜ	5	0.179	17.9%	$\frac{5}{28}$
28	/ / /	3	0.107	10.7%	$\frac{3}{28}$
29	ʜʜ / / /	7	0.250	25%	$\frac{7}{28}$
32	ʜʜ /	6	0.214	21.4%	$\frac{6}{28}$
35	/ / /	3	0.107	10.7%	$\frac{3}{28}$
36	/ / / /	4	0.143	14.3%	$\frac{4}{28}$
Total		28	1.000		

9) 302 **10)** 37 **11)** 30 **12)** $\frac{1}{3}$ **13)** $\frac{1}{2}$ **14)** 64.2%, 0.642

Pre–Test and Post–Test VIII

1)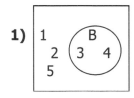

2) {1,2,5} **3)** {10,12}; {6,8,10,12,14} **4)** { } **5)** Natural numbers
6) {91 93, 95, 97, 99} **7)** {1, 3 , 5, 7, 9, 10, 11, 13, 15, 17, 19, 20} **8)** Re; Ra
9) 51; 27; 33;15 **10)** M and W; T and B; D and A; C and NY

9)
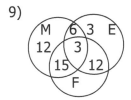

10)
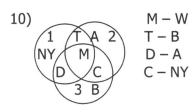

M – W
T – B
D – A
C – NY

W   was not chosen to win

Pre–Test and Post–Test IX

1) ←5 -4 -3 -2 -1 0 1 2 3 4 5 6→
• • • • • • •

2)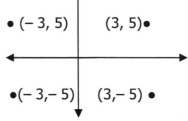

3) -5 -4 -3 -2 -1 0 1 2 3 4 5 6

Ans. {−3, −2, −1, 0 1, 2, 3}

4) {(1,1), (2,4)}

5)

• (− 3, 5)   (3, 5)•

•(− 3,− 5)   (3,− 5) •

6) No   • (3, 4)
• (4, 3)

7) {(1, 1), (2, 2), (3, 3) . . .}
• (4, 3)
• (3, 3)
• (2, 2)
•(1, 1)

8)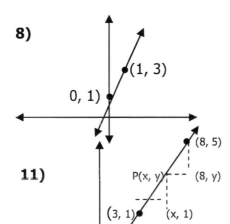

(1, 3)

0, 1)

9)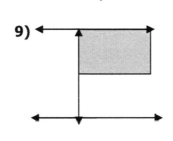

10) $\frac{3}{2}$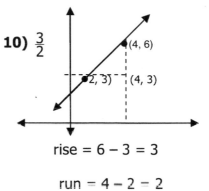
(4, 6)
(2, 3) (4, 3)

rise = 6 − 3 = 3

run = 4 − 2 = 2

slope = $\frac{3}{2}$

11)
(8, 5)
P(x, y) - - - (8, y)
(3, 1) (x, 1)

Pre–Test and Post–Test X

1) ABC has two equal sides

2)

p	q	p ∧ q
T	T	T
T	F	F
F	T	F
F	F	F

3)

p	q	p ∨ q
T	T	T
T	F	T
F	T	T
F	F	F

4) If two triangles are not similar, they are not congruent.

5)

p	q	~p	p v q	q v ~p
T	T	F	T	T
T	F	F	T	F
F	T	T	T	T
F	F	T	F	T

Columns 4 and 5 are different.

6)

p	q	p∧q)	q	(p ∧ q) ∧ q	p ∧ q
T	T	T	T	T	T
T	F	F	F	F	F
F	T	F	T	F	F
F	F	F	F	F	F

Columns 5 and 6 are the same.

314

Answers to the Exercises

The notation RC means Readers Choice, i.e. if there are different ways of solving a problem or the choice of the problem is left to the reader, then each reader may have a different answer.

Exercise 1

1a) < **b)** > **c)** > **d)** > **e)** < **f)** < **g)** = **h)** < **2a)** 5 + 0 = 4 + 1 = 3 + 2
b) 6 + 1 = 5 + 2 = 4 + 3 **c)** 8 + 1 = 7 + 2 = 6 + 3 **d)** 4 + 0 = 3 + 1 = 2 + 2
3a) < **b)** > **c)** > **d)** <

Exercise 2

1a) 4 **b)** 6 **c)** 8 **d)** 9 **e)** 6 **f)** 9 **g)** 12 **2a)** 5 **b)** 8 **c)** 9
d) 11 **e)** 14 **3)** $13 **4)** 17 **5)** 7 **6)** 18
7) 4 **8)**

③	①	①	③
⑤④ or	⑤⑥ or	⑥⑤ or	④⑤
①⑥②	③④②	②④③	②⑥①

Exercise 3

1a) 9 **b)** 13 **c)** 12 **d)** 17 **e)** 14 **f)** 15 **g)** 15 **h)** 16 **2a)** 9 **b)** 6 **c)** 15
d) 10 The order in which numbers are added will not alter the sum. **e)** (3 + 2) + 1, 3 + (2 + 1) and (1 + 2) + 3, 2 + (1 + 3) **f)** 17 **g)** 11 **h)** 8 **I)** 16 **j)** 11 **3)** six;
5 + 6 + 7 = 5 + 7 + 6 = 6 + 5 + 7 = 6 + 7 + 5 = 7 + 6 + 5 = 7 + 5 + 6
4a) (7 +3) + (8 + 2) = 20 **b)** (4 + 5) + (5 + 6) = 20 or (4 + 6) + (5 + 5) = 20
c) (3 + 5) + (7 + 5) = 20 or (3 + 7) + (5 + 5) = 20 **d)** (9 + 4) + (4 + 2) = 19 or
(4 + 4 + 2) + 9 = 19 **5a)** (9 + 6) + (8 + 7) = 30 **b)** (4 + 6) + (7 + 3) = 20
c) (5 + 0) + (9 + 1) = 15 **d)** (4 + 6) + (0 + 1) = 11 **e)** (2 + 8) + (7 + 3) = 20
f) (9 + 1) + (7 + 5) = 22 **g)** (7 + 3) + (6 + 4) = 20 **h)** (8 + 2) + (9 + 4) = 23
i) (5 + 4) + (7 + 3) = 19

Exercise 4

1a) 100 **b)** 151 **c)** 61 **d)** 94 **e)** 80 **f)** 70 **2)** $64 **3)** 58 **4)** 80 **5)** 57
6) 33 **7)** 57 **8)** They have the same sum. The order in which numbers are added will not alter the sum. **9)** 4; 6; 7 **10a)** 23 + 20 = 43 **b)** 7 + 30 = 37
c) 6 + 20 = 26 or 10 + 16 = 26 **d)** 7 + 30 = 37 **e)** 36 + 70 = 106 **f)** 50 + 19 = 69

Exercise 5

1a) 9 hundreds; 4 tens; 7 ones **b)** 4 hundreds; 3 tens; 5 ones **c)** 3 hundreds; 0 tens; 8 ones **d)** 7 hundreds; 2 tens; 6 ones **e)** 5 hundreds; 0 tens; 0 ones
f) 6 hundreds; 3 tens; 8 ones **2)** 1=111 **3a)** 200 **b)** 129 **c)** 141 **d)** 221 **4)** $101
5) 129

Exercise 6

1a) 861 **b)** 694 **c)** 950 **d)** 945 **e)** 811 **2a)** 6,622 **b)** 8,116
c) 9,330 **d)** 9,309 **e)** 9,164 **3)** 588 **4)** 1,476 **5)** $32,850 **6)** 1,348

Exercise 7

1a) 2 **b)** 2 **c)** 3 **d)** 2 **e)** 1 **f)** 4 **g)** 4 **h)** 3 **i)** 3 **j)** 3 **k)** 5 **l)** 5 **m)** 7
n) 5 **o)** 4 **p)** 0 **q)** 5 **r)** 7 **s)** 4 **t)** 7 **2)** $3 **3)** 5

Exercise 8

1a) 22 **b)** 12 **c)** 23 **d)** 35 **e)** 46 **f)** 57 **g)** 11 **h)** 16 **i)** 26 **j)** 28 **k)** 49
l) 39 **2)** 53 **3)** 18 **4)** 68 **5)** 28 **6)** $682: 750 −56 = 694 and 694 − 12 =
682 or 56 + 13 = 68 and 750 − 68 = 682. **7)** 26 **8a)** 5, **b)** 4, **c)** 5, **d)** 5, **e)** 7

Exercise 9

1a) 14 **b)** 51 **c)** 171 **d)** 348 **2a)** 91 **b)** 199 **c)** 396 **d)** 97 **e)** 209 **f)** 23

Exercise 10

1a) 193 **b)** 109 **c)** 289 **d)** 269 **2a)** 896 **b)** 1886 **c)** 3095 **d)** 556
3) 845 **4)** $2196 **5)** 4950

Exercise 11

1 a) 30 **b)** 56 **c)** 48 **d)** 28 **e)** 35 **f)** 24 **g)** 36 **h)** 36 **i)** 42 **j)** 5
k) 9 **l)** 0 **m)** 0 **n)** 0 **o)** 0 **p)** 63 **q)** 42 **r)** 63 **s)** 72 **t)** 11 **2a)** 105
b) 105 **c)** 105 **d)** 72 **e)** 72 **f)** 72 **g)** 20 **h)** 0 **i)** 5 **j)** 48 **k) 72** **l)** 0
3) 48 **4)** 54 **5)** 84 **6)** The order in which numbers are multiplied will not alter the
product **7)** 1,000 **8)** RC

Exercise 12

1a) 542 **b)** 779 **c)** 731 **d)** 982 **e)** 868 **f)** 928 **2a)** 728 **b)** 2,241
c) 4,560 **d)** 1,121 **e)** 2,150 **f)** 624 **3a)** 468 **b)** 960 **c)** 728 **d)** 304 **e)** 484
f) 893 **g)** 867 **4)** 154 **5)** 345 **6)** 660 **7)** 187 **8)** 912 **9)** 936 **10)** 544

Exercise 13

1a) 4,424 **b)** 1,930 **c)** 3,438 **d)** 6,712 **e)** 14,416 **f)** 10,422 **g)** 32,742
h) 13,000 **2)** $16,198; $3,276, 12,922 **3)** 5,542 **4)** 180,164

Exercise 14

1a) 3 **b)** 5 **c)** 5 **d)** 8 **e)** 6 **f)** 9 **g)** 6 **h)** 8 **i)** 12 **j)** 4 **k)** 7 **l)** 9
2) 4 **3)** 8 **4)** 8; 4; 10; 44; 56; 36; 48; 72; 98; 16; 66; 18; 40; 50; 92; 32; 64
5) 15; 45; 80; 55; 35; 65; 70; 75; 95; 100 **6)** 40; 60; 90; 10; 30; 80; 70 These numbers are also divisible by 5. 10 is divisible by 5. All numbers that are divisible by another number are divisible by all of its factors. **7)** 45; 33; 21; 60; 18; 48; 51; 69; 72; 81; 87; 96 **8)** 27; 45; 54; 63; 72; 81; 9 **9)** They all are. 9 is divisible by 3. All numbers that are divisible by another number (other than one and itself) are divisible by all of the factors of that number. **10)** 22; 33; 44; 55; 66; 77; 88; 99

Exercise 15

1a) 1, 3, 5, 15 **b)** 1, 2, 7, 14 **c)** 1, 2, 3, 4, 6, 12 **d)** 1, 17 **e)** 1, 2, 4, 8, 16
f) 1, 31 **g)** 1, 3, 17, 51 **h)** 1, 5, 11, 55 **i)** 1, 3, 9, 27 **j)** 1, 2, 3, 4, 6, 8, 9, 12, 18, 24, 36, 72 **k)** 1, 2, 3, 4, 6, 9, 12, 18, 36 **l)** 1, 2, 11, 22 **m)** 1, 2, 4, 8, 16, 32 **n)** 1, 2, 3, 4, 6, 8, 12, 24 **o)** 1, 2, 4, 8, 16, 32, 64 **2)** 2, 3, 5, 7, 11, 13, 17, 19, 23, 29, 31, 37 **3)** 36, 38, 39, 40, 42, 44, 45, 46, 48, 49, 50, 51, 52, 54, 55, 56, 57, 58, 60, 62, 63, 64, 65, 66, 68, 69, 70, 72, 74, 75 87, 75, 81, 90 **4)** only the numbers 2 and 3

Exercise 16

1a) 16 **b)** 132 **c)** 152 **d)** 52 **e)** 214 **f)** 365 **g)** 654 **h)** 211 **2)** 1,222
3) 408 **4)** 126 **5)** 36 **6)** 150

Exercise 17

1a) 24 **b)** 21 **c)** 42 **d)** 26 **e)** 25 **f)** 27 **g)** 18 **h)** 30 **2)** 39 **3)** 15
4) 48 **5)** 52 **6)** 82

Exercise 18

1) .34 **2)** 2 If each deck is dealt separately, 3 cards will be left over each time. Therefore, there are 9 cards and 1 card can be dealt to each player. Therefore, there are 2 cards left over. Or, if the 3 decks were dealt at once, 52 x 3 = 156 and 156 ÷ 7 is 22 with a remainder of 2. **3)** 3 scarves, 4 balls of wool **4)** 3 liters

Exercise 19

1) 45, 55, 65, 75 . . . **2)** 45, 55, 65, 75 . . . **3a)** 8:05 **b)** 8:55 **c)** 11:30 **d)** 9:10
4a) 15:15 **b)** 13:55 13:40 **c)** 12:50 **d)** 10:45 **5a)** 12:11:05 **b)** 12:01:15
c) 14:56:10 **6a)** 3:30:30 **b)** 4:55:05 **c)** 3:59:55 **7a)** 13:3 5 **b)** 17:05
c) 15:45 **8)** international travel, international business, used by the military, used by meteorologists **9)** 9:59 **10)** 54 minutes

Exercise 20

1a) 273 **b)** 1,035 **c)** 1,558 **d)** 990 **e)** 840 **f)** 564

Exercise 21

1) 8 **2)** 7 **3)** 7 **4)** the order of addition does not change the sum **5)** 7 **6)** 0
7) division is a shortcut for repeated subtraction **8)** 20; 20 **9)** 0
10) Error. Division by zero is undefined. **11)** 37 + 0 = 37 and 45 x 1 = 45
subtraction of the additive inverse or multiplication of the multiplicative inverse results
in 0 or 1 **12)** right; left

Exercise 22

1a) 0.33333333; 0.03030303; 0.00300300; 0.00030003 **b)** 0.11111111;
0.01010101; 0.00100100 0.00010001 **2)** 18.62 **3)** .0033 cm **4)** 44,392424,880
5) 102(100 −1) = 10,098 **6)** Multiply (58 − 1) by (78 − 1). The product is 4,389.
7a) 14 **b)** 17 **c)** 90 **d)** 80 **e)** 24 **f)** 31 **g)** 22.25 **h)** 14.73 **i)** 2.236
j) 2.2645 **k)** 3.317 **l)** 5.292

Exercise 23

1a) 22 **b)** 924 **c)** 0 **d)** 456 **e)** 348 **f)** 1,430 **2)** $544 **3)** $42.48

Exercise 24

1a) 20, 25, 30: Add 5 to the preceding number **b)** 8, 10, 12: Add 2 to the preceding
number. **c)** 16, 25, 36: The squares of consecutive numbers. **d)** 44, 55, 66:
consecutive numbers multiplied by 11. **e)** 64, 125, 216: the cubes of the Natural
numbers. **f)** 72, 61, 73: Add 12, subtract 11 **g)** 63, 55, 47 subtract 9, 7, 5 ... or,
decrease differences by 2 **h)** 63, 127, 255 add 2, 4, 8, 16 etc. **i)** 12, 6, 3 Multiply
by $\frac{1}{2}$ or divide by 2 **j)** 19, 15, 21, +4, − 2m +5, − 3, + 6 − 4 etc. **k)** 8, 81, 8, the
powers of 3 interspersed by an 8 **l)** 17, 23, 30. Add the sequence 1, 2, 3, 4, 5. . .
to the previous number **m)** 12, − 52, − 116, subtract twice the previous difference
2) 11 kg **3a)** 1234 x 8 + 4 = 9876
$\qquad$ 12345 x 8 + 5 = 98765
$\qquad$ 123456 x 8 + 6 = 987654

b) 1234 x 9 + 5 = 11111 **c)** 9876 x 9 + 4 = 88888
$\quad$ 12345 x 9 + 6 = 111111 $\qquad$ 98765 x 9 + 3 = 888888
$\quad$ 123456 x 9 + 7 = 1111111 $\qquad$ 987654 x 9 + 2 = 8888888

Exercise 25

F= Frog; H = Horse; L= Lion; P = Parrot and B = Blank. **1a)** P **b)** H **c)** H
d) P **e)** P **f)** B **g)** F **h)** F **2a)** P **b)** B **c)** H **d)** F **e)** B **f)** L **g)** H **h)** B

Exercise 26

1a) CCLVI I   **b)** C D X X IX   **c)** D C C C X X X VII   **d)** C M I I   **e)** CCXXXV
f) MMMC C XCIX   **g)** M I I   **h)** C M L X X X I X   **i)** MDX   **j)** CCC LX IV
ck) MMCXXXVIII   **l)** MI   **2)** clocks, Super Bowl Numbers, Introductory pages in a book
3a) 111 **b)** 1491   **c)** 112   **d)** 1453   **e)** 1903   **f)** 1600   **g)** 224   **h)** 1842
i) 1510   **j)** 1771   **k)** 345   **l)** 1557

Exercise 27

1) 118ml   **2)** 8.2   **3)** 15,256.08 ft^3 **4)** 144928.68 m^2 **5)** 7.3 hours or 7 hrs and 18 minutes

Exercise 28

1) 33.3°   **2)** 62.6°   **3)** 100   **4)** 0°   **5)** – 40°

Exercise 29

1a) cm   **b)** liters   **c)** kg   **d)** kg   **e)** liters   **f)** m   **g)** cm   **h)** m   **i)** m or kg
2) RC   **3)** 3; 2.75; 2; 5   **4)** The measure from the finger tip of one hand to that of
the other is approximately equal to the height of the person. **5)** 5 x 10 x 10 or 500
6) 266.5 U.S. gallons **7)** 200 liters   **8)** tsp, tbsp, cup, fl oz, ml   **9)** building a car,
the 100 yard dash, medical operations   **10)** the number of liters in a lake, the
distance from Earth to Moon, approximating a crowd   **(11, 12, 13)** RC   **14)** 3 by
325, 5 by 195, 13 by 75, 15 by 65, 25 by 39; 25 by 39.   **15)** A standard paper clip
measures approximately 3 cm. Therefore, 25 paper clips joined together will measure
approximately 75 cm.   **16)** RC

Exercise 30

1) Reader's Choice   **2)** Reader's Choice

The following are some examples.

3)
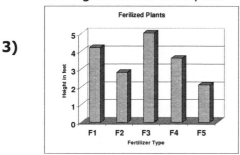

4a)
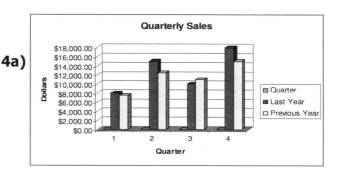

b)
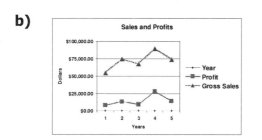

5)
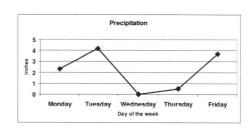

6) RC   **7)**

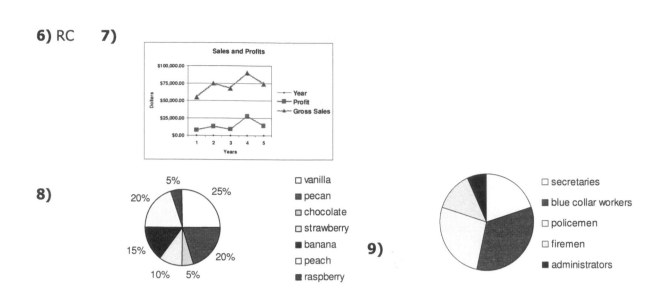

8)

9)

10) RC

Exercise 31

1) a) equilateral, **b)** right, **c)** scalene, **d)** isosceles   **2a)** 9, **b)** 8, **c)** 9, **d)** 9
3) 70 + 70 + 40 = 180; 60 + 60 + 60 = 180; 60 + 60 + 60 = 180

Exercise 32

1a) square, **b)** rectangle, **c)** triangle, **d)** parallelogram   **2)** window; card table; picture frame: door, dinner table, pad paper   **3a)** 2.5 cm, P = 5.2 cm   **b)** 1.5 cm and 2.5, P= 8 cm   **c)** 2 cm, 2 cm and 3 cm, P = 7 cm **d)** 3 and 1.5, P = 9
4) 20 cm^2; 2 cm^2; 18 cm^2; 6 cm^2; 18 cm^2; 14 cm^2; 5 cm^2; 15 cm^2 **5)** side squared
6) 4; 1 x 24, 2 x 12, 3 x 8, 4 x 6   **7)** 1, 6 x 6   **8)** 1, 9 by 9   **9)** 1, 6 by 6
10) 0 – if the sides are whole numbers   **11)** 9: 1 by 17; 2 by 16; 3 x 15 etc.   **12)** 0 – if the sides are whole numbers   **13)** 9 m   **14)** acute; obtuse; reflex; right **15)** =
16) RC   **17)** R C   **18a)** 6 cm^2, **b)** 5 cm^2; **c)** 24 cm^2 **19)** 21. The sides could be 2, 43, 43; 4, 42, 42; 6, 41, 41; 8, 40, 40 ...38, 25, 25; 40, 24, 24; 42. 23, 23. If we used 44, 22 and 22, no triangle would result because the sum of any two sides of a triangle must be greater than the third side. Try drawing a triangle with sides 10 cm, 4 cm and 5 cm. **20)** Yes. Opposite sides are equal and all angles are right angles. **21)** Yes. All sides are equal and opposite sides are parallel.   **22)** No – you can have a rhombus with an angle less than 90 degrees. **23)** No – one of the angles can be less than 90 degrees.   **24)** Yes . he opposite sides are equal and parallel   **25)** Yes – if the arms surrounding the right angle are equal. l

Exercise 33

1) 96 **2)** 10,000 **3)** 28 (105 ÷ 15 = 7 and 60 ÷ 15 = 4. 4 x 7 = 28.) **4)** 1 x 1; 2 x 2; 3 x 3; 5 x 5; 6 x 6; 10 x 10; 15 x 15; 30 x 30

Exercise 34

1a) 1,800 °; **b)** 1,440 °;   **2)** 108 °

Exercise 35

1a) shoe box, a box of cereal, book **b)** dice, jack-in-the-box, a block of ice
c) a ball, the earth, an orange **d)** soup can, a pail, a cooking pot **2)** 120 cm2
3) 520.026 cm^3 **4)** 64 cm^3 **5)** 512 cm^3 **6)** 60 cm^3 **7)** 45.6 **8)** 1846.32 **9)** No.
New area = (2s)(2s) = 4s². The area is quadrupled. **10)** No. If a side = 2 cm, the
volume is 2 x 2 x 2 or 8 cm^3. If the side is tripled, the volume is 8 x 8 x 8 or 512 cm^3.
The volume of the cube is 27 times that of the original cube.

Exercise 36

1) 5.6   **2)**    **3)** 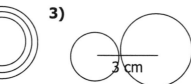   **4)** an indefinite number

5) an indefinite number

6)   The center of the field (rectangle is at the intersection of the two diagonals).
Therefore, the diameter is 3 cm and the radius is 1.5 cm. Since the rope is
1.5 cm, the cow can walk within 60 meters of the center of the field.

7a) Use any three points on the circumference. **b)** OQ **c)** MP **d)** NT **e)** MN or PQ
or PQM   **f)** POQ

Exercise 37

1a) scalene **b)** right **c)** equilateral **d)** isosceles **2)** cannot draw – the sum of the
lengths of any two sides must be greater than the length of the third side.
3a) 43.96 cm **b)** 21.98 cm

Exercise 38

1) 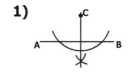   **2)** 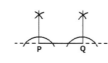   **3)**   ∠ABD and ∠DBC are 45⁰

∠DBE and ∠EBC are $22\frac{1}{2}$ °

Bisect a right angle to get an angle of 45⁰ and then bisect this angle to get an angle

of $22\frac{1}{2}$ °.   **4)** ∠QPR = 2∠QTR   **5)** RC   **6)** 19.2 cm

7)

3 cm

7 cm

3 cm

8)

9) same length AC = CD = DE

Exercise 39

1) yes − drawn through the middle   **2)** a pad of paper, a window, a flag, a rug
3a) 0 **b)** 3 **c)** 1 **d)** 0 (if isosceles, then 1) **e)** 4 **f)** 0 **g)** 4 **h)** 2 **i)** 4 **j)** 1
4) if they are the same size and the same shape **5)** 2 rulers, 2 plates, 2 CD's, 2 picture frames, 2 unused pencils, 2 license plates **6)** **7)** **8)** no-they have different lengths

Exercise 40

1a) 7 **b)** 6 **c)** − 12 **d)** b − a   **2a)**

-6 -5 -4 - 3 -2 -1 0 1 2 3 4 5 6

-2

b)

− 7 -6 -5 -4 -3 -2 -1 0 1 2 3 4 5

-2

c)

− 6 -5 -4 -3 -2 -1 0 1 2

-3

d) -9 -8 -7 -6 -5 -4 -3 -2 -1 0 1 2 3 4 5

-8

3) Show that −5 + (−3) = −8

$$8 + [(− 5) + (− 3)] = (5) + (3) + [(− 5) + (− 3)]$$ cancellation property
$$= [8 + (− 8)] + [3 + (− 3)]$$ associative property
$$= 0 + 0$$ additive identity
Therefore, 8 + (− 8) = 0   additive inverses
Therefore, 8 + [(− 5) + (− 3)] = 8 + (− 8)   transitive property
[(− 5) + (− 3)] + 8 = 8 + (− 8)   communicative property
Therefore, (− 5) + (− 3) = − 8   cancellation property

4a) 1   **b)** −3 **c)** 0 **d)** 6 **e)** − 25   **5)** left to right: − 2, 4, 0, − 6, −5, − 4

						a
	2	4	7	−3	−5	5
	−2	−4	3	−1	0	−4
	3	−6	0	2	4	3
	−1	4	−3	−6	7	1
	−4	3	−2	−1	−5	−9
b	−2	1	5	−6	1	−4

Exercise 41

1a) (− 2) − (− 4) = (− 2) + 4

−5 − 4 − 3 − 2 − 1 0 1 2 3

2

b) $(-5) - 8 = (-5) + (-8)$

-13 -12 -11 -10 −9 -8 -7 -6 -5 -4 -3 -2 -1   0 1

-13

c) $(-5) + 8 =$

-7 -6 -5 -4 -3 -2 -1   0 1 3 4 5

3

d) $(-7) - (-3) = (-7) + 3$ -8 -7 -6 -5 -4 -3 -2 -1 0 1 2 3

- 4

2a) 31   **b)** − 9   **c)** 0   **d)** − 4   **3a)** 2   **b)** − 2   **c)** 6   **d)** − 6   **e)** − 5   **f)** − 9
g) 28   **h)** 8   **4a)** 3   **b)** − 10   **c)** − 7   **d)** 1   **e)** 0   **f)** 10   **g)** − 9   **h)** − 2   **i)** 7
j) 1   **k)** − 11   **l)** 5

Exercise 42

1) 25, 20, 15, 10, 5, 0, − 5, −10, −15, −20   **2)** −20, − 16, − 12, − 8, − 4, 0, 4, 8, 12,
16, 20   **3)** − 40, − 32, − 24, − 16, − 8, 0, 8, 16, 24, 32   **4)** − 15, −12, − 9, − 6, −3,
0, 3, 6, 9, 12   **5)** 20, 16, 12, 8, 4, 0, − 4, − 8, − 12, − 16

Exercise 43

1a) − 4   **b)** − 3   **c)** − 2   **d)** − 7   **e)** 0   **f)** 3   **g)** − 3   **h)** − 1

Exercise 44

1) & 2)

$\frac{2}{4}$ or $\frac{1}{2}$ $\frac{3}{4}$ $\frac{3}{4} > \frac{2}{4}$ or $\frac{1}{2}$

3a) 12   **b)** $\frac{4}{12}$ or $\frac{1}{3}$ **c)** $\frac{1}{3}$ **d)** $\frac{1}{3}$ **e)** 1   **4a)** $\frac{4}{6}$, $\frac{6}{9}$, $\frac{8}{12}$, $\frac{10}{15}$, $\frac{12}{18}$

b) $\frac{8}{10}$, $\frac{12}{15}$, $\frac{16}{20}$, $\frac{20}{25}$, $\frac{24}{30}$ **c)** $\frac{10}{14}$, $\frac{15}{21}$, $\frac{20}{28}$, $\frac{25}{35}$, $\frac{30}{42}$ **d)** $\frac{8}{18}$, $\frac{12}{27}$, $\frac{16}{36}$, $\frac{20}{45}$,

$\frac{24}{54}$ **e)** $\frac{14}{16}$, $\frac{21}{24}$, $\frac{28}{32}$, $\frac{42}{48}$,   **5)** Multiply the fraction by $\frac{2}{2}$, $\frac{3}{3}$, $\frac{4}{4}$, etc.   **6)** an

infinite number; $\frac{2}{4}$, $\frac{3}{6}$, $\frac{5}{10}$, $\frac{6}{12}$, $\frac{49}{56}$ **7a)** P, **b)** P, **c)** I, **d)** P, **e)** I, **f)** P, **g)** I   **8a)** $\frac{2}{3}$

b) $\frac{3}{4}$ **c)** $\frac{3}{5}$ **d)** $\frac{1}{2}$ **e)** $\frac{1}{3}$ **f)** $\frac{1}{3}$ **9)** He placed 40 out of 80 or he took 4 of 8 items.

Exercise 45

1a) 12   **b)** 20   **c)** 35   **d)** 24   **e)** 12   **f)** 99   **2a)** $\frac{8}{15}$ **b)** $\frac{1}{4}$ **c)** $\frac{23}{56}$
d) $\frac{2}{3}$ **e)** $\frac{10}{27}$ **f)** $\frac{61}{45}$ **g)** $\frac{14}{15}$ **h)** $\frac{17}{24}$ **i)** $\frac{17}{12}$ **j)** $\frac{55}{24}$ **k)** $\frac{49}{30}$ **l)** $\frac{51}{56}$ **3a)** $\frac{1}{12}$
b) $\frac{7}{20}$ **c)** $\frac{19}{56}$ **4a)** $2\frac{1}{4}$ **b)** $3\frac{1}{2}$ **c)** $3\frac{1}{3}$ **d)** $4\frac{1}{5}$ **e)** $6\frac{1}{3}$ **f)** $6\frac{1}{4}$ **5a)** $\frac{17}{5}$
b) $\frac{15}{7}$ **c)** $\frac{17}{3}$ **d)** $\frac{31}{4}$ **e)** $\frac{33}{8}$ **f)** $\frac{56}{9}$ **6a)** $\frac{397}{40}$ **b)** $4\frac{2}{21}$ **c)** $\frac{61}{8}$ **d)** $\frac{1}{6}$
e) $\frac{154}{15}$ **f)** $7\frac{1}{8}$ **g)** $1\frac{5}{10}$ **h)** $\frac{49}{4}$ **i)** $\frac{17}{9}$ **7a)** $\frac{47}{30}$ **b)** $\frac{1}{4}$ **c)** $\frac{19}{16}$ **d)** $\frac{299}{24}$
e) $-3\frac{7}{15}$ **f)** $\frac{37}{18}$ **g)** $\frac{63}{10}$ **8)** 15, $\frac{5}{12}$ **9)** $\frac{13}{18}$, $\frac{5}{18}$ **10)** $\frac{91}{216}$, $\frac{125}{216}$ **11)** $\frac{1}{4}$, $\frac{3}{4}$
12) No – the fractions do not add up to one. **13)** $\frac{24}{35}$ **14)** 2   **15)** $6\frac{1}{4}$ **16)** $\frac{131}{12}$

Exercise 46

1a) <   **b)** <   **c)** <   **d)** >   **e)** <   **f)** >   **g)** <   **h)** >   **i)** >   **j)** =   **k)** >
l) >   **m)** >   **n)** <   **o)** >   **p)** <   **q)** <   **r)** <   **s)** =   **t)** >
2) They answered the same number. $\frac{15}{20} = \frac{3}{4}$ and $\frac{18}{24} = \frac{3}{4}$ **3)** neither, $\frac{1}{3} = \frac{2}{6}$
4) Steve $8\frac{7}{8}$, Jim $8\frac{3}{4}$, Roger $8\frac{1}{2}$, Paul $7\frac{3}{4}$, Henry $7\frac{1}{2}$

Exercise 47

1a) $\frac{6}{35}$ **b)** $\frac{1}{6}$ **c)** $\frac{35}{48}$ **d)** $\frac{4}{9}$ **e)** $\frac{3}{10}$ **f)** $\frac{7}{20}$ **g)** $\frac{85}{6}$ **h)** $\frac{55}{7}$ **i)** $\frac{58}{3}$
j) $\frac{23}{2}$ **2)** $\frac{3}{8}$ **3)** $\frac{1}{16}$ **4)** $\frac{1}{12}$ **5)** $\frac{21}{2}$ or 10.5   **6)** $35\frac{3}{4}$ **7)** \$1.50 ;
\$1.60 **8)** 6 kg   **9)** 63 kg   **10)** $\frac{11}{6}$ **11)** 82.5; 70.28   **12)** 25

Exercise 48

1a) $\frac{5}{6}$ **b)** $\frac{2}{3}$ **c)** 2   **d)** $\frac{10}{3}$ or $3\frac{1}{3}$ **e)** $\frac{25}{16}$ or $1\frac{9}{16}$ **f)** $\frac{40}{27}$ or $1\frac{13}{27}$ **g)** $\frac{14}{27}$
h) $\frac{119}{75}$ or $1\frac{44}{75}$ **i)** $\frac{35}{16}$ or $2\frac{3}{16}$ **2)** $\frac{1}{2}$ **3)** $11\frac{1}{4}$ **4)** 3   **5)** 3   **6)** 9   **7)** 72 **8)**
60   **9)** 100   **10)** 60

Exercise 49

1a) commutative with respect to addition   **b)** cancellation with respect to multiplication   **c)** existence of the additive inverse   **d)** distributive property of multiplication with respect to addition   **e)** associative property of addition   **f)** numbers are ordered **2a)** $3(4 - 2) = (3 \times 4) - (3 \times 2) = 12 - 6 = 6$ **b)** $5 + 0 = 5$ **c)** $3(4 \times 5) = (3 \times 4)5 = (3 \times 5)4$ **d)** If $x - y = z - y$ then $x = z$. **e)** If $x = y$ and $y = z$ then $x = z$ **3a)** Yes, because the Integers include the Natural numbers. **b)** No, because the negative numbers are not Natural numbers. **c)** $\frac{1}{3}$ **d)** $\frac{2}{5}$ **e)** Yes

f) Irrational

Exercise 50

1 a) $\frac{4}{5} = 0.80$

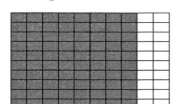

b) $\frac{3}{4} = 0.75$

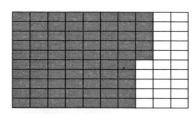

c) $\frac{1}{2} = 0.50$

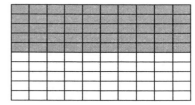

d) $\frac{3}{5} = 0.60$

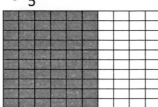

e) $\frac{63}{100} = 0.63$

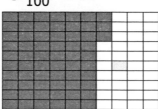

f) $\frac{87}{100} = 0.87$

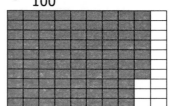

2a) $\frac{40}{100}$ or 0.4 **b)** $\frac{66}{100}$ or .666... **c)** $\frac{60}{100}$ or 0.60 **d)** $\frac{70}{100}$ or 0.70 **e)** $\frac{25}{100}$ or 0.25 **f)** $\frac{50}{100}$ or 0.5 **3a)** $\frac{35}{100}$ or $\frac{7}{20}$ **b)** $\frac{75}{100}$ or $\frac{3}{4}$ **c)** $\frac{63}{100}$ **d)** $\frac{42}{100}$ or $\frac{21}{50}$ **e)** $\frac{60}{100}$ or $\frac{3}{5}$ **f)** $\frac{99}{100}$ **4)** 30 and 50 ft. New area is 1500. Old area was 1200. Therefore increase in area is 300 sq ft. **5)** $7200 **6)** 300 **7)** Because 27.3 means $27 + \frac{3}{10}$, hence no "ones place".

Exercise 51

1. Shade the area shown in each of the following:

d) 3.8

 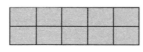 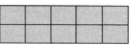 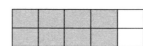

b) 2.6

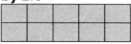 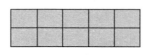 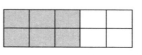 

c) 3.5

 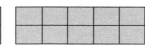 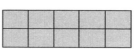 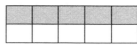

d) 3.7

 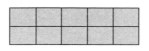 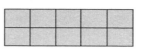 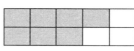

e) 1.6

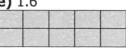 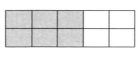 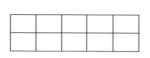 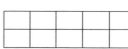

325

f) 2.30

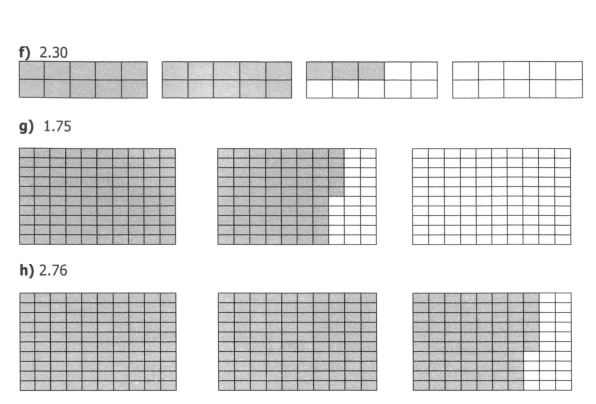

g) 1.75

h) 2.76

2a) 1.1   **b)** 1.4   **c)** 3.9   **d)** 6.2   **e)** 10   **f)** 12.2   **g)** 12   **h)** 0.3   **i)** 0
.6 **j)** 4.1 **k)** 7.021 **l)** 5.73 **m)** 8.131 **3a)** 0.3 **b)** 0.9 **c)** 0.9 **d)** 4.72 **e)** 1.78
f) 0.89 **4a)** 0.4 **b)** 4.05 **c)** 5.44 **d)** 10.26 **e)** 34.02 **f)** 10.675 **5a)** 0.7266
b) 7.5195 **c)** 3.301190 **d)** 11.511695 **6a)** 2.3 **b)** 4.6

Exercise 52

1a) 40%   **b)** 65%   **c)** 83%

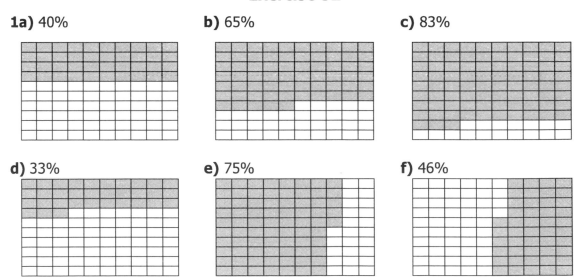

d) 33%   **e)** 75%   **f)** 46%

g) 60%   **h)** 80%   **i)** 10%

j) 20%   **k)** 50%   **l)** 90%

2) 60%; $180   **3)** 80%   **4)** $\frac{11}{20}$; 0.55 or $\frac{55}{100}$ **5)** 67%; $\frac{67}{100}$ **6)** Mary and Joan ate

$66\frac{1}{3}$ of the cake. Therefore, Helen ate $33\frac{2}{3}$ of the cake.

Exercise 53

1a) 40% = 0.4 = $\frac{2}{5}$;   **b)** 25% = 0.25 = $\frac{1}{4}$ **2a)** 70%   **b)** 60%   **c)** 55%   **3a)** 31%
b) 26%   **c)** 72%   **4a)** 10.81%   **b)** 5%   **c)** 8.55%   **5a)** 9%   **b)** 5%   **c)** 3.75%
6) 1.5   **7)** 20% of 20; 75% 0f 15 - .75 x 15 = 11.75 and 20% 0f 20 = 4.   **8)** $375
in each case because 75% = $\frac{3}{4}$ **9)** $70; $67.50; $2.50   **10)** The fourth because a
40% discount is the highest of the four. **11)** $100 **12)** $33\frac{1}{3}$%   **13)** 250 – 0.24 x 250
= 190; 0.76 x 250 = 190; 250 x $\frac{76}{100}$ = 190   **14)** 75 + 0.2 x 75 = 90; 75 x 1.2 =
90; 75 x 120/100 = 90   **15)** 75   **16)** 800,0000 x .20 = 160,000. 800,000 – 160,000
= 640,000; or 800,000 x 0.8 = 640,000   **17)** 4000 x 0.92 = 3680; 4000 – 0.08 x 4000
= 3680   **18)** $244,720   **19)** 14.29%   **20)** 60%. Won 6 of 10 games.

Exercise 54

1) 18%   **2)** .30 x $60 =$18; $\frac{30}{100}$ x $\frac{60}{}$ =18; 60 x .70 = 42 and 60 – 42 = 18
3) He was selling for less than his cost. For each $100, his Marked Price was $140. A
discount of 40% of $140 is $56. Therefore, his selling price was $84. **4)** 20%
5) 62.5%   **6)** 56% **7)** 4% **8)** 60% **9)** 15,000 –12,000 = 3,000 and
$\frac{3,000}{15,000}$ = $\frac{1}{5}$ or 20%; $\frac{3,000}{15,000}$ = $\frac{1}{5}$ or 20%; $\frac{12,000}{15,000}$ = $\frac{4}{5}$: decrease was $\frac{1}{5}$ or 20%;
100% = 15,000 and therefore, 1% = 150; 12,000 ÷ 150 = 80%. Therefore,
there was a decrease of 20%.   **10)** 60%   **11)** no – a 20% followed by a 10%
discount is equivalent to a 28% discount. **12)** 50%   **13)** $33\frac{1}{3}$%   **14)** $420

Exercise 55

1a) 12   **b)** 16   **c)** 18   **d)** 5   **e)** 3   **f)** 2   **g)** 18   **h)** 15   **i)** $\frac{1}{6}$ **j)** 1   **k)** $\frac{25}{2}$ or
$12\frac{1}{2}$ **l)** 4   **m)** $\frac{4}{3}$ **n)** $\frac{-14}{5}$ **o)** 4   **2)** 18   **3)** 8   **4a)** – 10   **b)** $-\frac{17}{3}$ **c)** – 2
d) – 4

Exercise 56

1) Yes – the sides are 5, 5 and 5;   No – the ratio is always $\frac{1}{4}$; Yes – the sides are 5 and 10.   **2)** $\frac{4}{10}$ $\frac{6}{15}$ $\frac{8}{20}$; $\frac{2}{5} = \frac{n}{35}$ implies that 5n = 70 and n = 14 or $\frac{2}{n} = \frac{5}{35}$ implies that 5n = 70 or n = 14; $\frac{2}{5} = \frac{100}{n}$ implies that 2n = 500 or n = 250 or, $\frac{2}{100} = \frac{5}{n}$ and this implies that 2n = 500 and n = 250   **3)** no. $\frac{3}{1} = 3$ but $\frac{1}{3} = 0.33333$ **4)** $\frac{1}{20} = \frac{15}{n}$ implies that n = 300 seconds; or, $\frac{1}{15} = \frac{20}{n}$ and this implies that n = 300 seconds   **5)** $\frac{1,000}{74,000} = \frac{10}{n}$ implies that 1,000n = 740,000 and therefore, n = $740, or if 1,000 watches cost $74,000, then 1 watch costs $74 and 10 watches cost $740.   **6)** It should be noted that if a log is to be cut into 4 pieces, then only 3 cuts are required

In a similar fashion, only 5 cuts are required to cut a log into six parts. If 3 cuts are made in 12 minutes, then 1 cut is made in 4 minutes and 5 cuts are made in 20 minutes. Or, $\frac{3}{12} = \frac{5}{n}$ and this implies that 3n – 50 or n = 20 min.

7) $\frac{o}{m} = \frac{2}{1}$, $\frac{o}{m} = \frac{3}{1}$ therefore, $\frac{o}{9} = \frac{2}{3}$ **8)** $\frac{3}{2} = \frac{n}{5}$, 2n = 15, n = 7.5 or,

$\frac{3}{n} = \frac{2}{5}$, 2n = 15, n = 7.5   **9)** 12 covers $\frac{2}{3}$ of the floor, 6 covers $\frac{1}{3}$ of the floor, therefore,

18 covers all of the floor; or $\frac{12}{\frac{2}{3}} = \frac{n}{1}$ implies that $\frac{2}{3}$n = 12 and therefore, n = 18.

10) $\frac{1}{4}$/n = $\frac{2}{80}$ implies that 2n = 20 and n = 10 ; $\frac{n}{80} = \frac{.25}{2}$ ⟶ 2n = 20 or n = 10 or 80 ÷ 2 = 40 and 40 x .25 = 10.   **11a)** $\frac{3}{20}$; 15%; .15;   **b)** $\frac{4}{8}$ or $\frac{1}{2}$, $\frac{1}{2}$, 0.5, 50%;

c) $\frac{5}{8}$; $\frac{5}{8}$; 38.46%   **d)** $\frac{4}{8}$ or $\frac{1}{2}$

Exercise 57

1) $\frac{2}{36}$ or $\frac{1}{18}$ (6, 1) (1, 6)   **2)** $\frac{1}{6}$; (1,1), (2,2), (3,3), (4,4), (5,5), (6,6)   **3)** MAO or MBP or AAB or PPP   **4)** 88 (87 and 1) and (29 and 3)   **5)** 30º   **6)** $\frac{32 + 46 - 63}{5}$

7) Yes. Color the opposite faces the same color.   **8)** 19: the sides measure 1 and 23: 2 and 22: 3 and 21: 4 and 20: 5 and 19...do you see a pattern? Finish listing the solutions.   **9)** 1 x 1, 1 x 36, 2 x 18, 3 x 12, 4 x 9, 6 x 6   **10)** add the first and the last numbers and multiply this result by $\frac{n}{2}$ **11)** 1400   **12)** 12   **13)** 1   **14)** $8

15 a) 100,000;   **b)** 60,000   **16)** saves $0.83   **17)** 63.5 kg   **18)** 30   **19)** 67   **20)** $1100   **21)** 10   **22)** 24   **23)** 8   **24)** 11   **25)** 212 (left) ; 102 (top); 59 (right)
26) 45   **27)** 75   **28)** $1\frac{1}{2}$ **29)** 40 (There are 50 even numbers and 10 numbers have a Ones digit of 5)   **30)** $\frac{1}{100}$ **31)** $\frac{1}{6}$ **32)**

Exercise 58

1) $\frac{1}{6}$ changing the numbers on a die will not change the probability

2) $(1 + 66) + (2 + 65) + (3 + 64)) = 67$. The sums of the numbers equidistant from the beginning and the end will equal 67. Since there are 66 numbers there will be 33 such pairs. Therefore, $33 \times 67 = 33(60 + 7)$ or $1980 + 231$ which equals 2211   **3)** When one or more of the factors is even.   **4)** 1111, 1112, 1121, 1122, 1211, 1212, 1221, 1222, 2111, 2112, 2121, 2122, 2211, 2212, 2221, 2222 **5)** 3333, 3335, 3353, 3355, 3533, 3535, 3553, 3555, 5333, 5335, 5353, 5355, 5533, 5535, 5553, 5555

6) 4.5 x 6, 5.6 x 7, 6.7 x 8   **7)** $50 + 5 + 30 - 1 + 10 + 6 = 90 + 10 = 100$ or $55 = 50 + 5$: $29 = 30 - 1$: $16 = 20 - 4$. Add $5 + (-1) + (-4) = 0$ and $50 + 30 + 20 = 100$ **8)** $888 + 88 + 8 + 8 + 8$; or five 8's in the ones column, 2 two eights in nthe tens column, and one 8 in the hundreds column. **9)** $777 + 7 + 777 + 777 + 7$ (or, ten 7's in the ones column, nine 7's in the tens column, and nine 7's in the hundreds column **10)** $7 \times 5 + 5 - 9 = 31$ **11)** 1 and 10000; 2 and 20,000; an infinite number – any ratio of $\frac{1}{10000}$ will work.   **12)** 77   **13)** 8, 8, 10, 10 or 12, 12, 6, 6

14) 88, $8.80   **15)** impossible   **16)** 2004   **17)** $78.60   **18)** 60

Exercise 59

1) $2832   **2)** $3960   **3)** 4.2857   **4)** 5%   **5)** $2500   **6)** $164.38
7) $8.94   **8)** $7.23   **9)** $1140   **10)** 20%   **11)** $54750   **12)** $82.50
13) $5500   **14)** $8000 @ 2.5% and $5000 @ 3%

Exercise 60

1) 8.243%   **2)** 4.06%   **3)** $3472.88   **4)** $1655.72   **5)** $414.25   **6)** $4700.97
7) $432.11   **8)** $7   **9)** 142,857.14   **10)** Ann by $4.51

Exercise 61

The following are some suggestions regarding the solution(s) to the problems.

1) The variable costs will be dictated by the size of the room. Assume the room accommodates 100 people and that it has a fully equipped kitchen. Also assume that all work will be done voluntarily. It is expected that 60 tickets will be sold at $12.00 each. Fixed costs for napkins, rolls, butter, cream, sugar etc. are estimated at $40.00. The variable costs for food can be determined as follows. $TR = F + vx$ or $720 = 300 + 40 + 60v$ which implies that $60v = 380$ or $v = 6.33$. $380 is the maximum that should be spent on food. Any reduction from 380 spent on food would be included in the profits. Mary could have started by deciding on a menu in which she would spend $380 for food. In this case, she would use the same formula to determine the number of tickets that must be sold. $12x = 300 + 40 + 380$ or $12x = 720$ or $x = 60$. This tells us that 60 tickets must be sold to break even and provide the profit of $300.

2) The food costs as estimated by caterer were $140. Therefore, the profit to the caterer was $420. The caterer and her husband were able to prepare and serve the meal and wash the dishes. The total revenue must be 420 + 140 or $560. Since 35 people will attend, the cost per person will be $16.

3) TR = P + F + vx. The profit was $100,000, the fixed costs were determined to $250,000 and if this type of pipe is selling at $6 a meter, then it can be determined how many meters must be sold. 6x = 350,000 implies that x = 58,333 and therefore, 58,334 meters must be sold to break even and have a profit of $100,000. The price per meters could have been determined if it was known that at least, this number of meters could be sold.

Exercise 62

1) $\frac{124}{623}$ = 20%; $\frac{98}{623}$ = 16%; $\frac{156}{623}$ = 25%; $\frac{87}{623}$ = 14%; $\frac{56}{623}$ = 9%; $\frac{102}{623}$ = 16%.

2) $\frac{175}{1250}$ = 14%; $\frac{83}{1250}$ = 6.6%; $\frac{137}{1250}$ = 10.96%; $\frac{212}{1250}$ = 16.96% **3)** 1990

4) 838; 83.8%

Exercise 63

1) RC

> 65				
51- 65				
36-50				
21-35				
< 21				
Total				

2)

27	////	5	0.179	17.9%
28	/ / /	3	0.107	10.7%
29	//// / /	7	0.250	25%
32	//// /	6	0.214	21.4%
35	/ / /	3	0.107	10.7%
36	/ / / /	4	0.143	14.3%
Total		28	1.000	100%

Exercise 64

1)

week		%
1	2,300	17.4
2	4,200	31.8
3	3,600	27.3
4	3,100	23.5
Total	13,200	100

2)

Period	Accidents	Injuries	Ra	Percent
Jan-March	8000	6000	$\frac{3}{4}$	75%
April-June	9000	7000	$\frac{7}{9}$	77.8%
July-Sept	7000	6000	$\frac{6}{7}$	86%
Oct-Dec	7000	5000	$\frac{5}{7}$	71%

Exercise 65

1) 297.6   **2)** 8.25 lbs and 3.75 kg (The difference results from using 1lb = 2.2 kg)
3) 3,000   **4)** the average weight of a group of children; the winning average of a team (usually expressed to three decimal places; the average number of sales in a particular month. **5)** to compare different units (for example, the average weight of the linemen on a football team) **6)** not good – use the height of the largest ship.
7) Not many people aged 104 were living.   **8)** Valid because when you multiply by a big enough number, the decimal disappears.   **9)** 40 yds.

Exercise 66

1) 37   **2)** 78   **3)** the median age within a group of people   **4)** the median is the middle number in a set of ordered numbers. If the set contains an even number of numbers, the median is the average of the two middle numbers.

Exercise 67

1) 30   **2)** 27 and 30   **3)** sales of new cars

Exercise 68

1) $\frac{4}{52}$ or $\frac{1}{13}$ **2)** $\frac{13}{52}$ or $\frac{1}{4}$ **3)** $\frac{9}{36}$ or $\frac{1}{4}$

4)

	1	2	3	4	5	6
1	(1 , 1)	(1 , 2)	(1 , 3)	(1 , 4)	(1 , 5)	(1 , 6)
2	(2 , 1)	(2 , 2)	(2 , 3)	(2, 4)	(2 , 5)	(2 , 6)
3	(3 , 1)	(3 , 2)	(3 , 3)	(3 , 4)	(3 , 5)	(3 , 6)
4	(4 , 1)	(4 , 2)	(4 . 3)	(4 , 4)	(4 , 5)	(4 , 6)
5	(5 , 1)	(5 , 2)	(5 , 3)	(5 , 4)	(5 , 5)	(5 , 6)
6	(6 , 1)	(6 , 2)	(6 , 3)	(6 , 4)	(6 , 5)	(6 , 6)

(1, 1), (2, 2), (3, 3), (4, 4), (5, 5), (6, 6) could be excluded on the basis that 0 is neither positive nor negative. The foregoing is a little picky and does not reflect the intentions of the problem. **4a)** 1 to 6   **b)** $\frac{6}{36}$ or $\frac{1}{6}$ **c)** $\frac{10}{36}$ or $\frac{5}{18}$ **d)** $\frac{8}{36}$ or $\frac{2}{9}$

e) $\frac{6}{36}$ or $\frac{1}{6}$ **f)** $\frac{4}{36}$ or $\frac{1}{9}$ **g)** $\frac{2}{36}$ or $\frac{1}{18}$ **h)** 0   **5)** {w_1w_2; w_1w_3; w_2w_3; y_1y_2;

w_1y_1; w_1y_2; w_2y_1; w_2y_2; w_3y_1; w_3y_2} **6a)** $\frac{3}{10}$ **b)** $\frac{1}{10}$ **c)** $\frac{6}{10}$ **7a)** H H, H T, T T. H

T, $\frac{1}{4}$ **b)** $\frac{3}{4}$ **8)** $\frac{11}{20}$

Exercise 69

1) $47619.05 **2)** $10,000 **3)** 221 **4)** $9.90 **5)** 16 **6)** 64.2%; 0.642 **7)** 0.864;
86.4%   **8)** $\frac{2}{1}$; 66.7%; 0.667; $\frac{2}{1}$.

Exercise 70

1a) {1,3,5,7,9,11,12,13,14,15}   **b)** {4,5,6,7,8,9,10,11,12}   **c)** {13,14,15}
d) {1,2,3,4,5,6,7,8,9}   **2)** {a, b} ; {c, d}.

Exercise 71

1a) 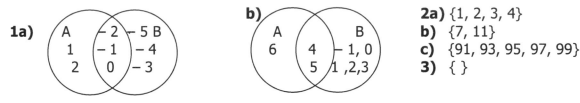   **b)**   **2a)** {1, 2, 3, 4}
b) {7, 11}
c) {91, 93, 95, 97, 99}
3) { }

4a) {5, 9} **b)** { } **c)** { } **d)** {10} **e)** {1, 2, 5, 6, 7, 9, 11, 12} **f)** {1, 2, 3, 4, 6, 11, 12} **g)** {1, 2, 3, 4, 5, 6, 7, 9, 11, 12}   **h)** {1, 2, 3, 4, 5, 6, 7, 9, 10} **i)** {1, 2, 3, 4, 6, 7, 9, 10, 11, 12}   **j)** {3, 4, 11,12}

Exercise 72

1a) B   **b)** D   **c)** either   **2a)** A   **b)** { }   **c)** A   **3a)** U   **b)** { }   **c)** A

Exercise 73

1a) {1, 2, 3, 4, 5, 6, 7, 8} **b)** {10, 11, 12, 13, 14, 15, 16} **2a)** I **b)** Re **c)** Ra **d)** Re
3a) {2, 6, 10, 14, 18}   **b)** {2, 4, 14, 16, 18, 20}   **c)** {4, 6, 8, 10, 12, 16, 20}
d) {2, 6, 8, 10, 12, 14, 18}   **e)** {2, 4, 8, 12, 14, 16, 18, 20}   **f)** U or {2, 4, 6, 8, 10, 12, 14, 16, 18, 20} **g)** U   **h)** U **4a)** {1, 2, 3, 4, 5, 8} **b)** { 1, 2, 3, 4, 11}
c) {1, 3, 4, 5, 9, 10} **d)** {1, 3, 4, 5, 8, 11} **e)** {1, 4, 5, 8, 9, 10, 11} **f)** {2, 9, 10, 11}
g) {1, 2, 3, 5, 11}   **h)** {9, 10, 11} **i)** {2, 3, 9, 10, 11} **j)** {1, 2, 4, 5, 8, 9, 10, 11}

Exercise 74

1) A = {1,2,3,4} and let B = {4, 5, 6}   **2)** A = {1,2,3,4}   B = {2,3,4,5}

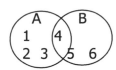

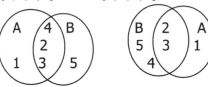

3 a) F ; T ; T ; T ; T ; F, F, F

Exercise 75

1a) 2   **b)** 3   **c)** 8   **d)** 5   **2a)** 9   **b)** 7   **c)** 5   **d)** 8   **3a)** 2   **b)** 6   **c)** 73

Exercise 76

1)

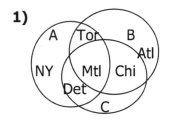

Washington was not picked to win

M – W; T – B; D – A; C-NY

2)

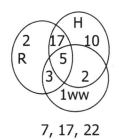

29, 24, 23

3)

7, 17, 22

Exercise 77

1a)

b)

2a)

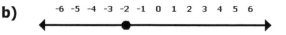

b)

3a)

b)

4a)

b)

5a)

b)

c)

d)

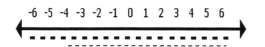

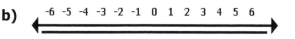

e)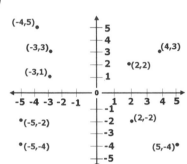

f)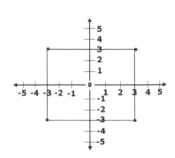

g)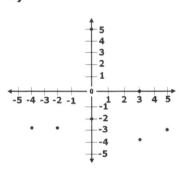

Exercise 78

1a) 9a   **b)** − 6   **c)** − 2   **d)** 0   **e)** $\frac{3}{2}$ **2)** {(1, 1),(1, 2),(2, 1),(2, 2)}

3) {(1, 1),(2, 4),(3, 9)}   **4)** No. Chart it on a Cartesian plane.

Exercise 79

1)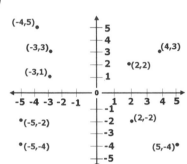

2)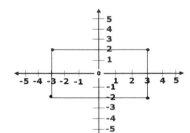

3a)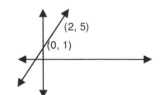

b)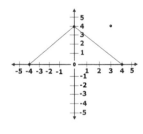

c)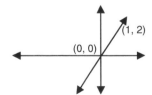

3a square

b) isosceles

    triangle

c) rectangle

Exercise 80

1 a) x = − y   **b)** y = 2x   **c)** y = 2x + 1

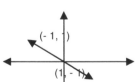

334

2a) x ≥ 3

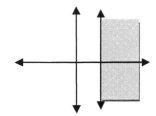

b) y ≥ 4

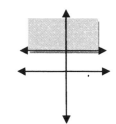

c) y > 2x − 3

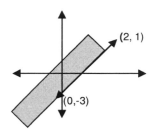

d) y ≥ 3x − 2

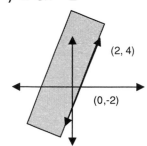

e) y ≤ 2x + 3

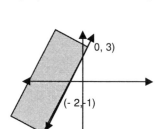

f) y ≥ x − 4

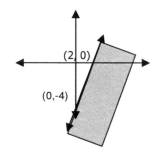

Exercise 81

1　**a)** x + y = 6 and
2x − 3y = 2

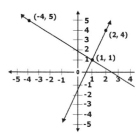

b) 2x − y = 5 and
2x + y = 7

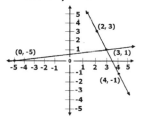

c) 3x + y = 10 and
4x − 5y = − 12

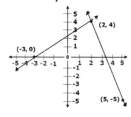

d) 4x + 5y = 9
and 3x − y = 2

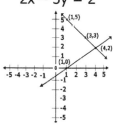

e) 2x + y = 6 and
6x − y = 2

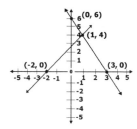

f) x + 2y = 5 and
2x − 3y = 4

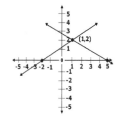

∩ = (1, 1)

∩ = (1, 4)

∩ = (1, 2)

2. a)

$x + y = 6$
$2x - 3y = 2$
$2x + 2y = 12$
$\underline{2x - 3y = 2}$
$\qquad 5y = 10$
$\qquad\ y = 2$
$x + y = 6$
$x + 2 = 6$
$x = 4 \qquad (4, 2)$

b)

$2X + y = 7$
$\underline{2x - y = 5}$
$4x \qquad = 12$
$\ x = 3$
$2x + y = 7$
$6 + y = 7$
$\quad y = 1 \ (3, 1)$

c)

$3x + y = 10$
$4x - 5y = -12$
$15x + 5y = 50$
$\underline{4x - 5y = -12}$
$\qquad 19x = 38$
$\qquad\ \ x = 2$
$3x + y = 10$
$6 + y = 10$
$y = 4 \quad (2, 4)$

d)

$4x + 5y = 9$
$3x - y = 2$
$4x + 5y = 9$
$\underline{15x - 5y = 10}$
$19x = 19$
$\ x = 1$
$4 + 5y = 9$
$\quad 5y = 5$
$\qquad y = 1 \qquad (1, 1)$

e)

$2x + y = 6$
$\underline{6x - y = 2}$
$8x \qquad = 8$
$\ x \qquad = 1$
$2x + y = 6$
$2 + y = 6$
$\qquad y = 4 \ (1,4)$

f)

$x + 2y = 5$
$2x - 3y = -4$
$2x + 4y = 10$
$\underline{2x - 3y = -4}$
$\qquad 7y = 14$
$\qquad\ y = 2$
$x + 2y = 5$
$x + 4 = 5$
$x \qquad = 1 \quad (1, 2)$

3a) $x \geq 0, y \geq 0$

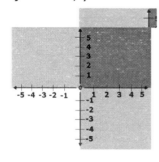

b) $x \geq y, \ y \leq 4$

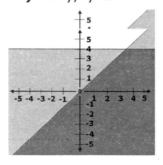

c) $x \leq 4, \ x - y \geq 0$

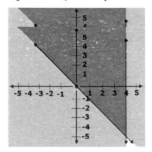

d) $0 \leq x \leq 3, 0 \leq y \leq 2$

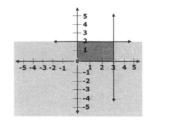

e) $2 \leq x \leq 5, -5 \leq y \leq -2$

f) $2 \leq x \leq 5, 1 \leq y \leq 4$

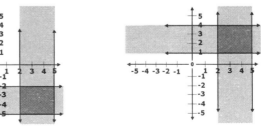

336

In all cases, U is all of the shaded areas and ∩ is all of the darkly shaded areas. including the lines drawn.

Exercise 82

1a) – 2   **b)** $\frac{17}{7}$ **c)** undefined   **d)** 0   **e)** $-\frac{1}{3}$ **2)** 0   **3)** undefined

Exercise 83

1a) (2, 3)   **b)** (6 ,2)   **c)** $(-2, \frac{1}{2})$ **d)** (– 3, 3)   **2)** $(1, -\frac{4}{5})$ **3)** (5, – 3)
4) same slope   **5)** 30   **6)** (0, 18)   **7)** (8, 6)

Exercise 84

1a) $4x - y - 10 = 0$ **b)** $5x - y + 13 = 0$ **c)** $3x + y - 9 = 0$ **d)** $2x + 3y + 15 = 0$
e) $y + 8 = 0$ **2a)** a horizontal line   **b)** a vertical line   **c)** slants left to right
d) slants right to left   **3a)** $x - 2y + 6 = 0$ **b)** $2x + y - 1 = 0$ **c)** $x + 3y - 5 = 0$
4a) $2x - y - 9 = 0$ **b)** $x - 3y + 2 = 0$ **c)** $x - 8y + 56 = 0$ **d)** $5x + y = 0$
e) $x - y - 5 = 0$

Exercise 85

1a) 6, 8, 10 and 9, 12, 15   **b)** an indefinite number. Note that we multiplied 3, 4, 5 by 2 and then by 3. However, there are others such as 1, 1, $\sqrt{2}$ since $1^2 + 1^2 + (\sqrt{2})^2 = 1 + 1 + 2$ **2)** The sum of the angles of a triangle is 180º. A square has four lines of symmetry.   **3a)** True – major and minor premises are true.   **b)** True – major and minor premises are true.   **c)** True – major and minor premises are true. **d)** False – the minor premise is false.   **e)** False – the major premise is false.
f) False – the major premise is false.   **4)** $\frac{BD}{BP} = \frac{BE}{BQ} = \frac{BF}{BR}$ and $\frac{BP}{EQ} = \frac{EQ}{FR}$.

Exercise 86

1) RC **2)** RC   **3)** Yes. 2n is even and therefore 2n + 1 is odd.   **4a)** $4 \times 5 \neq 30$

b) John is not smart.   **c)** Natural numbers are not integers

5a)

p	q	p ∧ q	q ∧ p
T	T	T	T
T	F	F	F
F	T	F	F
F	F	F	F

b) The commutative property.

6)

p	q	~p	~q	~p ∧ ~q
T	T	F	F	F
T	F	F	T	F
F	T	T	F	F
F	F	T	T	T

Exercise 87

1)

p	q	~q	p V ~q
T	T	F	T
T	F	T	T
F	T	F	F
F	F	T	T

2. Only when both statements are true.

3.

p	q	~p	~p V q
T	T	F	T
T	F	F	F
F	T	T	T
F	F	T	T

4.

p	q	~p	~q	p V q	~(p V q)	~ p ∧ ~q
T	T	F	F	T	F	F
T	F	F	T	T	F	F
F	T	T	F	T	F	F
F	F	T	T	F	T	T

5. If two triangles are not similar, then the two triangles are not congruent.

6 a) p implies q. If p is a triangle, then the sum of the angles is 180º. **b)** q V p is equivalent to p V q The truth table for p V q is the same as the truth table for q V p. 5 + 4 = 4 + 5. **c)** not q implies not p. If the two sides of a triangle are not equal, the triangle is not isosceles.

7.

p	q	~p	p ∧ q	q ∧ ~p
T	T	F	T	T
T	F	F	F	F
F	T	T	F	T
F	F	T	F	F
The columns 4 and 5 are not the same.				

8)

p	q	~p	p V q	q V (~p)
T	T	F	T	T
T	F	F	T	F
F	T	T	T	T
F	F	T	F	T
The columns 4 and 5 are not the same				

Exercise 88

1)

p	q	~(p V q)	~p	~q	(~p V q)	→	(~p V ~q)
T	T	F	F	F	T		F
T	F	F	F	T	F		T
F	T	F	T	F	T		T
F	F	T	T	T	T		T
1	2	3	4	5	6	7	8

Columns 6 and 8 are not the same.

2a) If n + 1 is not odd, then n is not a Natural number. **b)** If x ≠ 3, then 3x + 4 ≠ 13.   **3)** RC   **4)** If 2 + 6 = 8, then 8 = 2 + 6   **5)** RC

Symbols Used in this Book

+	addition
-	subtraction
x	multiplication
$\overline{)}$	division
=	is equal to
≠	is not equal to
>	is greater than
<	is less than
≥	is greater than or equal
≤	is less than or equal to
• • •	and so on
A = { }	A is the set {a, b, c . . .}
{ }	the empty set
lxl	the absolute value of x
→	implies (or, if then)
U	the universal set
U	the union of sets
∩	the intersection of sets
→	number line for the Natural Numbers
↔	a number line for the Real Numbers
→	a vector to the right
←	a vector to the left
( )	parentheses
{ }	braces
[ ]	brackets
$\sqrt{}$	the square root of. . .
$0.\overset{\bullet}{3}$	three tenths recurring
Σ	the sum of
$\bar{X}$	the mean (average)
π	pi an irrational number equal to approximately 3.14 . . .
∧	and (conjunction) (if both statements are true)
⊕	and (conjunction) (if at least one statement is true)
∨	or (disjunction)
↔	is equivalent to